MW00845737

Performance Improvement in Healthcare

A Tool for Programmed Learning

Chris Elliott, MS, RHIA
Patricia Shaw, MEd, RHIA
Polly Isaacson, RHIA, CPHQ
and Elizabeth Murphy, MEd, RN

AHIMA
AMERICAN HEALTH INFORMATION®
MANAGEMENT ASSOCIATION

ISBN 1-58426-045-9
AHIMA Product Number AB102700
Production Number PP-3000-900

American Health Information Management Association
233 North Michigan Avenue, Suite 2150
Chicago, Illinois 60601-5800

http://www.ahima.org

Contents

About the Authors

Chris Elliott holds a master's degree in information systems and is currently pursuing a doctorate in medical informatics at the University of Utah. He is currently associate professor and chairman of the Health Administrative Services Department, College of Health Professions, at Weber State University in Ogden, Utah. Before becoming a full-time health professions educator, he worked for 20 years in various positions related to health information management and quality improvement in the San Francisco bay area.

Patricia Shaw earned her master's degree in education in 1997 and has been on the faculty of Weber State University for over nine years, where she teaches in the Health Information Management and Health Services Administration programs. She has primary teaching responsibility for the quality and performance improvement curriculum in those programs. Pat maintains contact with practice settings as a consultant specializing in the areas of reimbursement and coding issues. Prior to accepting a position at Weber State University, Pat managed hospital health information services departments and was a nosologist for the 3M Corporation's Health Information Systems Division.

Polly Isaacson has 20 years of experience in acute, behavioral, and ambulatory healthcare, with a focus in facilitating organizations through licensure, accreditation, and/or certification based on JCAHO, CARF, LOA, Medicare, and Utah regulatory requirements. She has been a full-time healthcare consultant for the past six years. Polly has experience in teaching total quality management and continuous quality improvement processes, leading strategic leadership planning meetings, and facilitating performance (process) improvement teams in healthcare organizations. She holds certifications as a Registered Health Information Administrator and Certified Professional in Healthcare Quality.

Elizabeth Murphy holds a master's degree in education, with an emphasis in community counseling and addiction rehabilitation. She is a registered nurse and has worked in a variety of rehabilitation settings as a nurse administrator since 1987. Currently, she is the director of clinical services for Children's Comprehensive Services, Inc., which serves 4,500 children in psychiatric and rehabilitative settings across the nation. Her focus of practice in most of her positions has included accreditation and licensure, strategic planning, budgeting, performance improvement, and quality management.

Acknowledgments

The authors wish to thank the following individuals for their contributions to this text:

- Patrick Baggs for his real-life example regarding improving the environment of care
- Marcia Bottoms for her chapter on managing the human side of change and for editing the book so assiduously
- Melanie Brodnik, PhD, RHIA, for her review of the text and suggestions for improvement
- Shirley Eichenwald, MBA, RHIA, for her review of the text and excellent suggestions for improvement of it
- Danece Fickett, RN, for her real-life example regarding managing the continuum of care
- Beth Hjort, RHIA, for her review of the text and suggestions for improvements
- Merida Johns, PhD, RHIA, for reviewing the text and holding the authors to a higher standard
- Marie Kotter, PhD, for her case study on the organizational structure necessary for performance improvement programs
- Virginia Mullen, RHIA, for her real-life example regarding measuring customer satisfaction
- Gary Nielson, MS, MT (ASCP), CLS, for reviewing the infection control chapter and providing background materials on the Clinical Laboratory Improvement Amendments
- Karen Patena, MBA, RHIA, for her review of the text and excellent suggestions for its improvement
- Dorothy Grandolfi Wagg, JD, RHIA, for her chapter on the legal aspects of performance improvement

Preface for Health Professions Students

You will soon be entering your chosen profession in the healthcare field. The issues involved in the management of quality in healthcare span the various clinical and administrative disciplines and must be approached from a variety of perspectives. Many improvements for healthcare services are developed through team-based activities. Employers will expect you to be able to apply performance improvement data analysis and presentation tools. You may also find some time in the future that you will be asked to facilitate a performance improvement team meeting.

The authors of this text hope that this tool for programmed learning will prepare you well for the challenges you will face in your new career. If you use this text carefully, you will probably find yourself miles ahead of your fellow students in preparation for today's healthcare environment.

Preface for Healthcare Educators

This new textbook from AHIMA presents a comprehensive introduction to the theory, practice, and management of performance and quality improvement processes in healthcare organizations. Parts I and II are intended for use by students in technology-level programs of all kinds and provide a basic background in performance improvement philosophy and methodology for healthcare practice today. Each chapter has real-life examples and case studies from healthcare settings that bring home the importance of quality in healthcare services. QI toolbox techniques are presented both in theory and in practice so that your students can see how the techniques can actually be used in performance improvement activities. Healthcare information management students will find the textbook's unique programmed approach to the subject easy to use and understand. Students will also gain hands-on practice applying the analytical and graphic tools used in performance and quality improvement. Student projects are integrated into the chapter discussions, which range from designing specific improvement projects, to ongoing quality monitoring, to managing quality improvement programs and staff.

Part III is intended for use by students in management-level programs in the health services. Its chapters focus on the issues inherent in the management of quality and performance improvement programs in healthcare. Each chapter presents the issues and their backgrounds and concludes with a case study to reinforce student learning and encourage critical thinking about the issues.

An instructor's guide is provided for educators in an on-line format through the AHIMA Learning Institute. The instructor's guide includes supplementary materials specific to health information management and lesson plans applicable to students in two-year and four-year programs.

Introduction

People naturally expect their world to improve over time. This expectation affects everything people come into contact with: food, housing, cars, education, and healthcare. Such expectations stimulate general social progress. Progress may take considerable time to develop, and the desire for progress sometimes takes a counterproductive path, as during times of war and political upheaval. Still, the objective of making the human situation better is a constant in human endeavors.

Progress is commonly accomplished in one of two ways. First, progress can be achieved through an understanding of the scientific basis of the natural world and its constituent parts. Understanding the way the human body functions through biochemistry, for example, facilitated the development of the pharmaceuticals in use today. Second, progress can be achieved through improvements in the ways that people perform work. Understanding the procedures that healthcare professionals must perform to help people get well, for example, facilitated the development of one of the best healthcare delivery systems in the world. This textbook examines the second type of progress.

The focus of this textbook is healthcare quality and performance improvement in the United States and the means by which progress is accomplished in healthcare organizations. Every healthcare professional needs to understand the issues surrounding quality and performance improvement in healthcare because society expects that progress will result in better and better healthcare products and services. But are there other reasons why healthcare professionals should be concerned about quality improvement? For example, is there a tradition to be followed?

Early Quality Improvements in Healthcare

There is a long tradition of quality improvement in healthcare. From colonial times until the present, healthcare in the United States has undergone a series of developments and reforms, from the creation of hospitals in the eighteenth century to the scientific discoveries of the nineteenth century, to the professionalization of medical and nursing practice in the early twentieth century, to the technological advances of the late twentieth and early twenty-first centuries. Healthcare institutions, professional associations, individual leaders, and political visionaries all laid the foundations of modern healthcare.

Healthcare Institutions

During the mid-1700s, before the American colonies became a nation, the citizens of Philadelphia, Pennsylvania, recognized the need for a place to house the mentally ill and to provide relief to the sick and injured. They also recognized the need to sequester newly arrived immigrants, who often carried diseases they had contracted during their long voyages to America (Morton, 1895, p. 5). Thousands of people immigrated to the Pennsylvania colony in an attempt to improve their lives. Although most healthcare was provided in people's homes at that time, established inhabitants, particularly the poor, sometimes required a place to rest and mend during times of illness and injury. Recognizing these needs, Dr. Thomas Bond, with the help of Benjamin Franklin, persuaded the Pennsylvania legislature to undertake the organization and development of a hospital for the community, the famous Pennsylvania Hospital, the first in the growing nation (Morton, 1895, p. 6).

Over the next 150 years, the Pennsylvania Hospital became a model for the development of hospitals in other communities. It even attempted to standardize its care processes by publishing rules and regulations for its physicians and staff (Morton, 1895, pp. 549–58). These regulations represent early attempts at healthcare improvement.

The annals of Massachusetts General Hospital provide an early example of an action taken by a hospital board of trustees to ensure the quality of care provided in the institution. In 1837, the trustees became aware that the son of a resident surgeon (a surgeon who had not attained appointment to the hospital) had practiced in the hospital during his father's absence. The trustees reiterated to all of the medical staff the need for allowing only those accorded privileges at the institution to practice there (Bowditch, 1872, p. 135):

> . . . the Trustees have recently seen with great pain, that a violation of the rules of the institution by one of its officers has become the subject of newspaper animadversion. In an institution like this, to which it is so difficult to attract, and in which it is so important to command, public confidence, the strictest and most scrupulous adherence to rules, of which the propriety is unquestioned, is required by a just regard as well to its usefulness to the public, as to the character of those who have any agency in its direction and control. Where many persons are connected in different departments, the reputation of all is more or less affected by the conduct of each; and all are therefore bound, by respect for others as well as themselves to conduct in such a manner as to give no reasonable ground of complaint.

It is also interesting to note that the trustees believed that the expectations of the members of their community—their customers—should be considered.

The annals of Massachusetts General Hospital include other examples of the hospital's concern about service quality. For example, in 1851, the hospital hired a watchman to guard against the danger of fire during the night (Bowditch, 1872, p. 367). In 1853, the hospital commended one of its surgical staff for compiling an analytical index for the surgical records of the institution and reflected on the quality of the surgical services provided (Bowditch, 1872, p. 483). In 1872, the trustees decided to regulate the use of restraints at the institution, and they identified each by type and set the conditions under which the restraint could be utilized (Bowditch, 1872, pp. 679–80). Throughout the history of the institution, the trustees received regular reports on the number of patients treated as well as the classification of each patient's outcome as discharged "well," "relieved," "not relieved," or "dead" (Bowditch, 1872, p. 447).

Medical Practice

Human anatomy and physiology were not well understood before the twentieth century. At one time, it was believed that four basic fluids, called humors, determined a person's temperament and health and that imbalances in the proportion of humors in the body caused disease. The therapeutic bleeding of patients was practiced into the early twentieth century. Early physicians also treated patients by administering a variety of substances with no scientific basis for their effectiveness. The science of medicine began to evolve in the late nineteenth century but was not fully realized until the second and third decades of the twentieth century.

Early on, the medical profession recognized that some of its members achieved better results than others and undertook to regulate the practice of medicine. At first, the regulation took the form of licensure, beginning in New York in 1760 and New Jersey in 1771. The New Jersey law stated that ". . . no person whatsoever shall practice as a physician or surgeon, within this colony of New Jersey, before he shall have first been examined in physic and surgery, approved of, and admitted by any two of the judges of the supreme court." The examination was to be performed before a board of "medical men" appointed by the state medical society (Trent, 1977, p. 91). Various states developed similar legislation over the following decades.

By the middle of the nineteenth century, however, medical licensure had been repudiated as undemocratic, and the penalties for practicing medicine without a license were removed in most of the states. The buyer definitely had to beware because the title of doctor could be used by anyone who wanted to sell medical services (Haller, 1981, pp. 200–201). During this period, medical education consisted primarily of an apprenticeship with an already-established practitioner of some kind. Following the apprenticeship, the new doctor could then hang out a shingle and begin to treat patients. Some trainees did attend schools that claimed to teach them how to become physicians, but there was no established medical curriculum. Many people received diplomas just by paying a fee. Many others with no education, apprenticeship, or license just hung out a shingle and began piling up the fees. Effectively, doctoring had become a commercial enterprise. Any man with sufficient entrepreneurial talents could enter the practice of medicine. The emphasis was on making a living rather than joining a true profession. The result was an overabundance of "medical men" who provided medical care based on all kinds of traditions.

The American Medical Association (AMA) was established in 1840 to represent the interests of physicians across the United States. The organization was dominated by members who had strong ties to the medical schools and the status quo. The organization's ability to lead reform was limited until it broke its ties with the medical colleges in 1874. At that time, the association encouraged the creation of independent state licensing boards (Haller, 1981, pp. 210 and 214).

In 1876, the Association of American Medical Colleges (AAMC) was established. The AAMC was dedicated to standardizing the curriculum of U.S. medical schools and to developing the public's appreciation of the need for medical licensure.

Together, the AMA and the AAMC pushed for medical licensing. By the 1890s, thirty-five states had established or reestablished a system of licensure for physicians. Fourteen states granted medical licenses only to graduates of reputable medical schools. The state licensing boards discouraged the worst medical schools, but the criteria for licensing continued to vary by state and were not fully enforced (Haller, 1981, p. 223).

By the early twentieth century, it had become apparent that promoting quality in medical practice required regulation through curriculum reform as well as licensure. The membership of the AMA, however, was divided on this issue. Conservative members continued to believe that the organization should stay out of the regulatory arena. Progressive members advocated the continuing development of state licensure systems and the development of a model medical curriculum.

The situation attracted the attention of the Carnegie Foundation for the Advancement of Teaching and its president, Henry S. Pritchett. Pritchett offered to sponsor and fund an independent review of the medical curriculum and the medical colleges of the United States. The review was undertaken in 1906 by Abraham Flexner, an educator from Louisville, Kentucky.

Over the following four years, Flexner visited every medical college in the country and carefully documented his findings. In his 1910 report to the Carnegie Foundation, the AMA, and the AAMC, he documented the unacceptable variation in curriculum that existed across the schools. He also noted that applicants to medical schools frequently lacked a knowledge of the basic sciences. Flexner also reported how the absence of appropriate hospital-based training limited the clinical skills of medical school graduates. Perhaps most important, he documented the huge number of graduates who were being produced by the colleges each year, most with unacceptable levels of medical expertise.

Several reform initiatives grew out of Flexner's report and recommendations made by the AMA's Committee on Medical Education. One of the reforms required medical college applicants to hold a baccalaureate degree. Another required that the medical curriculum be founded in the basic sciences. Reforms also required that medical students receive practical, hospital-based training. Most important, Flexner recommended the closing of most of the medical schools in the country. The former recommendations were instituted over the decade after the release of Flexner's report, but only about half of the medical colleges actually closed. By 1920, most of the colleges met rigorous academic standards and were approved by the AAMC.

Nursing Practice

During the nineteenth century and throughout the first part of the twentieth, over half of the hospitals in the United States were sponsored by religious organizations. Nursing care at that time was usually provided by members of religious orders. As the U.S. population grew and more towns and cities were established, hospitals were built to accommodate the healthcare needs of new communities. Older cities were also growing, and city hospitals became more and more crowded.

In the late nineteenth century, nurses received no formal education and training. Nursing staff for the hospitals was often recruited from the surrounding community, and many poor women who had no other skills became nurses. The nature of nursing care at that time was unsophisticated, and ignorance of basic hygiene often promoted disease rather than wellness. In 1871 at Bellevue Hospital in New York City, for example, 15 percent of patients died while hospitalized, and hospital-acquired infections were common. Even simple surgical procedures and maternity care often resulted in death due to infection (Kalisch and Kalisch, 1995, p. 71).

In 1868, the president of the American Medical Association, Dr. Samuel Gross, called the medical profession's attention to the need for trained nurses. During the years that followed, the public began to call for better nursing care in hospitals.

A small group of women physicians working in the northeast area of the country created the first formal program for training nurses. Dr. Susan Dimock, working with Dr. Marie Zakrzewska at the New England Hospital for Women and Children, organized a general training school for nurses in 1872 (Kalisch and Kalisch, 1995, p. 68). The school became a model for other institutions throughout the United States. As hospital after hospital struggled to find competent nursing staff, many institutions and their medical staffs developed their own nurse training programs to meet staffing needs.

The responsibilities of nurses in the late nineteenth and early twentieth centuries included housekeeping duties such as cleaning furniture and floors, making beds, changing linen, and controlling temperature, humidity, and ventilation. Nurses also cooked the meals for patients in kitchens attached to each ward. Direct patient care duties included giving baths, changing dressings, monitoring vital signs, administering medication, and assisting at surgical procedures (Kalisch and Kalisch, 1995, p. 137). Nurses generally worked twelve-hour shifts, seven days per week.

During this time, nurses were not required to hold a license to practice. Because licensure was not required and because it was difficult to attract women to nursing staff positions, many women who had no training at all continued to work in the nation's hospitals and as private-duty nurses.

In the years immediately following the turn of the twentieth century, nurses began to organize state nursing associations to advocate for the registration of nurses. Their goal was to increase the level of competence among nurses nationwide. Despite opposition from many physicians who believed that nurses did not need formal education or licensure, North Carolina passed the first nurse registration bill in the United States in 1903. Many other states initiated similar legislation in subsequent years.

Allied Health Professions

Other healthcare professions in the United States developed as specialized areas of practice over the course of the twentieth century. Each underwent periods of formalization in similar ways. Each became regulated either by the states or by national professional associations as membership and professional responsibilities grew and the public demanded that they document their professional competence. These developments made important contributions to the quality of healthcare delivered in this country. The allied health professions include radiologic technology, respiratory therapy, occupational therapy, and physical therapy, among others. For example, health information management professionals today are certified and registered by the American Health Information Management Association.

Contributions of Individuals

Many individuals made significant contributions to the early improvement of healthcare delivery in the United States. Contributions included a variety of improvement strategies, all of which could not possibly be discussed here. It is important, however, to recognize the contributions that individuals can and have made. The following individuals and their contributions are typical of the progress that can be made when healthcare professionals care about the quality of their work.

Maude E. Callen, an African-American public health nurse/midwife, undertook the training of midwives in coastal South Carolina in 1926. A registered nurse, Callen recognized that the midwives' lack of training contributed to high infant and maternal mortality rates in the region, and she traveled extensively throughout the region to assist at deliveries and improve the expertise of midwives (Hill, 1997, p. 49).

Robert Latou Dickinson, an obstetrician and gynecologist practicing in New England around the turn of the twentieth century, developed a standardized patient questionnaire. He used the patients' answers on the questionnaire to structure his examinations. The questionnaire represents one of the first uses of a structured health assessment tool in the United States (Bullough, 1997, p. 76).

Lavinia Lloyd Dock, a nurse and early nurse educator, developed important approaches to disaster nursing at the end of the nineteenth century. After graduating from a nurse training program, Dock worked to institute appropriate nursing practices during the yellow fever epidemic in Jacksonville, Florida, in 1888, and during the aftermath of the Johnstown, Pennsylvania, flood in 1889 (Leighow, 1997, p. 79).

Roswell Park, a physician and surgeon during the late nineteenth century, helped to disseminate the principles of antisepsis during surgical procedures in the United States. On the basis of the findings of the English scientist Joseph Lister, Park advocated the use of antiseptic techniques and appropriate wound care in the treatment of surgical cases well before such approaches were common in the United States (Gage, 1997, p. 204).

Nicholas J. Pisacano, a physician who practiced in the middle and late twentieth century, recognized the need to upgrade the practice of the general practitioner as new technologies and treatments were developed. He worked tirelessly to found and promote the specialty of family practice in the United States (Adams and Moore, 1997, p. 221).

Ernst P. Boas, a physician who practiced in New York City during the first half of the twentieth century, was among the first to call for the coordinated, interdisciplinary care of the chronically ill. Prior to his advocacy, the chronically ill were often considered incurable. He believed that the development of new therapeutics and restorative technologies could return people with chronic illnesses to better health and productivity. His work led to the establishment of the Goldwater Memorial Hospital for Chronic Diseases on Welfare Island in New York City (Brickman, 1997, p. 21).

Mary Steichen Calderone, medical director of the Planned Parenthood Federation of America during the 1950s, launched a clinical investigation program to scientifically identify effective contraceptive methods. Hers was one of the first efforts to identify appropriate clinical practice through the use of scientific evidence in a controversial area (Meldrum, 1997, p. 45).

Hospital Standardization and Accreditation

In 1910, Dr. Edward Martin suggested that the surgical area of medical practice needed to become more concerned with patient outcomes. He had been introduced to this concept through discussions with Dr. Ernest Codman, a British physician who believed that hospital practitioners should track their patients for a significant time after treatment to determine whether the end result was positive or negative. Dr. Codman also advocated the use of outcome information to identify the practices that led to the best results.

Dr. Martin and others had been concerned about the conditions in U.S. hospitals for some time. Many observers felt that part of the problem was related to the absence of organized medical staffs in hospitals and to lax professional standards. In the early twentieth century, hospitals were used primarily by surgeons who required their facilities to treat patients with surgical modalities. Therapies based on medical regimens were not developed until later in the century. It was natural, therefore, for the impetus for improvement in hospital care to come from the surgical community.

In November 1912, the Third Clinical Congress of Surgeons of North America was held. At this meeting, Dr. Franklin Martin made proposals that eventually led to the formation of the American College of Surgeons. Dr. Edward Martin made the following resolution (Roberts, Coate, and Redman, 1987, p. 936):

> Be it resolved by the Clinical Congress of Surgeons of North America here assembled, that some system of standardization of hospital equipment and hospital work should be developed to the end that those institutions having the highest ideals may have proper recognition before the profession, and that those of inferior equipment and standards should be stimulated to raise the quality of their work. In this way patients will receive the best type of treatment, and the public will have some means of recognizing those institutions devoted to the highest levels of medicine.

Through the proposal and the resolution, the American College of Surgeons and the hospital improvement movement became intimately tied. Immediately upon formation, however, officers of the college realized how important their work would be. They were forced to reject 60 percent of the fellowship applications during the college's first three years because applicants were unable to provide documentation in support of their clinical competence (Roberts, Coate, and Redman, 1987, p. 937). Medical records from many hospitals were so inadequate that they could not supply information about the applicants' practice in the institutions. Because of this situation and many others of which they became aware, college officers petitioned the Carnegie Foundation in 1917 for funding to plan and develop a hospital standardization program.

In 1917, a committee on standards was formed by the college and met to consider the development of a minimum set of standards that U.S. hospitals would have to meet if they wanted approval from the American College of Surgeons. On December 20, 1917, the American College of Surgeons formally established the Hospital Standardization Program and published a formal set of hospital standards, which they called *The Minimum Standard.*

During 1918 and part of 1919, the college undertook the review of hospitals across the United States and Canada as a field trial to see whether *The Minimum Standard* would be effective as a measurement tool. In total, 692 hospitals were surveyed, of which only 89 met the standard entirely. Some of the most prestigious institutions in the United States failed to meet the standard. Brief and clear in its delineation of what was believed to promote good hospital-based patient care in 1918, *The Minimum Standard* (American College of Surgeons, 1930, p. 3) stated:

1. That physicians and surgeons privileged to practice in the hospital be organized as a definite group or staff. Such organization has nothing to do with the question as to whether the hospital is "open" or "closed," nor need it affect the various existing types of staff organization. The word STAFF is here defined as the group of doctors who practice in the hospital inclusive of all groups such as the "regular staff," the "visiting staff," and the "associate staff."

2. That membership upon the staff be restricted to physicians and surgeons who are (a) full graduates of medicine in good standing and legally licensed to practice in their respective states or provinces; (b) competent in their respective fields; and (c) worthy in character and in matters of professional ethics; that in this latter connection the practice of the division of fees, under any guise whatever, be prohibited.

3. That the staff initiate and, with the approval of the governing board of the hospital, adopt rules, regulations, and policies governing the professional work of the hospital; that these rules, regulations, and policies specifically provide: (a) That staff meetings be held at least once each month. (In large hospitals the departments may choose to meet separately.) (b) That the staff review and analyze at regular intervals their clinical experience in the various departments of the hospital, such as medicine, surgery, obstetrics, and the other specialties; the clinical records of patients, free and pay, to be the basis of such review and analysis.

4. That accurate and complete records be written for all patients and filed in an accessible manner in the hospital—a complete case record being one which includes identification data; complaint; personal and family history; history of present illness; physical examination; special examinations, such as consultations, clinical laboratory, X-ray and other examinations; provisional or working diagnosis; medical or surgical treatment; gross and microscopical pathological findings; progress notes; final diagnosis; condition on discharge; followup and, in case of death, autopsy findings.

5. That diagnostic and therapeutic facilities under competent supervision be available for the study, diagnosis, and treatment of patients, these to include, at least (a) a clinical laboratory providing chemical, bacteriological, serological, and pathological services; (b) an X-ray department providing radiographic and fluoroscopic services.

The adoption of *The Minimum Standard* marked the beginning of the **accreditation** process for healthcare organizations. A similar process is still followed today. (For more information, see chapter 14 of this textbook.) Basically, the process is based on the development of reasonable quality standards and an annual survey of the organization's performance on the standards. The accreditation program is voluntary, and healthcare organizations request participation in order to improve patient care (Roberts, Coate, and Redman, 1987, p. 937).

The American College of Surgeons continued to examine and approve hospitals for three decades. By 1950, however, the number of hospitals being surveyed every year had grown unmanageable, and the college could no longer afford to administer the program alone. After considerable discussion and organizing activity, four professional associations from the United States and Canada decided to join the American College of Surgeons to develop the Joint Commission on the Accreditation of Hospitals. These associations were the American College of Physicians, the American Medical Association, the American Hospital Association, and the Canadian Medical Association. The new accrediting agency was formally incorporated in 1952 and began accreditation activities in 1953. It continues its activities almost fifty years later as the Joint Commission on Accreditation of Healthcare Organizations.

Performance Improvement and Modern Healthcare

Until the Second World War, most healthcare was still provided in the home. Quality in healthcare services was considered a byproduct of appropriate medical practice and oversight by physicians. The positive and negative effects of other factors and the contributions of other healthcare workers were not given much consideration.

In the 1950s, the number of hospitals grew to support developments in diagnostic, therapeutic, and surgical technology and pharmacology. Fueled by an expanding economy, federal legislation (the Hill–Burton Act of 1946) funded extensive hospital construction. A renewed insurance industry helped to pay for the new healthcare services provided to groups of individual beneficiaries.

During this period, the Hospital Standardization Program was replaced by the Joint Commission on the Accreditation of Hospitals. A whole new set of standards covered every aspect of hospital care. The intent was to ensure that the care provided to patients in accredited hospitals would be of the highest quality.

The construction of new facilities and the growth of the medical insurance industry did not guarantee access to services. As new treatments and "miracle" drugs such as antibiotics were developed, healthcare services became more and more costly. Many Americans, particularly the poor and the elderly, could not afford to buy healthcare insurance or to pay for the services themselves.

Medicare/Medicaid Programs

The idea of federal funding for healthcare services goes back to the 1930s, the Great Depression, and Franklin Roosevelt's New Deal. Harry Truman also supported a universal healthcare program in the late 1940s. But it was not until the 1960s and the presidency of Lyndon Johnson that the federal government developed a program to pay for the healthcare services provided to the poor and the elderly (AHA, 1999).

In 1965, the United States Congress passed Public Law 89-97, an amendment to the Social Security Act of 1935. Title XVIII of Public Law 89-97 established health insurance for the aged and the disabled. This program soon became known as **Medicare.** Title XIX of Public Law 89-97 provided grants to states for establishing medical assistance programs for the poor. The Title XIX program became known as **Medicaid.** The objective of the programs was to ensure access to healthcare for citizens who could not afford to pay for it themselves. The Great Society of the 1960s marshaled billions of dollars to fund care for millions of Americans.

During the 1970s, attempts were made to further standardize and improve the clinical services provided by physicians and hospitals. Under the authority of Medicare officials, medical audits were conducted in attempts to identify physicians with substandard practice patterns. Peer review organizations tried to improve quality by disciplining substandard physicians. Such **quality assurance** efforts were only partially successful.

The changes that most significantly improved patient outcomes involved the development and use of sophisticated medical technology and pharmaceuticals. The overall benefits of modern healthcare were evident in increased life spans and better medical outcomes. Americans had come to expect the best and the newest medical care available as a personal right not to be taken away.

By 1980, however, it was obvious that healthcare spending in the United States would consume more and more economic resources if left unchecked. The Medicare and Medicaid programs were on their way to becoming the most expensive government programs in U.S. history. At the same time, healthcare experts also began to understand that increased spending and technological advancements did not automatically guarantee quality in healthcare.

In the early 1980s, a new nationwide system was developed to standardize reimbursement for hospital services provided to Medicare and Medicaid beneficiaries. Until 1983, Medicare/Medicaid reimbursement was based on a **retrospective payment system.** In a retrospective payment system, providers are reimbursed for the cost of services they provided at some point in the past. Retrospective payment is also called fee-for-service payment. In a **prospective payment system,** providers receive a fixed payment for the services they provide. The level of reimbursement is determined before the services are ever provided. Therefore, prospective payment systems encourage providers to control costs and avoid unnecessary services.

In the Medicare/Medicaid prospective payment system, reimbursement for hospital inpatient services is based on **diagnosis-related groups** (DRGs). The system assumes that similar diseases and treatments consume similar amounts of resources and therefore have similar total costs. Every hospital patient is assigned to an appropriate DRG on the basis of his or her diagnosis at discharge. Reimbursement levels for each DRG are updated annually and adjusted for the geographic location of the healthcare facility.

The HCFA Common Procedure Coding System (HCPCS) was developed in 1983. HCPCS codes are used to report the healthcare services provided to Medicare and Medicaid beneficiaries treated in ambulatory settings. HCPCS includes three separate levels of codes: (level I) Physicians' Current Procedural Terminology (CPT) codes, (level II) national codes, and (level III) local codes.

A prospective payment system for hospital outpatient and ambulatory surgery services provided to Medicare and Medicaid beneficiaries is scheduled for implementation in 2000 and 2001. This system is based on **ambulatory payment classification** groups (APCs). The APCs are generated on the basis of the CPT/HCPCS codes assigned for services such as outpatient diagnostic procedures and outpatient radiology procedures.

U.S. hospitals provide billions of dollars worth of care to Medicare/Medicaid patients every year. The implementation of prospective payment systems has made it necessary for healthcare organizations to devise ways to control costs without endangering safe and effective patient care.

Managed Care Revolution

The growth of managed care in the United States has also had a tremendous impact on healthcare providers. **Managed care** is a broad term used to describe several types of managed healthcare plans. Health maintenance organizations (HMOs) are one of the most familiar types of managed care. Members of an HMO (or their employers) pay a set premium and are entitled to a specific range of healthcare services. HMOs control costs by requiring beneficiaries to seek services from a preapproved list of providers, by limiting access to specialists and expensive diagnostic and treatment procedures, and by requiring preauthorization for inpatient hospitalization and surgery.

Other types of managed care include preferred provider organizations (PPOs) and point-of-service (POS) plans. These types of managed care plans negotiate discounted rates with specific hospitals, physicians, and other healthcare providers. Many also restrict access to specialists and require preauthorization for surgery and other hospital services. In PPOs, enrollees are required to seek care from a limited list of providers who have agreed in advance to accept a discounted payment for their services. Enrollees in POS plans pay for a greater portion of their healthcare expenses when they choose to seek treatment from providers who do not participate in their plan.

Together, the Medicare/Medicaid programs and the managed care insurance industry have virtually eliminated fee-for-service reimbursement arrangements. At the same time, healthcare consumers are demanding more services and greater quality. Hospitals and physicians now find that they have no choice but to become more efficient and effective if they are to stay in business. Programs that promote **efficiency** and **effectiveness** have become the only way for providers to add value to the services they provide and the only way for them to ensure their financial viability.

Total Quality Management in Healthcare

In the 1980s, leaders in the healthcare industry began to take notice of a theory from general industry called **total quality management (TQM).** This approach mobilizes the individuals directly involved in a work process to examine and improve the process with the goal of achieving a better product. It does not matter what the product might be. TQM is firmly based in the statistical analysis of objective data. It was developed by W. Edwards Deming in the early 1950s as an alternative to authoritarian, top-down management systems. Philip Crosby and J. M. Juran adapted TQM and developed similar approaches.

Total quality management revolutionized industrial production in Japan during the postwar period. When Japanese automobiles took over the U.S. market in the 1960s and 1970s, American manufacturers began to take notice of TQM. They understood that Deming's management philosophy might help them to create more efficient and effective manufacturing processes.

Avedis Donabedian was one of the first theorists to recognize that the TQM philosophy could be applied to healthcare services. Beginning in 1966, Donabedian advocated the assessment of healthcare from four perspectives: **structure, process, outcome,** and **cost.** Only in the 1990s, however, were his approaches widely adopted. Today, every major healthcare performance improvement model recognizes the importance of these four factors.

By the end of the 1990s, some individuals involved in the improvement of quality in healthcare had made a significant realization: quality in healthcare was tied very closely to the performance of individuals in the organization. Unlike manufacturing firms that utilize machinery to shape raw materials into physical products, the products of healthcare organizations were the services provided to patients by healthcare professionals. It was recognized that the performance of those professionals thereby determined the quality of the services. "Quality" improvement initiatives in healthcare organizations were renamed "performance" improvement initiatives.

Why Care about Performance Improvement?

So why should healthcare professionals care about performance improvement? Because performance improvement is the key to ensuring the quality of patient services. Today, most payers negotiate only with organizations that provide healthcare services of the highest quality at the lowest cost. And it is not enough to say that the quality of patient care is the highest priority of an organization. The organization must be able to prove its claims with reliable, objective data. Government-sponsored and commercial health plans, employers, and consumers alike are all asking for more information on the quality of the healthcare services they receive and pay for. Finally, quality is the key to meeting regulatory, licensure, and accreditation requirements. The agencies sponsoring these activities are extremely interested in how healthcare organizations improve the processes and products that they offer to the public.

Summary

Quality and performance improvement in healthcare have a long tradition in the United States. Improvement initiatives at the end of the twentieth century concentrated on refining improvement methodologies and making improvement processes more scientific. But the roots of the improvement tradition are still alive. The authors of this textbook believe that students of healthcare performance improvement should be aware of these roots as they proceed in their studies.

References

Adams, D. P., and A. L. Moore. 1997. Nicholas J. Pisacano in *Doctors, Nurses, and Medical Practitioners: A Bio-Biographical Sourcebook*. Lois N. Magner, editor. Westport, Conn.: Greenwood Press.

American College of Surgeons. 1930. *Manual of Hospital Standardization and Hospital Standardization Report*. Chicago: American College of Surgeons.

American Hospital Association. 1999. *100 Faces of Health Care*. Chicago: Health Forum.

Bowditch, N. I. 1872 (reprinted 1972). *History of the Massachusetts General Hospital*. Boston: Arno Press and *New York Times*.

Brickman, J. P. 1997. Ernst P. Boas in *Doctors, Nurses, and Medical Practitioners: A Bio-Biographical Sourcebook*. Lois N. Magner, editor. Westport, Conn.: Greenwood Press.

Bullough, V. L. 1997. Robert Latou Dickinson in *Doctors, Nurses, and Medical Practitioners: A Bio-Biographical Sourcebook*. Lois N. Magner, editor. Westport, Conn.: Greenwood Press.

Crosby, Philip B. 1980. *Quality Is Free*. New York City: Mentor Books.

Crosby, Philip B. 1984. *Quality without Tears*. New York City: Plume Books.

Donabedian, Avedis. 1966. Evaluating the quality of medical care. *Milbank Quarterly* 44:166–203.

Donabedian, Avedis. 1980. *The Definition of Quality and Approaches to Its Management*. Volume 1: *Explorations in Quality Assessment and Monitoring*. Ann Arbor, Mich.: Health Administration Press.

Donabedian, Avedis. 1988. The quality of care: how can it be assessed? *JAMA* 260(12):1743–48.

Gage, A. 1997. Roswell Park in *Doctors, Nurses, and Medical Practitioners: A Bio-Biographical Sourcebook*. Lois N. Magner, editor. Westport, Conn.: Greenwood Press.

Haller, John S. 1981. *American Medicine in Transition 1840–1910*. Chicago: University of Illinois Press.

Hill, P. E. 1997. Maude E. Callen in *Doctors, Nurses, and Medical Practitioners: A Bio-Biographical Sourcebook*. Lois N. Magner, editor. Westport, Conn.: Greenwood Press.

Kalisch, Philip A., and Beatrice J. Kalisch. 1995. *The Advance of American Nursing*. Philadelphia: J. B. Lippincott Company.

Leighow, S. R. 1997. Lavinia Lloyd Dock in *Doctors, Nurses, and Medical Practitioners: A Bio-Biographical Sourcebook*. Lois N. Magner, editor. Westport, Conn.: Greenwood Press.

Meldrum, M. 1997. Mary Steichen Calderone in *Doctors, Nurses, and Medical Practitioners: A Bio-Biographical Sourcebook*. Lois N. Magner, editor. Westport, Conn.: Greenwood Press.

Morton, Thomas G. 1895 (reprinted 1973). *The History of the Pennsylvania Hospital*. New York City: Arno Press.

Roberts, James S., Jack G. Coate, and Robert Redman. 1987. A history of the Joint Commission on Accreditation of Hospitals. *JAMA* 256(7):936–40.

Silin, Charles I. 1977. A state medical board examination in 1816. *Legacies in Law and Medicine*. C. R. Burns, editor. New York City: Science History Publications.

Trent, Josiah C. 1977. An early New Jersey medical license. *Legacies in Law and Medicine*. C. R. Burns, editor. New York City: Science History Publications.

Walton, Mary. 1986. *The Deming Management Method*. New York City: Perigee Books.

Walton, Mary. 1990. *Deming Management at Work*. New York City: G. P. Putnam's Sons.

Part I
A Performance Improvement Model

Chapter 1
Defining a Performance Improvement Model

Learning Objectives

- To understand the cyclical nature of performance improvement activities
- To describe the distinction between organizationwide performance improvement activities and team-based performance improvement activities
- To outline the organizationwide performance improvement cycle
- To outline the team-based performance improvement cycle

Background and Significance

QA (quality assurance), TQM (total quality management), QI (quality improvement), CQI (continuous quality improvement), QM (quality management), PI (performance improvement): efforts to ensure the quality of the healthcare services provided in the United States have gone by many names. The acronyms represent quality and performance improvement models and methodologies that have been used with varying degrees of success by healthcare organizations over the past thirty years. Many books and articles have been written on the subject, and new models and terminology will likely be developed in the future.

A professional just entering the healthcare field will probably work for many different organizations over his or her career and participate in many different quality and performance improvement projects. He or she will learn to use specific quality and performance improvement models and techniques as needed. With experience, he or she will develop the skill necessary to customize the models to specific organizations and healthcare services.

The goal of this chapter is to provide a general overview of quality and performance improvement as it is applied in healthcare organizations. The chapter describes a generic model of performance improvement. It also defines commonly used PI terms and explains the basic philosophy of continuous performance improvement.

Performance Improvement as a Cyclical Process

Accreditation organizations, groups of clinical professionals, quality management professionals, healthcare providers, and government regulatory and policy-making entities all have unique perspectives on quality in healthcare. Many have developed their own methodologies for quality and performance improvement. But most performance improvement models being applied in healthcare today share one organizing characteristic: they are cyclical in nature.

The models are based on the assumption that performance improvement activities will take place continuously and that services, processes, and outcomes can always be improved. Quality is not to be treated as a goal to be accomplished and then forgotten. It is to be treated as an ongoing mission that guides everyday operations.

Accreditation and licensing agencies expect hospitals and other healthcare facilities to strive for the highest quality of care possible at all times. Healthcare executives and boards of directors monitor the outcomes of the PI programs in their organizations. Most large healthcare organizations employ experts in quality management who are responsible for ensuring the success of PI activities and reporting results to the board and executive management.

The general PI model presented in this textbook includes two interrelated cycles. The cycle illustrated in figure 1.1 represents the organization's ongoing performance-monitoring function. The cycle illustrated in figure 1.2 represents the activities of individual PI teams working on specific PI projects. Together, the two cycles make up the healthcare performance improvement model (figure 1.3).

Performance Monitoring

As shown in figure 1.1, performance monitoring depends on the identification of **critical performance measures.** Critical performance measures are developed around the processes and products (sometimes called **hard issues**) and staff attitudes (sometimes called **soft issues**) upon which customers base their perceptions of quality. These issues represent the most important aspects of the services provided by the organization. (See chapter 2.) Critical performance measures must also reflect the organization's **mission, vision,** and **strategic plan.** (See chapter 13.)

For example, the strategic plan at Community Hospital of the West included a goal that called for improving physician satisfaction. Improvement was to be measured according to the results of the next biannual medical staff survey. One **action plan** for achieving the goal called for refining the centralized scheduling process. The associated performance measure was to improve physician satisfaction responses on the biannual survey with at least 10 percent of the responses moving to the "very satisfied" response category compared to the results of the previous survey.

A second strategic goal at Community Hospital of the West was to improve employee turnover rates. The associated performance measure involved improving employee satisfaction and decreasing employee turnover (the loss and replacement of qualified employees) by 10 percent during the next year. The organization's action plan included three objectives: to institute awards and recognition for years of service, to improve employee evaluation and training processes, and to implement a merit raise program.

The organizational unit that is responsible for achieving a critical performance measure continuously monitors performance on the measure. The unit compares the organization's performance to the performance of similar service units within and outside the organization. In some cases, the comparison may also be made to the national performance experience by using data from similar organizations across the country. This comparison of performance is called **benchmarking.**

When variation is discovered through continuous monitoring or when unexpected events suggest performance problems, members of the organization may decide that there is an **opportunity for improvement.** The opportunity may involve a process, a product, or an attitude that could be changed to better meet customers' expectations or accreditation and licensure requirements.

Who identifies opportunities for improvement? Many people may participate, but participation depends most on the attitudes of the individuals working in the organization. Ideally, performance improvement should be a bottom-up process in which those closest to care processes identify improvement opportunities. In such situations, nonmanagement personnel often identify the opportunities and decide for themselves what to work on.

In some organizations, however, employees may not feel free to offer suggestions for improvement. In addition, managers who have a traditional style of management—those

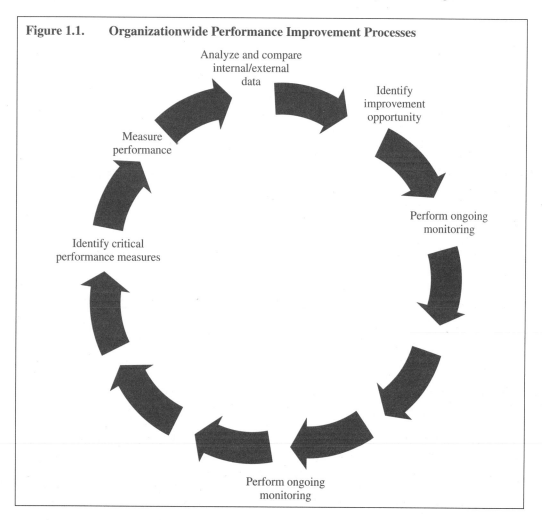

Figure 1.1.   Organizationwide Performance Improvement Processes

Analyze and compare internal/external data

Identify improvement opportunity

Measure performance

Perform ongoing monitoring

Identify critical performance measures

Perform ongoing monitoring

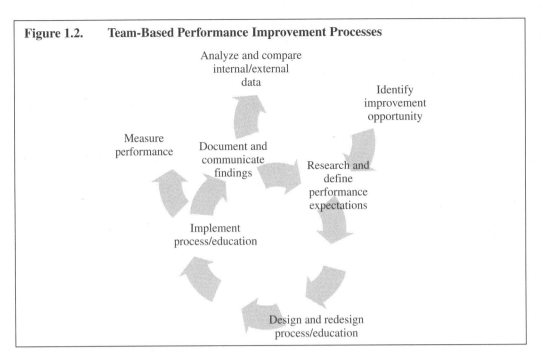

Figure 1.2.   Team-Based Performance Improvement Processes

who believe that only managers should direct change—may feel threatened by PI processes. In such situations, managers assume the responsibility for identifying opportunities for improvement. Because there is a wide spectrum of performance improvement mind-sets in real healthcare organizations, many subtly different approaches may be encountered.

Many healthcare organizations maintain a leadership group to oversee and stimulate performance improvement activities. After an improvement opportunity has been identified, the leadership group (sometimes called a **performance improvement council**) may respond in a variety of ways. When the improvement opportunity is believed to be the result of a lack of knowledge or experience, the leadership group may initiate an educational program. Educational programs are often developed in response to soft issues. The goal of the educational program is to eliminate counterproductive attitudes that have developed over time. When the improvement opportunity is the result of an inherent inefficiency or ineffectiveness in a work process, however, the leadership group may convene a **performance improvement team** to examine the process or product involved. (The relationship between organizationwide performance monitoring and team-based improvement process is illustrated in figure 1.3.)

Team-Based Performance Improvement Processes

The first task of a performance improvement team is to research and define performance expectations for the process or product targeted for improvement. Research involves comparing the current process or product to the organization's performance standards, national benchmarking standards, and customers' expectations and needs. After it has developed a clear picture of the factors that require improvement, the team designs or redesigns the product or process to better satisfy the customers' needs.

Performance improvement teams have a variety of tools that they can use to accomplish their goals. This textbook calls these quality improvement tools collected from traditional

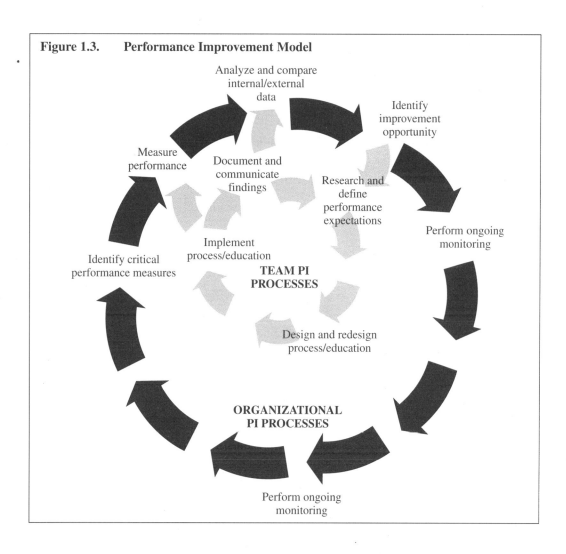

Figure 1.3.   Performance Improvement Model

quality improvement practice and theory **QI toolbox techniques.** The tools make it easier to gather and analyze information, and they help team members stay focused on PI activities and move the process along efficiently. Each of the subsequent chapters of part I of this textbook and all of the chapters in part II introduce at least one technique from the QI toolbox.

After implementation of a new process, performance is again measured against customers' expectations and other performance standards. The team may need to redesign the process or product when measurements indicate that there is room for further improvement. When measurements indicate that the improvement is effective, ongoing monitoring of the process is resumed (as in figure 1.1). The team documents and communicates its findings to the leadership group and other interested parties in the organization. Results may also be communicated to interested groups in the community.

The team is usually disbanded at this point in the cycle, and routine organizational monitoring of the critical performance measures is resumed. When another opportunity for improvement arises, the team-based improvement process is reinstituted.

Summary

Performance improvement in healthcare is a cyclical process. Healthcare professionals are expected to continuously look for opportunities to improve the quality of processes, products, and professional attitudes. Many performance improvement methodologies can be applied in healthcare organizations. Most methodologies, however, follow a model of continuous performance monitoring, ongoing identification of improvement opportunities, and team-based improvement processes.

References

McLaughlin, Curtis P., and Arnold D. Kaluzny. 1994. *Continuous Quality Improvement in Health Care: Theory, Implementation, and Applications.* Gaithersburg, Md.: Aspen Publishers.

Meisenheimer, Claire G., editor. 1997. *Improving Quality: A Guide to Effective Programs.* Gaithersburg, Md.: Aspen Publishers.

Tacket, S. A. 1991. The quality council: a catalyst for improvement. *Journal of Quality Assurance* 13(5):30–36, September–October.

Chapter 2
Finding Improvement Opportunities

Learning Objectives

- To identify the four principal aspects of healthcare that are targeted for performance improvement
- To understand the significance of outputs in performance improvement methodology
- To explain how brainstorming and the nominal group technique can be used in performance improvement activities

Background and Significance

The American healthcare system is extremely complex. The idea of improving even a tiny element of the system may seem daunting to students new to the concept of performance improvement. Where does the process begin? How are potential areas for improvement identified? To answer these questions, it is important, first, to develop a general understanding of the areas of healthcare services that are the focus of quality improvement efforts.

Most healthcare quality improvement philosophies focus on four areas of healthcare:

- **Structures:** The foundations of care giving, which include buildings, equipment, technologies, professional staff, and appropriate policies
- **Processes:** The interrelated activities of healthcare organizations, which include governance, managerial support, and clinical processes, that affect patient outcomes across departments and disciplines within an integrated environment
- **Outcomes:** The end results of healthcare services in terms of the patient's expectations, needs, and quality of life, which may be positive and appropriate or negative and diminishing
- **Cost:** The financial investment of individuals, healthcare organizations, and society in providing healthcare services and its relationship to the quality of care provided

All performance improvement programs in healthcare organizations should address these four aspects of patient care (Donabedian, 1988). Of course, not every improvement project can address all four areas, but every improvement project should address quality in one of these areas.

Continuous Improvement Builds on Continuous Monitoring: Steps to Success

In order to discover what processes, structures, outcomes, or costs need to be improved, a healthcare organization must first find out what is and what is not working with respect to the needs and expectations of its customers. (See the discussion of monitoring performance in chapter 1.) Most improvement methodologies recognize that the organization must continuously analyze the care environment to identify aspects of the organization that can be improved. (See figure 2.1 for an illustration of the process.)

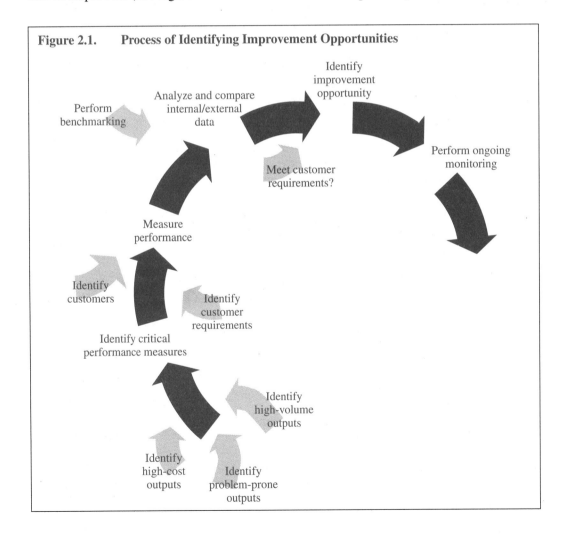

Figure 2.1.   Process of Identifying Improvement Opportunities

Step 1: The organization identifies its outputs

Outputs are the measurable products of the organization's work. In healthcare, outputs include:

- The things and actions provided to patients and clients (products and services)

- The effects services have on patients and clients (outcomes)

In addition, the processes of every organizational unit have outputs that affect other organizational units. This means that the members of the organization are each other's customers. For each process, the outputs must first be identified. Outputs received by patients and clients as well as outputs received by other members of the organization must be considered. (See the discussion of internal and external customers in chapter 4.)

Benchmarking is another means through which products, services, and outcomes can be identified for improvement. **Benchmarking** is the systematic comparison of the products, services, and outcomes of one organization with those of a similar organization. Benchmarking comparisons can also be made to regional and national standards.

Finally, organizations sometimes receive dramatic information about the ineffectiveness of a care process through sentinel events. **Sentinel events** usually involve the significant injury or death of a patient or an employee through avoidable causes. Such problem-prone outputs get the organization's attention very quickly. An analysis of the causes of a sentinel event usually allows the organization to make significant improvements in a process. (See chapter 7.)

The most important outputs are those related to strategically important product lines or to the organization's overall mission. Some organizations use the criteria high volume, high cost, and problem prone to identify the outputs that should receive the most scrutiny:

- Processes related to high-volume outputs affect numerous customers.

- Processes related to high-cost outputs affect the financial health of the organization.

- Processes related to problem-prone outputs can result in negative outcomes that might open the organization to malpractice suits or other legal actions.

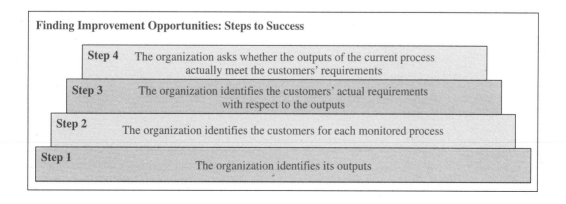

Finding Improvement Opportunities: Steps to Success

Step 4 The organization asks whether the outputs of the current process actually meet the customers' requirements

Step 3 The organization identifies the customers' actual requirements with respect to the outputs

Step 2 The organization identifies the customers for each monitored process

Step 1 The organization identifies its outputs

The outputs related to strategically important product lines and to the organization's overall mission become the organization's critical performance measures—those outputs by which the quality of the organization and its work units will be measured by patients, clients, visitors, and community leaders.

Step 2: The organization identifies the customers for each monitored process

The question to be answered in this step is who is the receiver of the outputs? The list must be exhaustive and must include internal and external customers (as described in chapter 4).

Step 3: The organization identifies the customers' actual requirements with respect to the outputs

Identifying actual requirements must be done from the customers' perspective. Identifying the factors most valued by customers is the objective, whether those customers are internal or external to the organization.

Step 4: The organization asks whether the outputs of the current process actually meet the customers' requirements

When the answer is yes, another process within the organization is selected and examined. When the answer is no, a performance improvement team may be formed to examine the process in greater detail. (See chapter 3.) Alternatively, an educational program may be developed to fine-tune the organization members' ability to execute the process effectively.

Real-Life Examples

Some ways that healthcare work units have identified improvement opportunities using the techniques introduced in this chapter are discussed in the following paragraphs.

Registration for Day Surgery

At one hospital, many patients had complained about having to come to the facility two and three times for preoperative testing. The PI team assigned to explore the problem identified the following outputs, customers, and customers' needs:

Outputs?	Registration information provided Preoperative workup completed Surgery scheduled
Customers?	Patient and patient's family Physician and office staff Surgery staff Registration staff
Customers' Requirements?	One-time communication of registration information Preoperative workup completed before surgery and coordinated in one visit Surgery date and time confirmed during the same visit

Customers' Requirements Met?	Patient satisfaction surveys showed only 76 percent satisfaction with same-day surgery registration and preoperative workup processes
	Registration staff and physician office staff were hearing complaints from patients that registration process was cumbersome and not user-friendly
	Duplicate data collection occurred between physician office registration and same-day surgery registration

Business Office and Health Information Management Departments

In another hospital, the number of accounts waiting to be billed had increased over the past six months. The business office and health information management (HIM) departments decided to look at the timeliness, appropriateness, and effectiveness of their information-processing procedures. A PI team assigned to examine the process developed the following information:

Outputs?	Patient insurance and benefits information
	Complete health record documentation
	Clinical codes
	Billed accounts

Customers?	Patients
	Physicians and other clinical staff
	Business office staff
	HIM staff
	Administration

Customers' Requirements?	Unbilled accounts continuously below $1 million
	Health record delinquency rate less than 50 percent
	HIM health record completion standards met
	Business office benefits verification standards met

Customers' Requirements Met?	Unbilled accounts greater than $3 million
	Health record delinquency rates greater than 50 percent
	HIM backlogs in all chart completion areas
	Business office benefits verification at admission occurring only 48 percent of the time

QI Toolbox Techniques

The most common toolbox techniques used to identify performance improvement opportunities include **brainstorming,** the **nominal group technique,** and **affinity diagrams.**

Brainstorming

Brainstorming can be conducted in a structured or an unstructured way. In *structured* brainstorming, the leader solicits input from team members by going from one to the next around the table or room. Each team member comments on the issue in turn or passes until the next round. This process continues until participants have no new ideas to suggest or until the time period set in the meeting's agenda has lapsed. In *unstructured* brainstorming, members of the team offer ideas as they come to mind. Some members may have no ideas to offer and others may contribute a number of ideas.

In either method of brainstorming, several general rules are followed:

- Everyone agrees on the issue to be brainstormed.

- All ideas are written down on a white board or flip chart in the team members' own words.

- Ideas are never criticized or discussed during the brainstorming period.

- The process is limited in the time allotted, 5 to 15 minutes at most.

Nominal Group Technique

The **nominal group technique** gives each member of the team an opportunity to select which ideas under discussion are the most important. This technique allows groups to narrow the focus of discussion or to make decisions without getting involved in extended, circular discussions during which more vocal members dominate. All of the ideas obtained during a brainstorming session are written in a place where everyone can see them. Teams usually use white boards or flip charts for this purpose.

Next, team members vote on the various issues or ideas to determine which should be considered first. The facilitator then writes a numeral 1 by the idea chosen by each team member in turn. This process continues until all of the team members have ranked all of the issues or ideas on a numerical scale. For example, if there were five issues listed, each team member would rank the five issues from 1 to 5, with 1 being the most important and 5 being the least important. Then the facilitator adds up the rankings for each issue. The issue with the lowest sum is selected as the team's choice as the most important. The team then works on this issue first, followed by the other four in ranked order.

Another way to vote is to use adhesive dots in various colors. Each team member chooses a color, and the members affix their dots to the five issues they feel are most important. The issue that has the most dots is the most important. This method works well because members can be influenced by other members' placement of votes, thus allowing consensus to begin to develop during the voting process.

Affinity Diagrams

Affinity diagrams are used to organize and prioritize ideas after the initial brainstorming session. This type of diagram is useful when the team generates a large amount of information. The team members agree on the primary categories or groupings from the brainstorming session and then secondary ideas are listed under each primary category. This process allows the team to tackle a large problem in a more manageable way (JCAHO, 1993). (See figure 2.2 for an example.)

Case Study

Students should watch the movie *The Doctor,* with William Hurt, or *Patch Adams,* with Robin Williams. In class, students should brainstorm positive and negative healthcare quality issues as portrayed in the film they watched. Then they should create an affinity

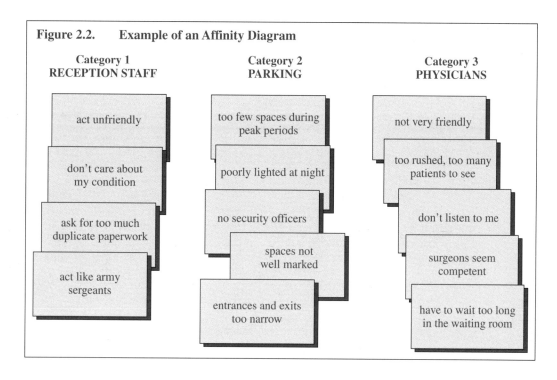

Figure 2.2.   Example of an Affinity Diagram

Category 1 RECEPTION STAFF	Category 2 PARKING	Category 3 PHYSICIANS
act unfriendly	too few spaces during peak periods	not very friendly
don't care about my condition	poorly lighted at night	too rushed, too many patients to see
ask for too much duplicate paperwork	no security officers	don't listen to me
act like army sergeants	spaces not well marked	surgeons seem competent
	entrances and exits too narrow	have to wait too long in the waiting room

diagram by writing the brainstormed issues on adhesive notes and group similar quality issues together on a white board or flip chart.

Project Application

Students should brainstorm issues or opportunities for improvement that they have observed in their academic environment, general community, work settings, or personal activities. The issues can be educational processes such as course sequencing, professional practice issues, or customer service issues in relation to the bookstore or registration area. Students who are working in a healthcare setting may have issues that student teams could work on and then offer recommendations to healthcare administrators. Governmental processes that do not seem to be working might be good opportunities for improvement. Processes needing improvement at the grocery store or at church might also be evident.

Summary

Four aspects of healthcare are considered the most important areas for performance improvement: structure, process, outcome, and cost. Healthcare organizations usually focus on these areas. Many organizations emphasize the need to monitor and evaluate services that are high volume, high cost, or problem prone. Identifying outputs for each organizational work unit helps define processes and products produced by the unit and valued by customers.

References

Abdelhak, Mervat, et al. 1996. *Health Information: Management of a Strategic Resource,* pp. 453–54. Philadelphia: W. B. Saunders.

Albright, J. M., et al. 1993. Reporting tools for clinical quality improvement. *Clinical Performance Quality in Health Care* 1(4):227–32, October–December.

Donabedian, Avedis. 1988. The quality of care: how can it be assessed? *JAMA* 260(12):1743–48, September.

Joint Commission on Accreditation of Healthcare Organizations. 1993. *The Measurement Mandate.* Oakbrook Terrace, Ill.: JCAHO.

Chapter 3
Applying Teamwork
in Performance Improvement

Learning Objectives

- To understand the effective use of teams in performance improvement activities

- To understand the composition of performance improvement teams

- To recognize the advantages that agendas lend to performance improvement team processes

- To understand the differences between the roles of the leader and the members in performance improvement teams

Background and Significance

Performance improvement (PI) teams involve a number of people working over long periods of time. They are expensive in terms of both time and money. Therefore, PI teams should be considered an organizational resource to be used appropriately and prudently.

The early quality improvement philosophies of Deming, Juran, and Crosby were based on team processes. Therefore, when quality improvement methodologies were first applied to healthcare organizations, it was assumed that PI activities were best accomplished by PI teams. Experience with PI processes in healthcare settings, however, has shown that PI teams are not always required.

Today, when an improvement opportunity is identified, the organization's leadership or performance improvement council can initiate one of three approaches:

- Establishing a **blitz team**

- Disseminating information or developing an educational training program

- Developing a cross-functional PI team

Sometimes the leaders of an organization may decide that they already have all of the facts they need about an improvement opportunity. In such cases, they may decide to establish a **blitz team.** Blitz teams do not spend a lot of time gathering data and reengineering processes. Instead, they construct relatively simple fixes that improve work processes without going through the whole PI process. Thus, an improvement can be implemented without a major investment of time and resources.

Some improvement opportunities involve only the dissemination of information or better individual training. Again, this approach to implementing an improvement can be accomplished without expending large amounts of resources.

When, however, the improvement opportunity is complex and involves multiple departments or multiple work units within a department, the team-based approach is required. A PI team is instituted to research, plan, and implement the improvement. This approach represents the traditional **total quality management** (TQM) process (which was discussed in chapter 1).

The goal of this chapter is to discuss the composition of PI teams and the roles of individual members. The purpose of team mission and vision statements is also explained.

Team Composition

When convening a PI team is appropriate, the leadership of the organization must determine the composition of the team. The PI team should be made up of individuals close to the process to be improved, because they are best qualified to accomplish the process review. This may mean that some teams will include more staff than managers. Some questions that should be asked to identify individual team members include:

- Which departments or disciplines are involved in the process?

- Who are the customers of the process? That is, who will receive the product or service that the process produces?

- Who supplies the process? That is, who provides materials or services for use in the process under investigation?

Limitations on the number of people who can participate on a team and other factors sometimes mean that all of the people involved in a process to be improved cannot participate directly on the PI team. When this happens, the team must make provisions to contact the other individuals affected by the improvement initiative. Because their perspectives and information are of critical importance, some means for obtaining their input must be developed.

A team should include no more than ten members. Once the team has been formed, the team members should determine which individuals, departments, and disciplines are key players in the process. Then they can bring other individuals, departments, and disciplines into the process on an ad hoc basis when necessary.

Team Roles

After the team has been selected, a **team leader** should be chosen. Having a leader is necessary to get the team organized in the most basic ways. The organization's leaders may select the team leader, or the team itself may select its own leader.

The team leader should be someone whom the team respects as well as someone who is organized and will take the initiative to see the team through the process. The team leader is primarily responsible for championing the effectiveness of the process in meeting customers' needs. He or she is also responsible for the *content* of the team's work. The team leader is responsible for the following specific activities:

- Preparing for and scheduling meetings (standard meeting day, time, and location)

- Sending out announcements of meetings and any other necessary materials

- Conducting meetings (the importance of following an agenda is discussed later in the QI toolbox techniques section of this chapter)

- Focusing the group's attention on the task at hand

- Ensuring group participation and asking for facts, opinions, and suggestions

- Providing expertise in the organization's performance improvement methodology and PI tools and techniques

- Overseeing data collection

- Making task assignments

- Facilitating implementation of action plan items

- Conducting critiques of the meetings

- Serving as the primary spokesperson and presenter for the team

- Keeping attendance records

- Contacting absent members personally to review the results of the meeting and provide any materials that were distributed during the meeting

The role of the **team member** includes the following functions:

- Participating in decision making and plan development for the team

- Identifying opportunities for improvement

- Gathering, prioritizing, and analyzing data

- Sharing knowledge, information, and data that pertain to the process being investigated

A variety of other roles may be implemented in performance improvement teams. (See chapter 16.)

Mission and Vision Statements

Healthcare organizations use **mission** and **vision statements** at many different levels. The corporation as a whole may have a mission and vision statement, as may the separate divisions of the corporation. Facilities and departments within facilities also may have mission and vision statements.

To be effective, mission and vision statements should be developed in concert with the organization's overall strategic plan. The statements should be coordinated throughout the organization, and each should reflect the mission and vision of the organizational levels above it. The mission statement for an organization identifies its name, what it does, and whom it serves.

After the team has been assembled and the leader has been chosen, the team should establish its mission. Developing a mission statement can help both the team and the larger organization identify the goals and purpose of the performance improvement initiative. The team's mission statement should answer the following questions:

- What process is to be improved?

- For whom is the process performed?

- What products does the process produce?

- What is not working with the current process?

- How well must the process function?

(See the example in figure 3.1.)

The team should also articulate its vision for the process. A vision statement is a description of the ideal end-state or a description of the way the process should function. (See the example in figure 3.2.)

The team's vision of the way a process should function may not be validated by existing data and observations of the process. In such cases, a disharmony between the vision and reality becomes apparent. This disharmony represents the team's opportunity for improving the process. Humans have a natural tendency to resolve disharmony. The more clearly the group maintains its focus on "what should be" and acknowledges "what is," the more powerfully the team will be drawn toward implementing its vision of the desired outcome.

Quite often, organizations give up their vision because of the discomfort connected with the disharmony between their vision and current reality. Some organizations focus on

---

Figure 3.1.   Sample Mission Statement

"Evaluate the HIM lab in regard to accessibility, resources,
library access, Internet access, quality of equipment,
and adequacy of equipment for HIM students."

Figure 3.2.   Sample Vision Statement

"The HIM lab provides access to a variety of application software resources,
library knowledge bases, and the Internet.
A convenient, comfortable work environment exists."

their vision and ignore the way things are or believe the current situation is better than it really is. In either case, the natural tendency for resolution or change is dissipated.

The team that focuses on "what should be" and at the same time maintains an accurate description of the current state of the process takes a powerful step toward creating the results they envision. When the PI team focuses clearly and consistently on its vision, it naturally and almost effortlessly gets a sense of what still needs to be done. New processes seem to announce themselves, and the group becomes increasingly aware of additional opportunities for continuing improvement.

Real-Life Examples

Three examples of the effectiveness of PI teams follow.

Continuum of Care Team

In a small, metropolitan hospital, the triage process in the emergency department was inadequate. Communication was fragmented. Precertification was not taking place in a timely manner. Intake processing time had increased. The main patient waiting area was not private, and referral volume was increasing.

To address these problems, a PI team was instituted. The team included the following people:

- *Team leader:* emergency department intake coordinator

- *Team members:* representatives from business office, health information services, administration, utilization review, and finance

- *Ad hoc members:* representatives from regulatory affairs, reception, nursing, and case management

After analyzing the situation, the team created a vision of a centralized clinical assessment center and a private family waiting area. Staffing changes and cross-training made implementation of the vision possible.

Health Information Services and Business Office Services

The health information services (HIS) department's mission was to "contribute and provide support to the effective organizationwide management of information." The business office's mission statement was to "give support to organizationwide financial viability and provide accurate and timely exchange of financial information that allows for an efficient and effective billing and collection process."

The team included three employees from the HIS department and three employees from the business office. Because the departments were relatively small, all of the departments' employees could participate on the team.

Clinical Laboratory Services

Safety issues and other problems concerning the laboratory department at one hospital increased 207 percent over a period of one year. The objectives of the PI team were to identify specific problem areas within laboratory services, conduct a baseline study to assess each area, analyze the survey results, develop an action plan, implement improvements, and evaluate the results of the changes. The team was made up of the following people:

- The chief clinical officer
- The laboratory manager
- An emergency department physician
- The director of clinical services
- The director of nursing
- Laboratory personnel
- A performance improvement representative

Registration for Day Surgery

The purpose of the PI team was to streamline the data collection process from physician offices to the surgery center. Information on day surgery schedules was being lost between the physicians' offices and the facility. Patients had to come to the facility two or three times or experienced long waiting times before being taken to surgery. Team members included representatives from the surgery department, admitting, medical staff, physician office staff, and ancillary departments (laboratory, radiology, and electrocardiography).

QI Toolbox Technique

For a meeting to be effective, the team must operate with a common purpose and specific goal. Communication of the meeting's common purpose and specific goal is usually accomplished by establishing an **agenda.** An agenda is a list of the tasks to be accomplished during a meeting. Using an agenda ensures that every team member knows what items will be discussed or worked on. The agenda should be sent to all team members before the meeting. This allows them to prepare ahead of time to discuss specific agenda items. The agenda should also include an indication of how long the team will spend on each item. (See the sample agenda in figure 3.3.) Setting time frames for agenda items helps the team leader to keep the group focused on the process and moving forward.

Standard agendas begin with a review and approval of the last meeting's minutes. Once this has been accomplished, the PI team should review the agenda for the current meeting and approve the time frames that have been set. This allows the individual team members to have input into how long a certain agenda item should be discussed. Next, the specific performance improvement steps for current discussion should be listed and discussed.

As a closing item of business, many teams find it helpful to evaluate the meeting itself in terms of its effectiveness. Asking the following questions may be helpful:

- Did the team accomplish what it set out to accomplish during the meeting?
- Is the PI process moving forward?

Figure 3.3.   **Sample Agenda**

AGENDA

Date: January 15   **Team:** Registration Process

Time: 10:00 a.m.   **Place:** Conference Room B

Time Allotted:	Agenda Item:
5 minutes	1. Review and approve minutes from last meeting
5 minutes	2. Review agenda and time frames
15 minutes	3. PI step: Registration process discussion on how the computer system affects the registration process
15 minutes	4. PI step: Registration process discussion on what happens now when the computer system is "down"
15 minutes	5. Brainstorm possible ideas to improve the computer system
10 minutes	6. Process (evaluate) meeting
10 minutes	7. Plan next steps and agenda for next meeting

- Does the team need to ask additional people to sit in on the process meetings?

- Did members participate appropriately, listen effectively to other members' suggestions, and stay focused on the agenda?

Finally, the next meeting's agenda should be agreed upon and tied to the current meeting's evaluation process and minutes. In other words, the next meeting should be designed in light of the accomplishments of the current meeting.

Case Study

"Well, why does it have to take so damn long?" the nurse shouted into the telephone receiver. "We've got to be able to order tests for our patients! They can't wait until next Christmas for their meds!" She punched the receiver onto its cradle and turned to the rest of the staff collected at the nursing station. "436 was transferred here from ICU two hours ago and I still can't enter any orders. How do those idiots in Admitting think we're supposed to get our work done? I will never understand why it has to take so long to get a patient transferred in that g.d. system."

"That witch!" exclaimed the admissions clerk to her supervisor as she hung up the phone. "If someone would let us know once in a while what they're doing with patients in this place, maybe we could do our jobs! Evidently, they transferred Mr. Campbell to 436 from ICU hours ago!"

The clerk walked over to the report printer. A long, wide ribbon of paper hung from it onto the floor where it curled in a short pile. She yanked at the hanging pages and ripped them along a perforation. Then she sat down at a desk, where she began to sort the half-sheet messages from the hospital network communication system into different piles.

When she was finished sorting, she began entering the changes in status and location for each of the patients on each message into the patient accounting and order-entry system.

"But NO, instead of giving us a call and telling us that the patient's been transferred, they'd rather wait 'til a couple of hours later and the patient doesn't have his meds and then call up and rag on us to death like it was OUR fault!" She entered "Campbell, Roy" from one of the half-sheets, and the patient's location data came up on screen. She keyed 4-3-6 in the location field and pressed Enter.

University Hospital employees had been confronted by this same kind of conflict for two years, ever since management purchased a new patient accounting and order-entry system from SMS. Both the new system and the clinical information system, ACIS, had patient census management applications. ACIS was used by clinicians to look up out-patient histories, laboratory reports, and other diagnostic data for both inpatients and outpatients. It also provided departments with information about the current location of the patient so that they would know where to send the final paper-based reports of blood tests, X rays, and other diagnostic reports. But the nursing staff had never been very careful about transferring or discharging patients in the system. It was one of those tasks that took secondary importance to the other patient-oriented duties that they had to perform in their hectic schedules.

University Hospital was the principal tertiary care hospital in a community of 200,000, and patients were referred to it from all over the state. The census never dipped below 70 percent. As a result, the nursing units were almost always full, and the patients had high acuity levels.

The admitting and patient accounting departments had been requesting a new information system for many years when administration finally agreed to make the investment in the SMS system. The new system allowed them to tie order-entry functions to the geographic location of the patient in the hospital. Thus, the system provided more accurate information to lab and other diagnostic testing personnel such as ECG and X-ray to inform them of the patient's whereabouts when a test was ordered. This feature would also ensure that the patient's account was charged correctly for room rate, which had never been the case when they were relying on the ACIS system. Nursing staff had never seemed to get changes in room location entered into the system in a timely fashion. And the census from the ACIS system was never accurate—*everyone* knew that.

The managers of the admitting and patient accounting departments had stood their ground when the new work procedures around the SMS system were developed. They were adamant that nursing was *not* going to be in charge of patient census management. It had been obvious for years that nursing could not take it seriously. The admitting department staff would be making all changes in patient location in the system. Finally, their system would generate an accurate daily inpatient census. They had IS programmers add a short utility in ACIS so that whenever a patient was discharged or transferred in the ACIS census management application, a notification message of same would print out on the admitting department printer. Periodically, during the day, the admitting clerks would take the messages and enter them into the SMS system. If for some reason they were not notified, they had the authority to go into the system and change the dates and times of the discharge or transfer so that the accounting files would be correct and the patients' bills would reflect correct charges. One additional feature of the SMS system, however, was that orders on a patient could only be entered from the nursing unit on which the system currently had the patient located.

Case Study Questions

1. In your opinion, is there an opportunity for improvement in this system? Why or why not?

2. If there is, is a performance improvement team appropriate in this context?

3. From your knowledge of hospital organizational structure, who should be on the team? What is your rationale for including each individual?

Student Project Application

Students should form teams of two to four members. Each team should select a process or product to evaluate for improvement opportunities. After each team has identified a process or product to evaluate, each should develop a mission statement for the team and a vision statement for its process. This will help each team to identify its goals and purposes for the performance improvement process as well as to clarify what it is trying to accomplish. Mission and vision statements can be written on newsprint flipchart paper similar to that used in healthcare organizations. The statements should then be displayed on the wall so that the students can share their initial mission and vision statements and introduce their proposed projects.

Summary

Cross-functional teams often undertake performance improvement activities in healthcare organizations. The team process allows the members to represent the varied perspectives of departments and other entities in the organization. At a minimum, a team should include a team leader and several team members. Mission and vision statements and team meeting agendas help keep the team focused on team activities.

References

Carboneau, C. E. 1999. Achieving faster quality improvement through the 24-hour team. *Journal of Healthcare Quality* 21(4):4–10, July–August.

LaVallee, Rebecca, and Curtis P. McLaughlin. 1994. Teams at the core. In *Continuous Quality Improvement in Health Care,* Curtis P. McLaughlin and Arnold D. Kaluzny, editors. Gaithersburg, Md.: Aspen Publishers.

Lynch, Robert F., and Thomas J. Werner. 1992. *Continuous Improvement: Teams and Tools.* Atlanta: QualTeam.

O'Malley, S. 1997. Total quality now! Putting QI on the fast track. *Quality Letter for Healthcare Leaders* 9(11):2–10, December.

Parisi, Lenard L. 1994. Quality improvement teams and teamwork. In *Improving Quality: A Guide to Effective Programs,* Claire G. Meisenheimer, editor. Gaithersburg, Md.: Aspen Publishers.

Part II
Continuous Monitoring and Improvement Functions

Chapter 4
Measuring Customer Satisfaction

Learning Objectives

- To understand the differences between internal and external customers
- To recognize the reasons why customers' perspectives are important to the performance improvement process
- To recognize the difference between surveys and interviews
- To be able to outline the characteristics that make surveys and interviews effective
- To be able to critique a survey or interview format

Background and Significance

As discussed in chapter 1, researching and defining performance expectations includes an investigation of what the **customers** of an organizational process expect from that process. Because there are many kinds of organizational processes, there are also many types of customers. Their **expectations** must be identified and incorporated into the design or redesign of an effective process.

The customers of a process are those individuals who receive a product or a service from the process. Just as one can identify the customers of a dress shop or an auto dealership, one can also identify the customers of a healthcare process. For example, when a nurse inserts a catheter into an artery to administer medication, the patient is receiving a service from the nurse. Similarly, when a pharmacist dispenses a medication to a patient, the patient is receiving a product from the pharmacist.

Identifying the patient as a customer should seem fairly straightforward. But customers can be identified for all kinds of healthcare processes. The families and friends of patients are the customers of volunteer services when they stop to ask what room a patient is in. Emergency care physicians are the customers of central supply services when they request sterile suturing trays to close a patient's laceration. Surgeons are the customers of the pathology laboratory when they request frozen-section examination of tissue in the operating room during resection of a breast lesion.

Types of Customers

Customers can be categorized as two types, **internal customers** and **external customers.** When the healthcare organization as a whole is considered, the internal customers of a process are those individuals within the organization who receive products or services from an organizational unit or department. In the preceding examples, surgeons are the internal customers of the pathology laboratory, and emergency care physicians are the internal customers of central supply services.

The external customers of a process are those individuals from outside the organization who receive products or services from an organizational unit or department. In the preceding examples, patients, family members, and friends of patients are external customers.

In determining the customers of a process, however, the organizational frame of reference must also be taken into consideration. Sometimes the frame of reference modifies the customer type. (See figure 4.1.) When one thinks of the organization as a whole, surgeons are identified as internal customers because they are members of an organizational unit, the medical staff. If the frame of reference were focused on the department level, however, with the pathology laboratory taken as the frame of reference, then the surgeons might be identified as the external customers of pathology lab processes, and the pathologists might be identified as the internal customers of the laboratory technicians who process the specimens.

It is important to recognize that internal and external customers must be identified in relation to the context of the organizational process under consideration. Every process has a unique set of customers whose needs and expectations must be recognized.

The opinions of internal and external customers regarding the effectiveness of a healthcare process should be of primary importance to healthcare organizations. Who is a better judge of the products and services provided than the customer? It is also important

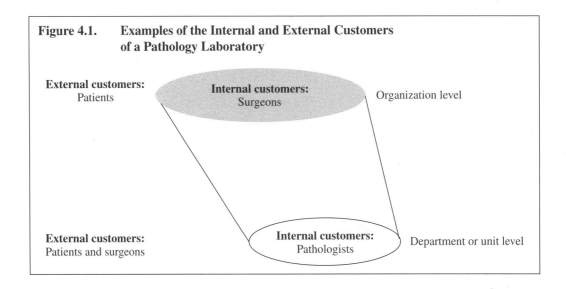

Figure 4.1.   Examples of the Internal and External Customers of a Pathology Laboratory

External customers:
Patients

Internal customers:
Surgeons

Organization level

External customers:
Patients and surgeons

Internal customers:
Pathologists

Department or unit level

to remember that a dissatisfied customer is said to tell ten times as many people of his discontent as the satisfied customer is of his contentedness.

How can the organization's staff get information about its customers' perceptions of the products and services it provides? That is actually a more complex question than one might think it to be.

With internal customers, it is easy. Simply ask them! Many internal customers never get the opportunity to express their expectations in a positive context. Often, the only time a department representative hears about the expectations of internal customers is when a process has been mismanaged or has resulted in a negative outcome. Just giving internal customers the opportunity to put their expectations forward for consideration significantly increases their satisfaction.

With external customers, particularly patients, identifying expectations about service quality is more complicated. Patients' expectations are multifaceted and often reflect the condition for which the patient is being treated. Any assessment of those expectations must be undertaken judiciously.

For many aspects of patient satisfaction, one could use a patient satisfaction survey. Subjects such as parking, hours of operation, room decor, and so forth can be handled with an anonymous survey. Information pertaining to the patient's condition and medical and nursing treatment, however, may need to be assessed with other methodologies. Some aspects of patient care should perhaps be assessed from the viewpoint of the clinicians involved in the patient's care and the outcomes achieved through that care. (See chapter 8.)

Other deeply subjective value systems, pain management, for example, may be completely different from one patient to the next. Another highly subjective area that influences a patient's expectations is quality of life: how patients decide that their quality of life has returned to a satisfactory state after treatment. One of the most important factors that influences how patients assess their care is how caring and respectful caregivers are in their relationships with patients (Atlantic Information Services, 1995, pp. 5–6).

Because of this inherent complexity, assessment of patient satisfaction might best be performed by multidisciplinary teams using carefully tailored assessment tools. Nationally recognized vendors offer patient satisfaction surveys. Their names and addresses can be found in table 4.1.

Monitoring and Improving Customer Satisfaction: Steps to Success

In order to monitor and improve customer satisfaction, the organization must know exactly who its customers are, what those customers want and value, and what improvements could be made to better meet the customers' needs.

Step 1: Identify internal and external customers

Assessing whether a process has met the expectations of its customers is difficult when all of those customers have not been identified. To identify customers, the PI team should list everyone who comes in contact with the process and takes away a product or a service. (See figure 4.2.)

**Table 4.1.   Vendors of Patient Satisfaction Surveys
(From Atlantic Information Services, 1995, pp. 5–6)**

Vendor Name/ Contact Information	Product Description
National Research Corporation Gold's Galleria 1033 O Street Lincoln, NE 69508 402-475-2525	• Provides customizable patient satisfaction surveys • Provides SF-36-based health assessment surveys • Conducts surveys through both telephone and direct mail • Maintains national databank for benchmarking • Provides extensive analysis of results
Dey Systems, Inc. 230 Executive Park Louisville, KY 40207 502-896-8438	• Developed Patient Satisfaction Information System (PSIS) for data analysis • Uses time-dependent, Functional Status Outcomes Measurement System (FSMS) developed from SF-36 questionnaire for health assessment • Offers consulting services for aid in survey design • Maintains processing center for mailing, collection, scanning, comment typing, coding, and reporting • Offers on-line access to benchmarking information
Press, Ganey Associates 1657 Commerce Drive South Bend, IN 46628 800-232-8032	• Specializes in patient satisfaction measurement via direct mail surveys • Produces quarterly reports detailing hospitalwide performance comparing individual units, noting satisfaction trends and national benchmarking statistics • Offers on-line access to completed surveys • Produces special annual reports containing detailed demographic analyses of individual hospital data and national comparative data
Parkside Associates, Inc. 205 West Touhy Avenue Suite 204 Park Ridge, IL 60068 847-698-9866	• Designs and distributes customizable surveys for patient satisfaction • Performs direct mail surveys • Performs data entry, analysis, and reporting • Offers individual departmental analysis • Provides national benchmarking data • Offers consultation on result application
The Gallup Organization The Gallup Building 47 Hulfish Street Princeton, NJ 08542 609-924-9600	• Conducts telephone surveys from lists of discharged patients • Uses patient satisfaction survey that is customized by specialty • Uses customizable, time-dependent telephone surveys developed from SF-36 questionnaire to assess functional outcomes • Analyzes collected data and creates quarterly reports • Generates recommendations on successful application of results • Provides national benchmarking results provided within quarterly reports
The Picker Institute 1295 Boylston Street Suite 100 Boston, MA 02215 617-667-2388	• Designs surveys that target dimensions of care that patients are most concerned about • Offers SF-36 surveying and analysis services only in conjunction with patient satisfaction surveying programs • Conducts continuous survey and analysis • Provides a priority matrix that helps clients to focus on areas needing improvement • Provides national benchmarks and comparisons with peer institutions
Professional Research Consultants 11326 P Street Omaha, NE 68137 800-428-7455	• Uses proven methodology for patient satisfaction telephone interviewing • Incorporates patient satisfaction and expectation assessments with outcomes research (not health assessment outcomes) • Provides statistically valid measurement of perceptions of "quality" with open-ended response capabilities

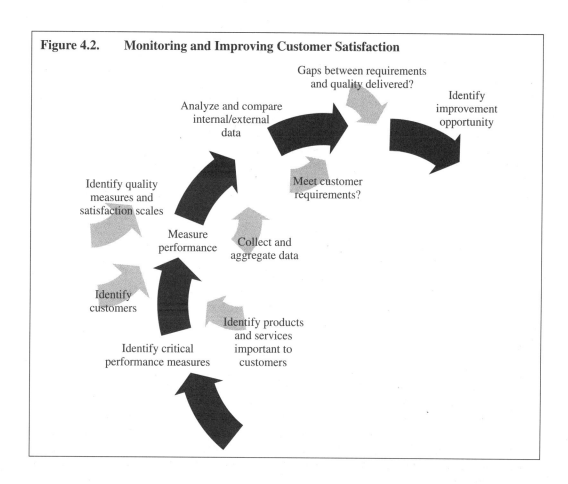

Figure 4.2.   Monitoring and Improving Customer Satisfaction

- Gaps between requirements and quality delivered?
- Identify improvement opportunity
- Analyze and compare internal/external data
- Meet customer requirements?
- Identify quality measures and satisfaction scales
- Measure performance
- Collect and aggregate data
- Identify customers
- Identify products and services important to customers
- Identify critical performance measures

Step 2: Identify products and services important to customers

The PI team then should develop a list of the products and services used by each internal and external customer. Not every product is tangible. Information, for example, may be collected in a database and used by many customers, but only rarely would the database be printed out on paper.

Outcomes of care are not necessarily tangible. One may not be able to see the outcome. The recipient of the care services may need some means of telling the team about the outcome.

Step 3: Identify quality measures and satisfaction scales for each product and service

For each product and service that a customer takes away from the process, associated **performance measures** must be identified. For example, if one were assessing the patient's experience of going to a physician's office for a medical appointment, waiting time would be a relevant performance measure. After waiting time has been identified as a performance measure, a scale for measuring waiting time would need to be developed. For example, the team would need to decide whether it would be best to measure waiting time in seconds, minutes, or hours.

Step 4: Collect and aggregate data on each performance measure

The best methods for collecting data on each performance measure currently under assessment should be determined. In assessments of customer satisfaction, the principal methods of collecting data are **survey tools, interviews,** and **direct observation.**

The construction of an effective survey tool requires a significant investment of time. (See the discussion of survey tools later in this chapter.) Interviews are often considered easier to use because they consist of a series of open-ended questions. Aggregation of data (the summing of responses) from a survey is easier than aggregation of information gathered in an interview because surveys are often made up of checkoff-type responses. The responses to interview questions must be analyzed to identify common themes and perceptions.

The healthcare organization's Institutional Review Board (IRB) must preapprove the use of any data-gathering tool. IRB approval is mandated by federal regulations on the use of human subjects in biomedical and health services research. Although an in-depth consideration of IRB approval cannot be provided here (every institution has its own policies and procedures), PI teams using such data-gathering methodologies must recognize their responsibility for obtaining IRB approval.

Step 5: Analyze and compare the data collected

The aggregate satisfaction ratings on performance measures are next compared with previous trends within the organization or with satisfaction levels achieved by other organizations. Such comparisons may be performed using patient satisfaction data collected within the enterprise or satisfaction ratings published by state departments of health, national accrediting agencies, or other national organizations specializing in healthcare quality assessment. (The vendors of patient satisfaction surveys noted in table 4.1 can provide national data.)

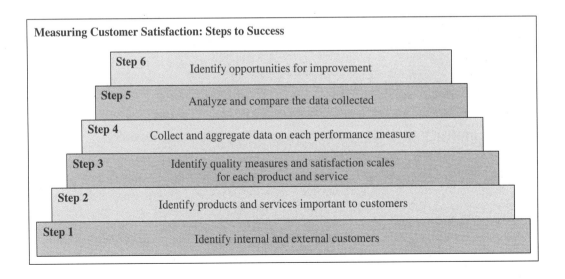

Measuring Customer Satisfaction: Steps to Success

Step 6	Identify opportunities for improvement
Step 5	Analyze and compare the data collected
Step 4	Collect and aggregate data on each performance measure
Step 3	Identify quality measures and satisfaction scales for each product and service
Step 2	Identify products and services important to customers
Step 1	Identify internal and external customers

Step 6: Identify opportunities for improvement

Next, areas for improvements are developed on the basis of the comparisons with aggregate satisfaction ratings on quality measures. Performance improvement teams should be implemented to define appropriate performance expectations and design/redesign processes.

Real-Life Examples

The following two examples help illustrate the process of measuring customer satisfaction.

External Customers of a Food Services Department

Virginia Mullen, RHIA, is the director of quality and service excellence for a large U.S. healthcare corporation. She was working with one of her corporation's smaller facilities, a small acute care hospital with 80 beds. In evaluating the service excellence of the facility, Mullen and the administration had decided to use a satisfaction survey. The survey was to be mailed to patients after they had been discharged from the hospital.

One part of the survey asked for patient feedback on inpatient food services. The quality of food services was rated on a five-point scale, with 5 indicating very satisfied and 1 indicating very dissatisfied. The survey contained the following items (see figure 4.3):

26. Taste of the food

27. Temperature of the food

28. Appearance of the food

29. Variety of menu items

30. Overall satisfaction with food services

After administering the survey for several months, Mullen and the administration noted that patient ratings on food services generally showed responses in the excellent category of only 10 to 30 percent.

Mullen considers the percentage of responses in the excellent category to be a measure of the loyalty of a facility's customers. The loyal customers are the ones who will reliably return in the future. Customers who respond at levels less than excellent on satisfaction surveys may or may not return to the facility for future care. In a highly competitive environment, developing this loyal segment of the market is extremely important to the survival of the facility.

Historically, institutional food is not an area that gets rave reviews. On review of the literature for institutional nutrition services, the investigators found that the research noted that assessment of food quality is highly subjective. Everyone has his or her own idea about what is good. In addition, the fact that the respondents are hospitalized further complicates the assessment because illnesses and medications often significantly affect taste sensation. Food services have traditionally received the lowest ratings across the healthcare industry. Despite the historic experience, administration and the management of the food services for this hospital decided to see whether the ratings for this area could be improved.

Figure 4.3.   Example of a Patient Satisfaction Survey

Patient Satisfaction Survey

Instructions:
- ► Use a pencil or black pen to fill in your answers to the questions on the survey.
- ► Mark your answers in the circles provided.
- ► Answer only the questions that apply to your stay in the hospital.

Please choose one of the responses provided for the following questions:

1. Was this the first time you came to this hospital for inpatient care?
   ○ Yes   ○ No

2. Would you recommend this hospital to a friend or family member who needed inpatient care?
   ○ Yes   ○ No

3. Where were you admitted into the hospital?
   ○ Registration Area   ○ Emergency Department   ○ Other

4. How long did you wait before you were taken to your room?
   ○ Less than 20 minutes   ○ 21 to 30 minutes   ○ 31 to 60 minutes   ○ More than 1 hour

5. Did you have surgery while you were hospitalized?
   ○ Yes   ○ No

6. Were you in an intensive care unit at any time during your stay?
   ○ Yes   ○ No

Fill in the circle to the right of each statement that best describes how satisfied you were with the care and services you received while you were in the hospital.

Registration Process	Very Dissatisfied	Somewhat Dissatisfied	Neutral	Somewhat Satisfied	Very Satisfied
7. Courtesy and friendliness of the registration staff	○	○	○	○	○
8. How well the registration staff answered your questions	○	○	○	○	○
9. Amount of time needed to complete the registration process	○	○	○	○	○
10. Overall satisfaction with registration procedures	○	○	○	○	○
Nursing Staff					
11. Caring and concern of the nurses who cared for you	○	○	○	○	○
12. Skill of the nurses who cared for you	○	○	○	○	○
13. Time it took for nurses to respond to your calls	○	○	○	○	○
14. Willingness of your nurses to listen to your concerns	○	○	○	○	○
15. Amount of time your nurses spent with you	○	○	○	○	○
16. Overall satisfaction with nursing staff	○	○	○	○	○

PLEASE COMPLETE THE SURVEY ON THE REVERSE SIDE OF THIS PAGE.

Figure 4.3.   *(Continued)*

Medical Staff	Very Dissatisfied	Somewhat Dissatisfied	Neutral	Somewhat Satisfied	Very Satisfied
17. Caring and concern of the doctors who cared for you	○	○	○	○	○
18. Availability of your doctors	○	○	○	○	○
19. Ways your doctors worked together and with your nurses	○	○	○	○	○
20. Information your doctors provided about your condition	○	○	○	○	○
21. Amount of time your doctors spent with you	○	○	○	○	○
22. Overall satisfaction with medical staff	○	○	○	○	○
Housekeeping Services					
23. Cleanliness of your room	○	○	○	○	○
24. Overall cleanliness of the hospital	○	○	○	○	○
25. Overall satisfaction with housekeeping services	○	○	○	○	○
Food Services					
26. Taste of the food	○	○	○	○	○
27. Temperature of the food	○	○	○	○	○
28. Appearance of the food	○	○	○	○	○
29. Variety of menu items	○	○	○	○	○
30. Overall satisfaction with food services	○	○	○	○	○
Other Hospital Services					
31. Overall satisfaction with X-ray services	○	○	○	○	○
32. Overall satisfaction with respiratory therapy services	○	○	○	○	○
33. Overall satisfaction with rehabilitation services	○	○	○	○	○
34. Overall satisfaction with emergency department services	○	○	○	○	○
35. Overall satisfaction with the care and services your received	○	○	○	○	○

36. What did we do really well? (Please be specific.) _____

_____

_____

37. What do we need to improve? (Please be specific.) _____

_____

_____

REMEMBER: ALL OF YOUR RESPONSES ARE CONFIDENTIAL.
THANK YOU FOR PARTICIPATING.

Working in a performance improvement team methodology, the participants developed an entirely new approach to menu selection for inpatients. The PI team focused on lunch and dinner, leaving breakfast as it was, with a standard provision of the usual breakfast items. The directors had read about a few hospitals trying a new approach of using room service, just as in a hotel. They contacted a hospital in Washington State that had implemented a similar program and invited the staff to give a presentation about the pros and cons of the program. Following the presentation, the team did additional research to see whether the system was being used anywhere else and identified successes and challenges. It became apparent that every facility needed its own process for designing this new service. The features of the new service needed to be based on the organization's patient population, staffing, equipment, and financial resources. The pilot hospital put together a multidisciplinary team to identify all the issues that would come up with such a change. The food service team needed the buy-in from administration, their own staff, ancillary staff, and especially nursing.

The program was implemented at lunch and dinner as planned. Patients on regular diets had a three-and-a-half-hour window during which they could order whatever they specifically wanted from a menu similar to a hotel room service menu. Patients on therapeutic diets were still visited by the dietician, who helped them develop appropriate diets for their medical conditions.

Over the following months, Mullen and the administration of this hospital saw the ratio of very satisfied ratings increase from the 10 to 30 percent range to over 50 percent. The ratio of ratings in the satisfied and very satisfied responses rose to over 80 percent. Annual projected costs in food services decreased $20,000 owing to a decrease in the amount of wasted food. Patients could now eat what they wanted when they wanted it, and they were more likely to eat all of it and not select foods they did not intend to eat.

In the long term, the system is working extremely well. Food service staff members who were skeptical initially would not go back to the old way of doing things. Satisfaction scores have stayed high. There is less food waste because patients are ordering what they want, and the nursing staff keeps all of the items for liquid diets on the units so that patients have access to the liquid foods when they want them. Nursing also knows when patients are moving from a liquid to solid diet, and they help their patients order appropriate food.

Food service at the hospital has become a revenue-generating department because the room service menu has been expanded to serve visitors. Families are thrilled to be able to have meals with the patients who are in the hospital and are willing to pay for the meals. The most recent change has been to expand this program to the hospital staff. The hospital cafeteria is closed on weekends, and the staff can call for room service at any time. They love it, and so the program has been of benefit with respect to employee satisfaction as well.

Internal and External Customers of a Pathology Laboratory

Dr. Lagios had been chief pathologist at Western States University Medical Center for two months. He moved from a large, tertiary care, private hospital in a metropolitan community to the university setting because he wanted to expand his responsibilities. As many managers do when they come into new positions, he began an inventory of the pathology laboratory's functioning and examined each of its processes.

In general, the lab appeared to be functioning well, particularly in the area of processing surgical specimens. But in the area of autopsy report dictation, he found a huge backlog of reports that had not been dictated and finalized. The backlog of forty reports extended back more than two years. When he asked his secretary for an explanation of the backlog, she reacted with amazement and was totally unaware of the situation. No one had been monitoring the status of the autopsy reports on a continuing basis.

Dr. Lagios began his investigation by interviewing his fellow pathologists. Each of them told a similar story. Autopsies were usually performed on the day following the death of a patient, and the remains were then picked up by a mortician. Organ specimens were harvested during the procedure, and microscopy slides were processed during the immediately following days. During the autopsy procedure, the pathologist would dictate notes about the findings to the diener, the nonphysician assistant who managed the remains and the specimens. The diener would write the notes on a photocopied form that outlined the order in which the autopsy was performed. But then the reports never got dictated because the pathologists had so many surgical specimens to process that they never seemed to have time to do the autopsy reports. When a physician needed the autopsy findings to fill out a death certificate, he had to call the assigned pathologist, who would verbally report the results.

Dr. Lagios believed that there was definite room for improvement in this process. He decided to convene a performance improvement team to examine the situation and come up with better ways for the process to work. He asked that two of his fellow pathologists, who had been around longer than he, to serve on the team as well as the diener. In addition, he requested the participation of the director of health information services, who managed pathology and autopsy report transcription processing, and two internal medicine physicians, whose previous patients had been autopsied most frequently in the past two years.

At the first meeting, the two internists talked the most. It was obvious that there was a fair amount of suppressed frustration about the current situation. If the two internists on the team were unhappy, then other physicians were probably unhappy, too. The internists had morticians after them for cause of death to put on the death certificates, and tracking down the pathologists to get any findings from autopsy considerably delayed the death certificate process.

Mrs. Castle, director of health information services, reported that it was becoming difficult to tell which autopsies had been done and which had not because there were so many of them. She was very willing to try and find a solution if the pathologists were willing to accept some change in procedures. She felt that there might be an information management solution available, because it was, she felt, an information management problem.

The group decided to meet again to determine whether new procedures could be developed. Mrs. Castle volunteered to contact the local Lanier representative to see whether he had any suggestions on how to deal with the problem.

QI Toolbox Techniques

Surveys and interviews are commonly used as data collection techniques in measuring levels of customer satisfaction. As mentioned earlier in this chapter, direct observation of behavior may also be used, but behavior is difficult to analyze. Behavior often changes when people realize that they are being observed. All three methods can be used to measure outcomes and processes, however. Some of the design considerations for surveys and interviews are discussed next.

Survey Design

When designing a survey, the PI team must define the goal or goals of the survey in clear and precise terms. The purpose and audience of the survey must also be kept in mind during the design phase. Careful consideration of the questions asked on the survey is imperative. The team must have a reason to include every item on the survey. It should avoid asking for information that is interesting but not needed to measure process capabilities.

Survey items should be arranged in logical fashion, that is, general to specific; for example, demographic data followed by process-specific questions. It is helpful to identify the broad categories of information necessary and then determine the order for these categories. Specific process issues about which the team needs information should not be placed at the beginning of the survey. That is, the first question should not attempt to elicit information that is emotionally charged or sensitive. For example, if physicians were being surveyed about the quality of the transcription system, the first question should not ask whether they are happy with the transcription system. The initial questions should ask how much they use the system, what types of reports they generate, and so on. The next set of questions can be used to determine their level of satisfaction with the system.

After the team has determined the broad categories of information it needs, it should think about the individual questions or items. The single most important factor in item construction is clarity (Jagger, 1982). Item format and content should be consistent. Similar questions should be formatted in the same way using the simplest arrangement possible. (See figure 4.4.)

The survey should be written at the reading level of the respondents. The average reading level in the United States falls at the sixth grade. Simple wording should be used, not sophisticated medical or technical terminology that the average person would not understand. Also, the items should be written in an objective manner, so that they do not imply that any particular response is either desired or correct. (See figure 4.5.)

Surveys may incorporate a variety of question types. Open-ended questions allow respondents to construct a free-text answer in their own words. Responses to open-ended questions, however, are difficult to score and response data are difficult to aggregate, because there is no defined scale of responses. Numerous responses may show no clear connection or pattern.

Therefore, open-ended questions should only be used at the end of the survey. They should not be used to elicit information that could more easily be collected in a structured format. (See figure 4.6.) When the researcher wants specific information about a particular area of investigation, the items must be worded precisely so that comparable data can be collected.

The use of closed-ended questions on a survey limits the number of possible responses and standardizes the data collected. Care should be taken to include all possible responses to each question. Respondents must be able to select their answers from the choices provided. One method of ensuring this is to include a choice of "Other (specify)" so that respondents can write in an answer when the desired answer is not among the choices offered. Even then, it is important to provide as many of the common answers as possible to minimize the number of write-in responses. When items include categories of response, the categories must be mutually exclusive; that is, categories should not overlap. (See figure 4.7.)

Another important issue in survey design involves the use of terms, phrases, and words that are known to both the PI team and the respondent. Careful word choice reduces ambiguity. This clarity of terminology is called an operational definition (Jagger, 1982). (See figure 4.8.)

A survey may be personally administered or mailed to the respondents. Either method is effective, but the response rate decreases and turnaround time is greater when the survey is mailed.

Figure 4.4.   Examples of Consistent and Inconsistent Format

Inconsistent Format	Consistent Format
What is your ZIP code? _____	Check which ZIP code you live in:
	___ 84065
Sex (circle one): Male Female	___ 84070
	___ 84092
	___ 84094
	___ Other (specify): _____
	What is your sex?
	___ Male
	___ Female

Figure 4.5.   Examples of Wording

Poor Wording	Simple Wording
Why were you admitted to the hospital?	Why were you in the hospital?
To deliver a child ___	___ To have my baby
To have a C-section ___	___ To have an operation
To have a surgical procedure___	___ To obtain medical treatment
For medical reasons ___	___ Other (specify): _____
Other (specify): _____	

Figure 4.6.   Example of an Open-Ended Question

Open-Ended Question	More Structured Question
How has your coronary artery disease affected your lifestyle?	Now that you have heart disease, are you exercising:
	___ More than before
	___ Same as before
	___ Less than before
	___ Not at all, before or now

Figure 4.7.   Examples of Closed-Ended Questions

Poor Question Construction	Good Question Construction
What is your present age?	What is your present age?
0–17 ___	___ 20 or younger
17–35 ___	___ 21–30
35–45 ___	___ 31–40
45–60 ___	___ 41–50
60–75 ___	___ 51–60
	___ 61–70
	___ 71 or older

Figure 4.8.   Examples of Terminology

Unclear Terminology	Clear Terminology
Have you received treatment in the ambulatory surgery unit?	Have you had surgery at this hospital for which you came to the hospital in the morning and left after surgery in the afternoon or evening?
Yes ___	___ Yes
No ___	___ No
Don't know ___	

Interview Design

An **interview,** whether conducted face-to-face or over the telephone, can provide important insight into quality issues in healthcare. Interviews may be unstructured or structured. In the unstructured type, the sequence of questions is not planned in advance. Instead, the interview is accomplished as though it were a friendly conversation. This type of interview is helpful when the interviewer is trying to uncover preliminary issues that may need a more in-depth analysis and investigation.

In contrast, a predetermined list of questions is used in a structured interview. The team knows exactly what information is needed. The interviewer must know and understand the purpose and goal of each question so that a meaningful response can be recognized.

During the interview process, rapport must be established between the interviewer and the respondent. Without this trust, the interviewee may not reveal his or her true opinions. Some techniques to keep in mind during the interview process include funneling, using unbiased questions, and clarifying responses. *Funneling* is the process of moving questions from a broad theme to a narrow theme in an unstructured interview. Funneling helps the interviewer to establish trust in the respondent as well as to get to the quality issues in the process.

The interviewer must state each question in a clear and somewhat benign manner so that bias is not introduced. If a specific word or phrase were overemphasized, it might elicit a different response than if all the words were spoken in the same tone. The interviewer should restate each response for clarification. This ensures the correct interpretation of each response.

Sometimes the interviewer may choose to use closed-ended questions, with all of the possible responses specified. In such cases, the interviewer must examine each question carefully to ensure that the wording and delivery of the questions do not bias the response. Questions should begin with broader issues and work toward more specific areas of concern.

Case Study

As previously discussed, one common method of measuring customer satisfaction in healthcare involves conducting a survey. Figure 4.9 shows a survey that was used in a healthcare organization. Students should critique this survey against the criteria listed in the preceding discussion of survey design. Careful consideration should be given to format, wording, appearance, and other factors.

Project Application

For their performance improvement projects, students should identify the expectations of internal and external customers regarding the process being examined. Then the students should design a survey, interview, or a combination of the two to collect data on the process. A minimum of thirty responses should be collected for a survey, or five interviews should be conducted. Student surveys and/or interviews should be critiqued by the instructor before they are administered.

Summary

In healthcare performance improvement, making decisions about process or product improvements must be done on the basis of meaningful data on the level of customer satisfaction. Customers may be either internal or external to the organization. Effective ways to collect customers' opinions include surveys and interviews, but each must be constructed carefully to collect relevant and unbiased data.

References

Atlantic Information Services. 1995. *A Guide to Patient Satisfaction Survey Instruments.* Washington, D.C.: Atlantic Information Services.

Bowling, Ann. 1997. *Research Methods in Health.* Philadelphia: Open University Press.

Jagger, Janine. 1982. Data collection instruments: side-stepping the pitfalls. *Nurse Educator,* May–June: 25–28.

Joint Commission on Accreditation of Healthcare Organizations. 1995. *Understanding the Patient's Perspective,* pp.16–19. Oakbrook Terrace, Ill.: JCAHO.

Sekaran, Uma. 1992. *Research Methods for Business.* New York City: John Wiley & Sons.

Vavra, Terry G. 1997. *Improving Your Measurement of Customer Satisfaction.* Milwaukee, Wis.: ASQ Quality Press.

Figure 4.9.   Sample Survey Instrument for the Case Study

SSS Questionnaire

Date of Short Stay Surgery _____
    Type of Procedure _____

Your general impression of the hospital:
    ___ Excellent   ___ Good   ___ Average   ___ Poor

When you spoke with the staff prior to surgery, were they courteous?   ___Yes   ___ No

Did they answer your questions about SSS satisfactorily?
___Yes   ___ No Comments: _____
_____

Were your accommodations in the SSS room:
a.   Clean   Yes ___   No ___
b.   Comfortable   Yes ___   No ___

Treatment by other hospital personnel:

Recovery	**exc**	**good**	**needs improvement**	**poor**
Concern	☐	☐	☐	☐
Efficiency	☐	☐	☐	☐
Courtesy	☐	☐	☐	☐
Adequate Explanation	☐	☐	☐	☐

Surgery

	exc	**good**	**needs**	**poor**
Concern	☐	☐	☐	☐
Efficiency	☐	☐	☐	☐
Courtesy	☐	☐	☐	☐
Adequate Explanation	☐	☐	☐	☐

X-ray

	exc	**good**	**needs**	**poor**
Concern	☐	☐	☐	☐
Efficiency	☐	☐	☐	☐
Courtesy	☐	☐	☐	☐
Adequate Explanation	☐	☐	☐	☐

When you were discharged, did you receive adequate information and instructions?   ___Yes   ___ No

If your surgery was delayed, was an explanation given?
___Yes   ___ No

What determined your selection of Community Hospital of the West as a hospital?
☐ Physician   ☐ Convenience   ☐ Insurance
☐ Friend   ☐ Previous experience
☐ Other:_____

How did you choose the physician who provided your care? _____

Given a choice of hospitals, would you return to Community Hospital of the West?
___Yes   ___ No

In your opinion, how could we improve or add to our services?
_____
_____
_____
_____
_____
_____
_____
_____
_____
_____
_____
_____
_____
_____
_____

We appreciate your confidential opinion of our services. It provides us with the valuable feedback we need in order to continually improve our patient care.

Chapter 5
Optimizing the Continuum of Care

Learning Objectives

- To understand the reasons why processes are being developed to optimize the continuum of care

- To be able to identify and discuss the steps in the case management function

- To understand how criteria sets contribute to the management of care in the U.S. healthcare system

Background and Significance

Today, American consumers are demanding more and more healthcare services in the hope of improving the quality of their daily lives and lengthening their life expectancies. Physicians are working to satisfy their entrepreneurial objectives or to realize a professional career with upper-middle-class living standards. Third-party payers (private and governmental) are trying to maximize profits and/or to minimize costs. The mission of healthcare organizations is to make a positive contribution to the health of their communities (and perhaps to make some profit on the side). In the United States, this collision of objectives and values has led to a variety of attempts to control the healthcare market, none of which has been entirely successful. It is not the intent of the authors to review the history, successes, and failures of the U.S. healthcare system. A basic understanding of the system's history, successes, and failures, however, is important to anyone trying to understand the issues surrounding the concept of the **continuum of care.**

Healthcare in the United States

In discussions of healthcare in the United States, point of view is everything. Common viewpoints include public and private regulation, healthcare economics, and the human desire to benefit personally and collectively.

Over the decades of the twentieth century, attempts have been made to balance the competing needs and expectations of consumers, providers, and payers. At various times, each group has dominated the marketplace, although none of the three has been on top for long. The products of this competition have included the voluntary hospital system, the finest healthcare technological infrastructure in the world, private health insurance plans, the broadest range of the most effective pharmaceuticals available, Medicare, Medicaid, preferred provider arrangements, health maintenance organizations, and so on and so on. The culmination has come in the most recent experimental solution—managed care. The student of healthcare quality and performance improvement is encouraged to review the economic and policy issues inherent in U.S. approaches to delivering healthcare.

The overall goal of the healthcare system is to accomplish equilibrium, as illustrated in figure 5.1. As the figure shows, a finite level of optimal collective health can be realized in U.S. society. Although many factors influence collective health, the system today seeks to identify the optimal level of spending that will achieve the optimal level of collective health. Expenditures are funded by a combination of public and private resources: public health, Medicare, Medicaid, insurance, private pay, public sanitation, and others. But there comes a time when more spending does not realize more collective health.

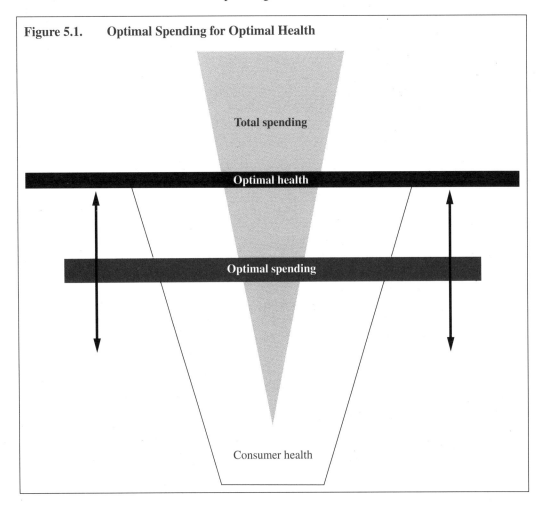

Figure 5.1.   Optimal Spending for Optimal Health

Total spending

Optimal health

Optimal spending

Consumer health

In figure 5.1, the light blue triangle that represents total spending extends above the black line that represents optimal health. This representation acknowledges the realization that all the healthcare spending a society could possibly do would not necessarily achieve the goal of optimal collective health. At some point for every patient the healthcare system serves, no additional health benefit would be achieved by further spending. Any additional expenditures would in effect be wasted. The money could have been used for another patient who could still have benefited. Because millions of Americans never approach the optimal health condition, that waste is considered intolerable. The system today seeks to provide benefits up to the point of optimal health for each individual, thereby realizing optimal health collectively. That is what optimizing the continuum of care is about.

For example, Mr. Abraham Smith is a 90-year-old, Caucasian male who has, in recent years, developed a heart condition known as chronic ventricular fibrillation. The condition is manageable with medication, but patients often continue to experience occasional periods of the arrhythmia even when they are taking their medications as prescribed. Mr. Smith experiences such arrhythmias. Each time the fibrillation begins, Mr. Smith feels weak and unwell, his face flushes, and he can feel his heart fluttering in his chest. He is afraid that he is going to die. Immediately, he calls to his wife to take him to the emergency department of his local hospital. By the time the couple drives to the hospital and Mr. Smith is checked by a physician, the fibrillation has subsided, and his heart has returned to a normal sinus rhythm. The emergency department physician on duty examines him, performs an EKG, and draws blood studies, all of which are negative. Each time, however, the symptoms could be those of a heart attack, but they are not.

Mr. Smith does not want to accept the fact that his heart condition cannot be managed any better than it currently is managed. His demand for services at the emergency department accomplishes nothing, but no one is prepared to tell him not to go there for this problem. Emergency visits are among the most expensive types of ambulatory care. Every visit Mr. Smith makes to the emergency department wastes services that could have been given to someone for whom the emergency visit would have been more helpful. Mr. Smith's use of healthcare services is not optimal, either for him or for society.

Regulatory approaches have sought and still seek to control expenditures on individuals in the hope of making more resources available to those who can still benefit. Medicare regulations mandated utilization review in the mid-1960s. The system required physician committees to review the practice patterns of their colleagues at institutions receiving Medicare dollars. In the 1970s, Medicaid programs in most of the states trained their own reviewers to visit hospitals and make sure that Medicaid patients were staying in the hospital only as long as absolutely necessary. In the mid-1980s, the prospective payment system was implemented for Medicare and Medicaid patients. Under this system, standardized payments are made to hospitals according to the diagnostic category (diagnosis-related groups [DRGs]) into which a patient falls. In the 1990s, the private and public sectors wrestled with the sometimes unfortunate decisions of managed care officials. All of these efforts have attempted to accomplish a balance between health benefit and health spending.

The issue remains important in the administration of healthcare organizations today. Services are to be accorded and expenditures made on individuals who can still benefit, no more and no less. The organizations must be able to demonstrate that rational decisions were made about a patient's care and that those decisions were in the patient's and society's collective best interest. The organizations must be able to demonstrate that the services provided to the patient were appropriate to the patient's physical and quality-of-life needs across the continuum of care.

The continuum of care consists of all of the settings in which patients or clients may receive care. (See figure 5.2.) Today, care is delivered in homes, physicians' offices, ambulatory care centers, hospitals, long-term care facilities, and residential care facilities. Each of these care settings provides a more or less complex set of services, all of which depend on the identified needs of the patient. In addition, each patient's needs may change, depending on the time that the needs are identified: prior to hospital admission, during the admitting process, during the hospital stay, during the discharge process, and during any immediately subsequent care episode. The expectation of the public and private regulatory agencies is that those needs will be identified and that the patient will be cared for in the setting most appropriate to fulfilling those needs.

Optimizing the Continuum of Care: Steps to Success

The principal process by which organizations optimize the continuum of care for their patients is **case management.** Case managers review the condition of patients to identify each patient's care needs and to integrate patient data with the patient's course of treatment. The case manager in many organizations matches the patient's course with a predetermined optimal course (often called a care map or a critical path) for the patient's condition. He or she identifies the actions to be taken when the patient's care is not proceeding optimally. The same concept (under the name managed care) is used by many payers to clearly define when a patient may have a procedure or to stipulate a particular course of treatment that the payer believes will be equally effective but less costly.

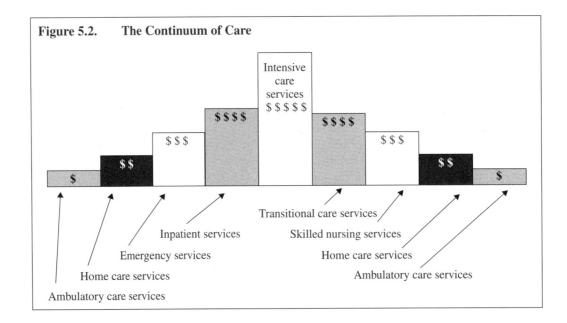

Figure 5.2.   The Continuum of Care

Step 1: Perform preadmission care planning

Preadmission care planning is initiated when the patient's physician contacts a healthcare organization to schedule an episode of care service. The case manager reviews the patient's projected needs with the physician. The manager may also contact the patient directly to obtain further information.

In addition, the manager may contact the patient's payer to confirm that all of the necessary preadmission authorizations have been obtained and that the payer will pay for the patient's services. As part of preauthorization, the payer's representative will have compared the planned services with the payer's criteria of care for the patient's diagnosis.

When a patient is to be transferred from one facility to another, the case manager will contact the case manager at the original facility to coordinate the transfer of services.

Step 2: Perform care planning at the time of admission

At the time the patient is admitted to the hospital, the case manager will review all of the information that has been gathered by the clinicians assigned to the case to confirm that the patient meets the admission criteria for the patient's admitting diagnosis. The manager will confirm that the patient requires services that can be performed in the facility. If it were determined that the facility could not perform the services needed, the case manager would arrange for the patient to be transferred to another facility.

At this time, the case manager will assign the case to the appropriate critical path if the facility utilizes care-mapping methodology. He or she would verify that all of the services stipulated in the critical path have been initiated.

Step 3: Review the progress of care

The case manager periodically reviews the patient's progress throughout the entire episode of care. When a critical path is being used, the manager will reintegrate care data each time the case is reviewed and compare the patient's progress to the path. When variations from expected progress occur, the case manager coordinates interventions among the clinicians and therapists assigned to the case to move the patient along the path.

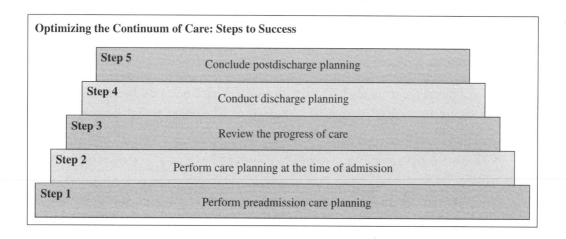

Optimizing the Continuum of Care: Steps to Success

Step 5 — Conclude postdischarge planning

Step 4 — Conduct discharge planning

Step 3 — Review the progress of care

Step 2 — Perform care planning at the time of admission

Step 1 — Perform preadmission care planning

From the beginning of the episode of care, the case manager continuously monitors the patient's acuity level and requirements for services. At the same time, he or she plans for the services the patient will need after discharge. The manager will make arrangements for the patient to be transferred to another facility or nursing unit to meet the patient's care needs. The goal is to maintain the patient at the least costly level of care possible.

Step 4: Conduct discharge planning

As the patient's requirements for care decrease and the patient moves toward discharge, the case manager undertakes final discharge planning. In this step, the patient's continued care after discharge is planned. Postdischarge medications are prescribed and therapies are scheduled. Arrangements to transfer the patient to a subacute facility are made when necessary. Effective discharge planning often begins at the time of admission to ensure that the patient will be prepared to leave the facility as scheduled.

Step 5: Conclude postdischarge planning

Once the patient has been discharged, the case manager conveys the information about the patient's course of treatment to the clinicians who will continue to care for the patient after discharge. At this point, the case management function is returned to the patient's physician and office staff. Some healthcare organizations, however, follow up on patients after discharge to ensure that the transition has gone smoothly and that the patient is receiving all of the services required.

Real-Life Example

Information collected in the form of valid and reliable data is the starting point for the management of the continuum of care. Established criteria for care and clinical paths are crucial to the quality of patient care. (See the discussion in the QI toolbox technique section later in this chapter.) Such guidelines, coupled with the clinical expertise of the case manager, can make the process of case management more effective. (Danece Fickett, RN, provided the following real-life example.)

At one hospital, care guidelines used internal criteria as well as external criteria for the process of utilization review and case management. It also used the feedback information provided by the third-party payers. Unfortunately, the organization lacked the ability to share that information.

The quality leadership had noted through data collection that the process of admission, treatment, and discharge planning was not well coordinated among all the associated caregivers and the business operations of the organization. Key issues included the following:

- Hospital stays were continued after symptoms and treatment had reached a point where the patient could have received appropriate care in a less intensive care setting.

- Patients were admitted to the hospital for diagnosis and treatment in cases where the patients could have received appropriate care in a less intensive care setting.

- Discharge planning was not completed in a timely fashion. (Families were not involved in the decisions regarding discharge placement options or care plans. Home health agencies, skilled nursing care facilities, and hospices were not being contacted early in the patient's stay to facilitate postdischarge transition to other levels of care.)

- Insurance carriers and Medicare were denying payment because services had not been preauthorized. Insurance carriers and Medicare were denying payment because services had been rendered after discharge criteria had been met and documented.

- Medical records contained inadequate documentation of medical conditions, interventions, and outcomes.

At first, hospital utilization/quality department personnel organized themselves to better communicate the needs, problems, and obstacles to an effective case management system. It quickly became apparent, however, that they alone could not make the kind of differences necessary to improve the ailing systems.

A PI team was formed. The team included a representative from the admitting/registration department, business office and financial counselors, the admissions nurse, the operating room scheduler, the operating room manager, a representative from outpatient services, representatives from the nursing units, discharge planners, the utilization review/case managers, and the director of the utilization/quality department.

The team implemented Shewart and Deming's model of performance improvement. The team discovered, however, that the team did not include all of the individuals and departments who were closely associated with the process. The team realized that it also needed representatives and participants from physicians' offices. It invited key office personnel to participate on the team.

The newly composed team spent several weeks working on team building. The result of their work was a team of individuals who had a common mission and goals. Departmental barriers were ignored. Leading this group of people to form a cohesive team was the most difficult task. Obstacles included finger-pointing, feelings of failure, and fault finding. Eventually, an important breakthrough occurred. After repeated reinforcement of the concept that improvement of the process would benefit all departments, the team was able to get down to work.

Team members found more purpose and pleasure in their work and felt less powerlessness and frustration. The team collected, analyzed, and reported the information to those persons who could directly help in making a difference. The medical staff was educated regarding the problems and proposed solutions that could help develop an effective case management model. Other office personnel and service departments were included to complete the circle of participants.

The team's achievements included the following:

- Critical information was shared about postdischarge planning, such as treatment plans, goals of care, and financial information, including benefits, limits, out-of-pocket expenses, and deductibles.

- Providers of primary care were included in the decision-making process, and they were given information that benefited not only patients and their families, but also the physicians' practices and the hospital.

- Coordination of services was improved and access to specialists and special services was provided in a timely manner, including options for alternative placement for care and the wise use of financial resources. Often, with completed care plans, the payers were willing to discontinue the patient's insurance contract and pay for services that would complete the healing process and avoid readmission or duplicate extended care and testing.

- The numbers and dollar amounts of denials of payment decreased. The organization's fiscal situation improved, thus allowing the purchase of equipment and expansion of services.

- The quality of documentation in medical records was improved as was access to records and reports. Some forms and the flow of some medical information were changed.

- Having a proven method of case management served as an asset in subsequent contracting with new providers and payers.

- Departments, personnel within the organization, and providers' offices became more unified. The team approach served as a catalyst for change within the organization. Individuals realized that they could make a difference and that they had the ideas and power to make change happen. The PI activity strengthened the commitment of employees to the mission and vision of the organization.

QI Toolbox Techniques

Indicators, or criteria, and Gantt charts are often used in assessments of continuum-of-care issues.

Indicators

An **indicator,** or criterion, is a performance measure that enables healthcare organizations to monitor a process to determine whether it is meeting process requirements. The criteria may be established and implemented internally, externally, or generically.

Internal criteria are usually developed by an interdisciplinary team made up of physicians, nurses, and other clinical staff from the healthcare organization. This type of criterion is developed to monitor specific processes within the organization.

External criteria are created by some organizations outside the healthcare facility. Organizations such as insurance companies, peer review organizations, the Health Care Financing Administration, and other regulatory agencies develop healthcare criteria.

Generic criteria have been developed by many of the same agencies for use across the continuum of care and in various regions of the country. The term *generic* implies that the criteria are applicable across many organizations and with many different kinds of patients.

One of the most common applications of generic criteria measures is in the area of admission certification. Admissions criteria are used to establish the fact that each patient actually requires care at the level to which he or she has been admitted. Usually, admission criteria in acute care settings have two categories, intensity of service and severity of illness. For a patient to meet the admission criteria, he or she must meet a clinical measure in each of the categories. Intensity of service refers to the type of services or care the patient will require. Severity of illness refers to how "sick" the patient is, or what level of care the patient will require, for example, intensive care unit or general medical unit. (See the list of admission criteria in the case study that follows.)

Each indicator, written in the form of a ratio, is used as a tool for monitoring care and service. An indicator for the number of admissions that meet set admission criteria might be the following ratio:

$$\frac{\text{Number of admissions meeting criteria}}{\text{Total number of admissions}}$$

A target or goal set by a healthcare facility might be, "Admission criteria met 99 percent of the time." Meeting such high levels of expectation is very important to healthcare organizations today because care rendered to patients who do not meet admission criteria is not usually reimbursed.

These kinds of indicators can also be used to monitor other important processes in the organization. For example, the Joint Commission on Accreditation of Healthcare Organizations (JCAHO) has developed clinical indicators such as the following:

$$\frac{\text{Number of comatose trauma patients with selected intracranial injuries}}{\text{discharged from emergency department prior to endotracheal intubation or cricothyrotomy}}{\text{Total number of comatose trauma patients with selected intracranial injuries}}{\text{discharged from emergency department}}$$

$$\frac{\text{Number of patients with resections of primary colorectal cancer}}{\text{whose preoperative evaluation, by a managing physician,}}{\text{includes examination of the entire colon}}{\text{Total number of patients with resections of primary colorectal cancer}}$$

Monitoring these indicators allows the organization's leadership to identify the cases in which the best care may not have been provided to a patient. The indicators also identify excessive numbers of cases in which this was true, thus providing an opportunity for improvement in organizational processes. A set of hospital standard measures (or indicators) utilized by one community hospital is provided in table 5.1. These indicators were used to provide standardized reporting (which is discussed in chapter 15). A corresponding JCAHO standard is cited for each criterion, and the formula is given. Each criterion indicates the benchmark that the organization wants to meet, how often the indicator is measured, which organizational unit is responsible for the measure, where data are pulled to compute the measure, and where the results are reported.

Table 5.1.   Hospital Standard Measures (Copyright © 2000 by Polly Isaacson. All rights reserved.)

Standard	Measure of Process	Type Out/Proc	Measured Y/N	Indication/Formula	Benchmark	How often measured	Owner	Source of Data	Results Given to
				Operative & Invasive Procedures					
PI.3.2.1	Discrepancies--Pre-op/Post-op/Path	O	Y	# cases with discrepancy / # of pathology cases	0%	Quarterly	OR	OR data sheet	QC, Med-Exec, & the Board
PI.3.2.1	Procedure appropriateness: Surgical criteria not met	P	Y	# of appropriate cases / # of cases	100%	Quarterly	OR	OR data sheet	QC, Med-Exec, & the Board
PI.3.2.1	Patient preparation for procedure	P	Y	# of pts w/incomplete prep / # of pts requiring prep	0%	Quarterly	OR	OR data sheet	QC, Med-Exec, & the Board
PI.3.2.1	Procedure performance & patient monitoring: Intraoperative complications	P	Y	# patients w/intraoperative complications / # patient procedures	0%	Quarterly	OR	OR data sheet	QC, Med-Exec, & the Board
PI.3.2.1	Procedure performance & patient monitoring: Unplanned returns to OR	P	Y	# pts w/unplanned return to the operating room / # patients operated on	0%	Quarterly	OR	OR data sheet	QC, Med-Exec, & the Board
PI.3.2.1	Complications of post-procedure care	P	Y	# pts w/complications / # patients operated on	0%	Quarterly	OR	OR data sheet	QC, Med-Exec, & the Board
PI.3.2.1	Complication of post-procedure patient education	P	Y	# pts w/pt ed completed / # patients operated on	100%	Quarterly	OR	OR data sheet	QC, Med-Exec, & the Board
				Medication Use					
PI.3.2.2	Drug selection: DUE--Primaxin appropriateness	O	Y	# meeting criteria / # patients on Primaxin	100%	Quarterly	Pharmacy	DUE	P&T Med-Exec
PI.3.2.2	Prescribing or ordering: DUE--Toradol dosing appropriateness	O	Y	# meeting criteria / # patients on Toradol	100%	Quarterly	Pharmacy	DUE	P&T Med-Exec
PI.3.2.2	Preparing and dispensing: Dispensing Errors	O	Y	# dispensing errors / # inpatient days	0%	Quarterly	Pharmacy	Pharmacy tracking system	P&T Med-Exec
PI.3.2.2	Preparing and dispensing: Med. Delivery Time--Antibiotics	P	Y	# meeting criteria / # patients on med	<120 min	Quarterly	Pharmacy	Meditech documentation	P&T Med-Exec
PI.3.2.2	Administering: Medication Delivery Time--Thrombolytics	P	Y	# meeting criteria / # patients on med	<52 min	Quarterly	Pharmacy	Meditech documentation	P&T Med-Exec
PI.3.2.2	Administering: DUE--Gentamycin appropriateness (peak/trough)	P	Y	# meeting criteria / # patients on med	100%	Quarterly	Pharmacy	DUE	P&T Med-Exec
PI.3.2.2	Monitoring the effects on patients: Adverse drug reactions	O	Y	# ADR's / # of admissions	0%	Quarterly	Pharmacy	Incident report	P&T Med-Exec

Table 5.1. *(Continued)*

				Blood and Blood Components					
PI.3.2.3	Ordering: Blood usage appropriateness	P	Y	# episodes appropriate / # transfusion episodes	100%	Quarterly	Lab	Patient's records	QC & Med-Exec
PI.3.2.3	Ordering: Written order for blood/ components	P	Y	# episodes with orders / # transfusion episodes	100%	Quarterly	Lab	Physician's orders	QC & Med-Exec
PI.3.2.3	Distributing, handling, & dispensing: Protocol for checking unit out of bloodbank	P	Y	# units correctly dispensed / # units dispensed	100%	Quarterly	Lab	Bloodbank log	QC & Med-Exec
PI.3.2.3	Administration: Blood hung within 20 minutes of dispensing	P	Y	# units hung w/in 20 mins. / # units dispensed	100%	Quarterly	Lab	Blood slips	QC & Med-Exec
PI.3.2.4	Administration: Blood slips posted in the chart	P	Y	# blood slips posted / # units transfused	100%	Quarterly	Lab	Blood slips	QC & Med-Exec
PI.3.2.5	Administration: Blood slips completed	P	Y	# slips completed / # units transfused	100%	Quarterly	Lab	Blood slips	QC & Med-Exec
PI.3.2.5	Administration: Blood transfusion forms completed	P	Y	# forms completed / # units transfused	100%	Quarterly	Lab	Blood slips	QC & Med-Exec
PI.3.2.3	Administration: Crossmatch: Transfusion ratio	O	Y	# crossmatches / # transfusions	<=2 (l)	Quarterly	Lab	Bloodbank log	QC & Med-Exec
PI.3.2.3	Monitoring effects on patients: Potential transfusion reactions	O	Y	# patients with potential transfusion reactions / # pts receiving transfusions	<=1 (l)	Quarterly	Lab	or phone notification	QC & Med-Exec
PI.4.5.3	Monitoring effects on patients: Confirmed transfusion reactions	O	Y	# of true reactions / # transfusion episodes	0% (l)	Quarterly	Lab	transfusion reaction investigations	QC & Med-Exec
PI.3.2.3	Transfusion report form completed	P	Y	# forms completed / # pts receiving transfusions	100%	Quarterly	Lab	report log	QC & Med-Exec
				Miscellaneous Measures					
PI.3.2.4	Utilization Management: Patients admitted to observation who should have been inpatients	P	Y	# pts not admitted as IP's who met inpatient criteria / # pts admitted	0%	Quarterly	UR	Utilization mgmt. form	QC & Med-Exec
PI.3.2.4	Utilization Management: Pts admitted who meet criteria on initial review	P	Y	# appropriate admissions / # of admissions	100%	Quarterly	UR	Utilization mgmt. form	QC & Med-Exec
PI.3.2.4	Utilization Management: Pts admitted meeting continued stay criteria	P	Y	# pts no longer meeting continued stay criteria / # of patients discharged	100%	Quarterly	UR	Utilization mgmt. form	QC & Med-Exec
PI.3.2.4	Utilization Management: Pts remaining inpatients after discharge criteria met	P	Y	# pts remaining after discharge criteria met / # pts discharged	0%	Quarterly	UR	Utilization mgmt. form	QC & Med-Exec

(Continued on next page)

55

Table 5.1. *(Continued)*

		P/O	Y	Numerator / Denominator	Target	Frequency	Responsible	Data Source	Reporting
	Miscellaneous Measures (cont'd)								
PI.3.2.4	Utilization Management: # of pts for whom discharge planning was done	P	Y	# pts who had discharge planning done / # pts discharged	100%	Quarterly	UR	Utilization mgmt. form	QC & Med-Exec
PI.4.5.2	Adverse events during anesthesia	O	Y	# adverse events / # pts given anesthesia	0% (I)	Quarterly	OR	or OR data sheet	QC & Med-Exec
TX.7.1.3.2.3	Restraint & Seclusion: Evidence of less restrictive measures used	O	Y	# pts w/evidence of less restrictive measures used / # patients in restraints	100% documnt.	Quarterly	Nursing	Patient restraint record	QC & Med-Exec
PI.3.3	Mortality Rate	O	Y	# deaths / # IP & OB discharges	1.4% (L)	Quarterly	HIM	Patient record	QC & Med-Exec
PI.3.3.1	Autopsy Results	P	Y	# performed / # met criteria		Quarterly	OR	Patient record & Autopsy criteria	QC & Med-Exec
PI.3.3	C-Section Rate	O	Y	# C-Sections performed / # of deliveries	17% (L)	Quarterly	Labor & Delivery	Obstetric report	QC & Med-Exec
PI.3.3	Vaginal deliveries with complications (ORYX)	O	Y	# vaginal deliveries w/comp. / # vaginal deliveries		Quarterly	OR	Patient report	QC & Med-Exec
PI.3.3	VBAC Rate	O	Y	# VBAC / # repeat C-sections	36% (S)	Quarterly	Labor & Delivery	Obstetric report	QC & Med-Exec
PI.3.3	Attempted VBAC Rate	O	Y	# pts w/previous C-sections who receive trial of labor / # pts w/previous C-sections	36% (L)	Quarterly	Labor & Delivery	Monthly obstetric	QC & Med-Exec
PI.3.3	Joint Replacements with complications (ORYX)	O	Y	# joint replacements with complications / # joint replacements	0%	Quarterly	OR	Patient record & Surgical stats	QC & Med-Exec
	Risk Management Activities								
PI.3.3.2	Notice of Intent	O	Y	# for current quarter	1	Quarterly	Risk Mgmt.	Receipt of atty letter or notice	QC & Med-Exec
PI.3.3.2	Summons and Complaint	O	Y	# for current quarter	1	Quarterly	Risk Mgmt.	Receipt of atty letter or notice	QC & Med-Exec
PI.3.3.2	Potentially Compensable Events	O	Y	# for current quarter	1	Quarterly	Risk Mgmt.	Complaint system	QC & Med-Exec
PI.3.3.2	Small Claims	O	Y	# for current quarter	1	Quarterly	Risk Mgmt.	Complaint system	QC & Med-Exec
PI.3.3.2	Patient/Family Complaints--Care	O	Y	# complaints / # patient days	<=2%	Quarterly	Risk Mgmt.	Complaint system	QC & Med-Exec
PI.3.3.2	Patient/Family Complaints--Billing	O	Y	# complaints / # patient days	<=2%	Quarterly	Risk Mgmt.	Complaint system	QC & Med-Exec
PI.3.3.2	Medical Device Reporting (Manufacturer)	O	Y	# complaints / # patient days	<.1%	Quarte:ly	Risk Mgmt.	Incident Report	QC, Med-Exec & Safety Comm

Table 5.1.   (Continued)

				Risk Management Activities (cont'd)					
PI.3.3.2	Medical Device Reporting (FDA)	O	Y	# of reportings / # patient days	<.1%	Quarterly	Risk Mgmt.	Incident Report	QC, Med-Exec & Safety Comm
PI.3.3.2	Tracking Requirements - Operating Room	O	Y	# pts successfully tracked / # pts required to track	100% (I)	Quarterly	Risk Mgmt.		QC, Med-Exec & Safety Comm
PI.3.3.2	Total Product Recalls	O	Y	# recalls / # patient days	<.2%	Quarterly	Risk Mgmt.	Notification from Manufacturer	QC, Med-Exec & Safety Comm
PI.3.3.2	Pharmacy	O	Y	# recalls / # patient days	<.1%	Quarterly	Risk Mgmt.	Notification from Manufacturer	QC, Med-Exec & Safety Comm
PI.3.3.2	Nutrition	O	Y	# recalls / # patient days	<.1%	Quarterly	Risk Mgmt.	Notification from Manufacturer	QC, Med-Exec & Safety Comm
PI.3.3.2	Materials Management	O	Y	# recalls / # patient days	<.1%	Quarterly	Risk Mgmt.	Notification from Manufacturer	QC, Med-Exec & Safety Comm
PI.3.3.2	Bio Medical	O	Y	# recalls / # patient days	<.1%	Quarterly	Risk Mgmt.	Notification from Manufacturer	QC, Med-Exec & Safety Comm
				Quality Control Activities					
PI.3.3.3	Clinical Lab	P	Y	# of QC measures at 100% / # QC measures in dept.	100% (I)	Quarterly	Lab	QC Logs	QC, Med-Exec & the Board
PI.3.3.3	Dietary	P	Y	# of QC measures at 100% / # QC measures in dept.	100% (I)	Quarterly	Dietary	QC Logs	QC, Med-Exec & the Board
PI.3.3.3	Diagnostic Radiology	P	Y	# of QC measures at 100% / # QC measures in dept.	100% (I)	Quarterly	Imaging	QC Logs	QC, Med-Exec & the Board
PI.3.3.3	Nuclear Medicine	P	Y	# of QC measures at 100% / # QC measures in dept.	100% (I)	Quarterly	Imaging	QC Logs	QC, Med-Exec & the Board
PI.3.3.3	Equipment used to administer meds	P	Y	# of QC measures at 100% / # QC measures in dept.	100% (I)	Quarterly	Pharmacy	QC Logs	QC, Med-Exec & the Board
PI.3.3.3	Pharmaceutical equipment used to prepare medications	P	Y	# of QC measures at 100% / # QC measures in dept.	100% (I)	Quarterly	Pharmacy	QC Logs	QC, Med-Exec & the Board
				Patient Rights					
PI.3.2.5	Patient satisfaction: Inpatient	O	Y	percentage reported only	93% (C)	Quarterly	QRS	Gallup results	QC, Med-Exec & the Board
PI.3.2.5	Patient satisfaction: Outpatient tests & treatment	O	Y	percentage reported only	93% (C)	Quarterly	QRS	Gallup results	QC, Med-Exec & the Board
PI.3.2.5	Patient satisfaction: Outpatient surgery	O	Y	percentage reported only	93% (C)	Quarterly	QRS	Gallup results	QC, Med-Exec & the Board
PI.3.2.5	Patient satisfaction: Emergency Room	O	Y	percentage reported only	93% (C)	Quarterly	QRS	Gallup results	QC, Med-Exec & the Board
				Human Resources					
PI.3.2.6 & HR.4.3	Staff views regarding performance and improvement opportunities	O	Y	# employees completing self appraisal forms / # of employees	100% (I)	Annually	Human Resources	Performance Appraisal form	QC, Med-Exec & the Board

(Continued on next page)

Table 5.1. *(Continued)*

				Human Resources (cont'd)					
HR.4.3	Collection of data on patterns & trends: Employee Turnover Rate	O	Y	# employees leaving / # of employees		Annually	Human Resources	Resource records	QC, Med-Exec & the Board
HR.4.3	Collection of data on patters & trends: Perf. Review Outcomes	O	Y	# employees scoring <=2 / # of employees	0% (I)	Annually	Human Resources	Performance Appraisal results	QC, Med-Exec & the Board
HR.4.3	Completion of competency testing of employees	O	Y	# employees completing competency testing / # of employees	100% (I)	Annually	Human Resources	Results of tests	QC, Med-Exec & the Board
	Environment of Care								
	Safety Plan Performance Measure								
EC.1.3	Patient Incidents--Total	O	Y	# of incidents / patient days	<15% (I)	Quarterly	Risk Mgmt.	Incident Report	Safety, QC & the Board
EC.1.3	Medication	O	Y	# of incidents / patient days	<2%	Quarterly	Risk Mgmt.	Incident Report	Safety, QC & the Board
EC.1.3	IV	O	Y	# of incidents / patient days	<2%	Quarterly	Risk Mgmt.	Incident Report	Safety, QC & the Board
EC.1.3	Adverse effect of medication	O	Y	# of incidents / patient days	<=5%	Quarterly	Risk Mgmt.	Incident Report	Safety, QC & the Board
EC.1.3	Falls	O	Y	# inpatient falls / patient days	<1%	Quarterly	Risk Mgmt.	Incident Report	Safety, QC & the Board
EC.1.3	Diagnostic/Procedure	O	Y	# of incidents / patient days	<5%	Quarterly	Risk Mgmt.	Incident Report	Safety, QC & the Board
EC.1.3	Other	O	Y	# of incidents / patient days	<5%	Quarterly	Risk Mgmt.	Incident Report	Safety, QC & the Board
EC.1.3	Home Health Patient Falls	O	Y	# of falls / # of patients	<10% (I)	Quarterly	Risk Mgmt.	Incident Report	Safety, QC & the Board
EC.1.3	Home Health Medication Errors	O	Y	# of errors / # of patients	<5% (I)	Quarterly	Risk Mgmt.	Incident Report	Safety, QC & the Board
EC.1.3	Visitor Incidents--Total	O	Y	# of incidents / patient days	<.2% (I)	Quarterly	Risk Mgmt.	Incident Report	Safety, QC & the Board
EC.1.3	Falls	O	Y	# of falls / patient days	<.1% (I)	Quarterly	Risk Mgmt.	Incident Report	Safety, QC & the Board
EC.1.3	Other	O	Y	# of other incidents / patient days	<.1% (I)	Quarterly	Risk Mgmt.	Incident Report	Safety, QC & the Board
EC.1.3	Worker's Comp Claims--Total	O	Y	# of claims x 100 / productive man hours	<2%	Quarterly	Risk Mgmt.	Incident Report	Safety, QC & the Board
EC.1.3	Hospital Employees	O	Y	# of claims x 100 / productive man hours	<2%	Quarterly	Risk Mgmt.	Incident Report	Safety, QC & the Board
EC.1.3	Home Health Employees	O	Y	# of claims x 100 / productive man hours	2%	Quarterly	Risk Mgmt.	Incident Report	Safety, QC & the Board
EC.1 3	Employee Infection/Illness	O	Y	# of claims x 100 / productive man hours	2%	Quarterly	Risk Mgmt.	Incident Report	Safety, QC & the Board

Table 5.1. *(Continued)*

Code	Measure			Performance Measure	Threshold	Frequency		Report	Committee
Safety Plan Performance Measure (cont'd)									
EC 1.3	OSHA Reportables	O	Y	# of reportables x 100 / productive man hours	<1%	Quarterly	Risk Mgmt.	Incident Report	Envir of Care, QC & the Board
EC 1.3	Occupational Injuries	O	Y	# of reportables x 100 / productive man hours	<2%	Quarterly	Risk Mgmt.	Incident Report	Envir of Care, QC & the Board
EC 1.3	Occupational Illness	O	Y	# of reportables x 100 / productive man hours	<1%	Quarterly	Risk Mgmt.	Incident Report	Envir of Care, QC & the Board
EC 1.3	Lost Work Days	O	Y	# of reportables x 100 / productive man hours	<1%	Quarterly	Risk Mgmt.	Incident Report	Envir of Care, QC & the Board
EC 1.3	Restricted Work Days	O	Y	# of reportables x 100 / productive man hours	<2%	Quarterly	Risk Mgmt.	Incident Report	Envir of Care, QC & the Board
EC 1.3	Back Injuries	O	Y	# of reportables x 100 / productive man hours	<1%	Quarterly	Risk Mgmt.	Incident Report	Envir of Care, QC & the Board
EC 1.3	Neddlesticks	O	Y	# of reportables x 100 / productive man hours	<1%	Quarterly	Risk Mgmt.	Incident Report	Envir of Care, QC & the Board
EC 1.3	Blood Body Fluid Exposures	O	Y	# of reportables x 100 / productive man hours	<1%	Quarterly	Risk Mgmt.	Incident Report	Envir of Care, QC & the Board
EC 1.8	Chemical Exposures	O	Y	# of reportables x 100 / productive man hours	<1%	Quarterly	Risk Mgmt.	Incident Report	Envir of Care, QC & the Board
Security Plan Performance Measures									
EC 1.4	Total Security Incidents	O	Y	# of incidents / 91 days or 1/4 yr	<5%	Quarterly	Risk Mgmt.	Incident Report	Envir of Care, QC & the Board
EC 1.4	Violence in Workplace	O	Y	# of incidents / 91 days or 1/4 yr	<1%	Quarterly	Risk Mgmt.	Incident Report	Envir of Care, QC & the Board
EC 1.4	Other Suspicious Circumstances	O	Y	# of incidents / 91 days or 1/4 yr	<5%	Quarterly	Risk Mgmt.	Incident Report	Envir of Care, QC & the Board
Control of Hazardous Materials and Waste Plan Performance Measures									
EC 1.5	Radiation Monitoring (Over-exposures)	O	Y	# of overexposures / Patient days	0	Monthly / Quarterly	Risk Mgmt.	Monitor tags	QC, Med-Exec & the Board
EC 1.5	Environmental Hazards Inspections	O	Y	# comp / 22 areas / # comp / 10 pt care areas	100%	Annually	Risk Mgmt.	Envir of Care Meeting	QC, Med-Exec & the Board
Emergency Preparedness Plan Performance Measures									
EC 1.6	Disaster/Disaster Drills	P	Y	# of drills / 1	100% 2/yr	Quarterly	Risk Mgmt.	Envir of Care Meeting	QC, Med-Exec & the Board
Life Safety Plan Performance Measures									
EC 1.7	Fire Drills	P	Y	# of drills / 3	100% or 3/quarter	Quarterly	Risk Mgmt.	Envir of Care Meeting	QC, Med-Exec & the Board
EC 1.7	Safety Inspections	P	Y	# comp / 22 / # comp / 10	100%	Quarterly	Risk Mgmt.	Envir of Care Meeting	QC, Med-Exec & the Board
EC 1.7	Orientation within 30 days	P	Y	# attended orientation w/in 30 days / # new hires	95%	Quarterly	Risk Mgmt.	Human Resources	QC, Med-Exec & the Board

(Continued on next page)

Table 5.1. *(Continued)*

				Life Safety Plan Performance Measures (cont'd)					
EC.1.7	Yearly Safety Education Compliance	P	Y	# completed education / # of employees	100%	Quarterly	Risk Mgmt.	Human Resources	QC, Med-Exec & the Board
EC.1.8	Biomedical Equipment P.M.'s	P	Y	# pieces of equip done / # pieces of equip due	95%	Quarterly	Risk Mgmt.	National MD	QC, Med-Exec & the Board
EC.1.8	Repairs	P	Y	# pieces of equip repaired / # pieces of failed equipmt	<3%	Quarterly	Risk Mgmt.	National MD	QC, Med-Exec & the Board
EC.1.8	User Errors	P	Y	# user errors identified / # pieces of failed equipment	<3%	Quarterly	Risk Mgmt.	National MD	QC, Med-Exec & the Board
EC.1.8	Laser Safety Procedures	P	Y	# procedures done / # op encounters	no benchmark	Quarterly	Risk Mgmt.	Operating Room	QC, Med-Exec & the Board
EC.1.8	Number of Related Incidents	P	Y	# incidents / # procedures done	<1%	Quarterly	Risk Mgmt.	Operating Room	QC, Med-Exec & the Board
				Utility Systems Plan Performance Measures					
EC.1.9	Plant Ops P.M.'s	P	Y	# PM's done / # PM's due	90%	Quarterly	Risk Mgmt.	Plant Operations	QC, Med-Exec & the Board
EC.1.9	Equipment/Utility Incidents	P	Y	# of incidents / patient days	<.5%	Quarterly	Risk Mgmt.	Plant Operations	QC, Med-Exec & the Board
				Management of Information					
IM.3.2.1	Data Quality Monitoring: Documentation appropriateness	P	Y	# cases w/appropriate doc / # cases reviewed	80% (I)	Quarterly	HIM	DQM form	QC, Med-Exec & the Board
IM.3.2.1	Medical Record Delinquency: Overall	O	Y	# charts 21 days delinq. / # discharges for month	<50% (J)	Quarterly	HIM	Record report	QC, Med-Exec & the Board
IM.3.2.1	Suspensions	O	Y	# suspensions / # physicians	0%	Quarterly	HIM		QC, Med-Exec & the Board
				Infection Control					
IC.2	Overall Nosocomial Infection Rate	O	Y	# nosocomial infections / # patients	<1% (I)	Monthly / Quarterly	Infection Control	Culture reports & Pt records	QR IC Committee
IC.2	Surgical Wound Infection Rate	O	Y	# post op infections / # surgeries	0.8% (L)	Monthly / Quarterly	Infection Control	Culture reports & Pt records	QR IC Committee
				Withholding Services					
RI.1.2.5	Advance Directives: Patients asked	P	Y	# pts asked about AD / # patients 18 or older	100%	Quarterly	Admitting	Patient record	QC, Med-Exec & the Board
RI.1.2.5	Advance Directives: Patients receiving info about Advance directives	P	Y	# pts receiving AD info / # pts 18 or older	100%	Quarterly	Admitting	Patient record	QC, Med-Exec & the Board
RI.1.2.5	Advance Directives: Advance directives received by the hospital	P	Y	# AD's hospital obtains / # pts claiming to have AD	100%	Quarterly	Admitting	Tracking form	QC, Med-Exec & the Board
				New Programs					
PI.3	New program effectiveness						CNO		

Gantt Charts

A **Gantt chart** is a project management tool used to schedule important activities. Gantt charts divide a horizontal scale into days, weeks, or months and a vertical scale into the project activities or tasks.

Gantt charts are used in clinical process improvement to depict clinical guidelines or critical paths in the treatment of common medical conditions. The tool provides a graphic method for showing the simultaneous and interdependent treatments for a clinical condition that are most likely to result in the best possible outcome. Figure 5.3 is an example of a Gantt chart. The chart depicts the clinical guidelines used for cases of myocardial infarction at a large medical center.

Case Study

Table 5.2 is a set of admission criteria for medical/surgical admissions. Figure 5.4 shows an example of a report of one patient's history and physical. Students should compare the patient's history to the admission criteria and determine whether the patient meets or does not meet the criteria for admission to the hospital. The patient must meet at least one criterion in severity of illness and at least one criterion in intensity of service.

Project Application

Students should refer back to chapter 4 and the data they collected for their student projects with surveys and interviews. Students then should identify the performance criteria that could capture data about those customer satisfaction issues. For example, if the students were looking at bookstore services, some of the criteria for bookstore performance might be book pricing, availability of books, and buy-back percentage.

Summary

Appropriate utilization of healthcare services has long been a major issue in the United States. Utilization management strategies led to the managed care approach common in the last decade of the twentieth century. Various approaches, including admission criteria and critical pathways, have been developed to assist reviewers in determining the nature and extent of required care. Management and analysis of these issues remains a major component of performance improvement activities in every healthcare organization in the nation.

References

Abdelhak, Mervat, et al. 1996. *Health Information: Management of a Strategic Resource,* pp. 336–42. Philadelphia: W. B. Saunders Company.

Meisenheimer, Claire G., et al. 1997. *Improving Quality: A Guide to Effective Programs,* pp. 207–24. Gaithersberg, Md.: Aspen Publishers.

O'Leary, Margaret. 1996. *Clinical Performance Data: A Guide to Interpretation.* Oakbrook Terrace, Ill.: Joint Commission on Accreditation of Healthcare Organizations.

Zander, K. 1997. Use of variance from clinical paths: coming of age. *Clinical Performance and Quality Health Care* 5(1):20–30.

Figure 5.3.   Sample Gantt Chart Format in an Excerpt of a Critical Pathway

Western University Regional Medical Center
Department of Nursing
Case Management Plan

Diagnosis: Idiopathic pediatric scoliosis, with surgery, without complications   **Unit:** 9 East   **DRG:** 215

Average Length of Stay: 7 days   **Usual OR Day (admission day = 1):** 2

Clinical Milestones:

	Prior to Admission	Day 1	Day 2	Day 3	Day 4	Day 5	Day 6	Day 7	Day 8	Day 9	Day 10	Day 11	Day 12
Self-donation of blood	X												
Chest X ray, chem panel	X												
Labs, EKG, blood type & crossmatch	X												
PM admission		X											
H&P		X											
Care planning		X											
Surgery			X										
Surgical ICU			X										
Catheter removed				X									
Patient sits up in bed					X								
Transfer to surgical floor					X								
Physical therapy					X	X	X						
Patient walks down corridor					X								
Patient education for self-care							X						
Patient receives meds and instructions for follow-up care										X			
Outpatient physical therapy scheduled						X							
Patient discharged to home										X			

Health Outcomes:

Diagnosis	Outcome (The patient . . .)	Day–Visit	Intermediate Goal (The patient . . .)	Day–Visit	Process (The nurse . . .)	Day–Visit	Process (The physician . . .)
Fluid–electrolye imbalance: third space shifting secondary to large volume loss and replacement	Has stable vital signs consistent with base-line at admission	5–6 4–14	Is afebrile	4	Takes vital signs every 2 hours	PTA	Arranges for self-donation of blood before surgery
		4–6	Maintains urine out-put over 1 cc/kg/hr while catheterized	4	Measures and records urine output every hour	1	Assesses patient's cardiac status on admission
	Has a baseline nor-mal voiding pattern	6–8	Voids 8 hours after Foley is discontinued			1	Orders lab workup
		4–14	Maintains specific gravity under .1020	4	Monitors specific gravity		
	Has no edema	8–9	Returns to baseline skin turgor	4–8	Balances IV and oral intake to achieve maintenance fluid requirements		

Table 5.2.   Admission Criteria

Severity of Illness	Intensity of Service
Sudden onset of unconsciousness or disorientation	Intravenous medications and/or fluid replacement
Pulse rate: <50/min or >140/min and not typical for patient	Inpatient-approved surgery or procedure within 24 hours of admission
Blood pressure: systolic <90 or >200 mm Hg or diastolic <60 or >120 mm Hg *and* not typical for patient	Vital signs every 2 hours or more often
Acute loss of sight or hearing	Chemotherapeutic agents requiring continuous observation
Acute loss of ability to move body part	Treatment in an ICU if indicated
Persistent fever	Intramuscular injection every 8 hours
Active bleeding	Respiratory care at least every 8 hours
Severe electrolyte/blood gas abnormality	Glucose monitoring at least 4 times daily
EKG evidence of acute ischemia	
Wound dehiscence or evisceration	
Widely fluctuating blood glucose levels	
Hemoglobin levels 1.4 times upper limit of normal	

Figure 5.4.   Example of a History and Physical Report

Reason for Admission: Severe, short-distance, lifestyle-limiting right lower extremity claudication

History of Present Illness: This is a 32-year-old woman who developed new-onset right lower extremity claudication following right transfemoral cardiac catheterization for routine follow-up 10 years after cardiac transplantation. The catheterization was approximately 10 days ago. Since that time, she describes symptoms of pain in her calf after walking approximately 20 yards or less. If she walks too far, she develops paresthesias and complete numbness in the right foot. The pain is relieved by rest. She does not have rest pain at night. She has never had any symptoms similar to this or any symptoms in the contralateral leg.

She underwent cardiac transplantation 10 years ago. Since that time, she has had annual routine evaluation by transfemoral cardiac catheterization. Dr. Smith, who reviewed the films from the catheterization, reports that there is evidence of mild narrowing in the common femoral artery, possibly due to prior catheterizations. There is also some concern regarding the possibility of arterial dissection more proximally, although this may be an artifact on the angiogram.

Allergies: No known drug allergies

Past Medical History: (1) History of hypertrophic cardiomyopathy, now status post cardiac transplantation. (2) Intermittent episodes of rejection. (3) History of herpes zoster.

Past Surgical History: Cardiac transplantation

Medications: Pepcid 20 mg po bid, Vasotec 5 mg po bid, magnesium oxide 400 mg po bid, aspirin 81 mg po bid, CellCept 1 gm po bid, Neoral 100 mg qam and 75 mg qpm

Social History: The patient is a schoolteacher.

Habits: She drinks alcohol occasionally and does not smoke cigarettes.

Review of Systems: The patient has no active cardiopulmonary symptoms of which she is aware and no history of hepatorenal dysfunction. She has had no other episodes of bleeding or thrombotic disorders.

Physical Examination:

HEENT:	Unremarkable
CHEST:	Clear throughout to auscultation
CARDIOVASCULAR:	Regular rhythm without murmur, gallop, or rub
ABDOMEN:	Soft, nontender with no obvious masses or organomegaly
GENITALIA/RECTAL:	Deferred
EXTREMITIES:	No clubbing, cyanosis, or edema. There is no dependent rub or pallor on elevation. The patient has normal sensation and motor function in the lower extremities. Pulses are 3/3 except in the right lower extremity, where no palpable pulses are present.
LABORATORY DATA:	Potassium 3.8; hematocrit 45; sodium 142
TEST RESULTS:	Angiography demonstrated occlusion of the external iliac artery from near the bifurcation to the distal common femoral artery, which reconstitutes just above its own bifurcation. A guide wire passed easily through this, suggesting soft thrombus. There is excellent collateralization and no evidence of distal abnormalities.
	Duplex ultrasonography performed earlier demonstrated no evidence of deep or superficial thrombophlebitis. Noninvasive vascular studies also suggested aortoiliac/femoral occlusive disease with good collateralization distally.

Impression:
1. Occluded right external iliac and common femoral artery following transfemoral cardiac catheterization
2. Status post cardiac transplantation for hypertrophic cardiomyopathy
3 History of herpes zoster

Plan: The patient will be admitted to the hospital to undergo operative intervention to repair the femoral artery injury. Several possibilities exist, including possible dissection of the artery and injury to the artery during the catheterization or development of a collagen plug post angiography. I have discussed these possibilities with the patient, and I plan to perform an exploration of the right femoral area and, if necessary, a right lower quadrant, retroperitoneal incision to expose the proximal bifurcation and a bypass if necessary. Discussed the possibility of vein patch angioplasty as well. We also discussed the risks of the operation including MI, CVA, death, infection, bleeding, nerve injury, embolization and tissue loss, bowel injury, etc. She understands all these things as well as the indications for operative intervention. We plan operation tonight as soon as an operating room is available.

Chapter 6
Managing the Infectious Disease Experience

Learning Objectives

- To understand why the control of infection is so important in healthcare organizations

- To be able to differentiate nosocomial infections from community-acquired infections

- To be able to explain the various approaches that healthcare organizations use to manage the occurrence of infection

- To be able to identify the governmental organizations that develop regulations in this area and explain the regulatory approaches often taken

Background and Significance

Infectious disease is not new to the world's human populations. Epidemics of infectious disease have resulted in major loss of life throughout the centuries. The discovery of the "germ" as the causative agent of infection presented the human species with its most important breakthrough in preventing human disease. Even today, the most effective means by which humans prevent disease is through sanitation procedures of all kinds.

Understanding how various germs (pathologic organisms: bacteria, viruses, and parasites) function presented humans with their most important opportunity to control and cure disease. Vaccines developed as a result of this understanding now limit the spread of infectious disease within a population, and antibiotics help limit the growth and spread of pathologic organisms within the human body.

New diseases still erupt onto the world landscape: hanta virus pneumonia, acquired immune deficiency syndrome (AIDS), and Legionnaire's disease have all been recognized and investigated within the past thirty years. But today, healthcare researchers and providers utilize vaccines, medications, and various other interventions to identify, limit spread, and eliminate disease so that a smaller proportion of the population is affected than in historic times.

In developed countries, governmental agencies such as the Centers for Disease Control (CDC) in the United States maintain national standards for disease prevention and treatment. Professional groups such as the Association of Professionals for Infection and Epidemiology and the American Public Health Association are involved in training communicable disease specialists and establishing standards of care for infectious diseases. In addition, most state licensing agencies and healthcare accrediting agencies publish standards of care for the management of infection and disease prevention.

Infections and infectious disease processes play a prominent role in the management of quality and performance in every healthcare facility, whether it is an acute care hospital, a residential care facility, or a community daycare program for senior citizens. Consumers avoid healthcare facilities that have high rates of **nosocomial infection.** Patients who acquire an infection while they are hospitalized spread the word about their experience to their families, friends, neighbors, and coworkers. Clearly, the infectious disease experience in healthcare facilities is of paramount importance, both in terms of its effect on patients' lives and its effect on a healthcare facility's reputation and accreditation status.

Managing the Infectious Disease Experience: Steps to Success

Infection control, surveillance, and management can be performed in a variety of ways. In some facilities, an infection control committee made up of physicians, nurses, and clinical laboratory staff performs weekly reviews of the facilitywide incidence of infectious disease. In others, one individual is specifically assigned to infection surveillance and control.

Infection management should be based on an infection control plan developed by the facility's clinical staff. The plan should be specific to that facility's case mix, service lines, and care resources. It should include methods of surveillance and tracking for infections in every area of the facility, from infectious disease units to dietary services, from newborn nurseries to clinical laboratories.

Step 1: Control infection through the use of universal precautions

The mandate for applying universal precautions in healthcare services has been the cornerstone of infection control since the 1980s. **Universal precautions** can be defined as the application of a set of procedures specifically designed to minimize or eliminate the passage of infectious disease agents from one individual to another during the provision of

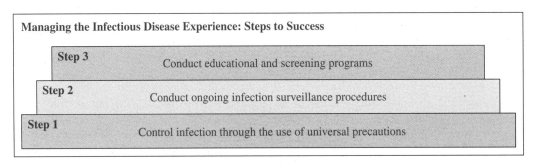

Managing the Infectious Disease Experience: Steps to Success

Step 3   Conduct educational and screening programs

Step 2   Conduct ongoing infection surveillance procedures

Step 1   Control infection through the use of universal precautions healthcare services. The precautions are called *universal* because they are meant to be followed by all caregivers as they provide services to all patients at all times.

Universal precautions require that caregivers wash their hands between patients and wear gloves when they examine patients or administer therapies. Caregivers must also wear gloves, gown, mask, and eye protection whenever they perform procedures that disrupt the patient's skin or mucous membranes. All patients are presumed to carry infectious disease agents. Therefore, barriers are erected between patients and other patients and between patients and caregivers when blood or bodily fluids are involved in any way.

Step 2: Conduct ongoing infection surveillance procedures

Occurrences of infection are evaluated to determine whether the infections were acquired in the healthcare facility or in the community. A **nosocomial infection** is defined as an infection that was acquired as a result of an exposure that occurred in the healthcare facility after the patient was admitted. A **community-acquired infection** is an infection that was present in the patient before he or she was admitted to the facility.

Specific guidelines have been developed to determine whether an infection is nosocomial or community acquired. For example, if a child were admitted to a hospital with a fever and within 24 hours developed measles, this disease would be considered community acquired. The incubation period for measles is at least 14 days; therefore, it can be determined that the patient's exposure to the disease occurred prior to admission. If, however, a patient was admitted for treatment of an intervertebral disk injury and then developed a urinary tract infection with fever after undergoing surgery, the infection was probably acquired while the patient was hospitalized. Infection after a patient's admission is classified as a nosocomial infection.

Both of these instances of infectious disease would be tracked and reported but for different reasons. The measles would be tracked to document the fact that the facility's staff took appropriate action to prevent the exposure of other patients. The urinary tract infection would be tracked to document initiation of appropriate treatment interventions and to identify any measures that might be taken to prevent such infections in the future.

It is important to track nosocomial infection rates for each area of the facility that deals with patients. Rates of nosocomial infection vary greatly depending upon the nursing unit and the types of patients cared for. For example, looking at central vascular catheter-related bloodstream infections (CR-BSIs) in the intensive care setting, one finds rates varying from 2.1 (respiratory ICU) to 30.2 (burn ICU) per 1000 central catheter days. Looking at noncentral vascular catheter-related bloodstream infections in other intensive care settings (cardiac ICU, postsurgical ICU), one finds rates varying from 0 to 2.0 per 1000 noncentral catheter days (CDC, 2000). Other types of procedures commonly associated with nosocomial infection that should be tracked include the use of indwelling urinary catheters and mechanical ventilation devices.

Decubitus ulcers and surgical site infections are often associated with hospital care. Other possible sources of nosocomial infection include exposure to clinical or nonclinical staff who themselves carry infectious diseases, substandard surgical or postsurgical care, and noncompliance with universal precautions. For a more in-depth discussion of the complexities of tracking and managing nosocomial infection in healthcare facilities, the reader is referred to the Web site of the Centers for Disease Control at www.cdc.gov/ncidod. In most facilities, a multidisciplinary approach to infection management involves the patient's physician, a pharmacist, an epidemiologist, a clinical laboratorian, the patient's nurse or case manager, and the patient. The goal is to initiate appropriate treatment, which usually involves the administration of an appropriate antibiotic medication prescribed in an effective dosage. A certified professional trained to evaluate the appropriateness of infection management measures may be assigned to review unusual cases of infection.

The appropriate use of antibiotics has been a subject of debate in recent years. Several strains of bacteria are becoming resistant to commonly prescribed antibiotics. Some medical experts implicate the indiscriminate use of antibiotics in cases without clear indication through laboratory culture and sensitivity processes. Specific antibiotics are approved for the treatment of specific conditions but not for all conditions. Antibiotics are not interchangeable, and an antibiotic approved for the treatment of cellulitis might not be appropriate for the treatment of a respiratory infection. In general, antibiotics are not effective against viral infections, but patients often request and receive antibiotics for common viral infections such as colds.

Another aspect of infection surveillance involves employee health and illness tracking. Policies related to the tracking of employee absences exist for the specific purpose of preventing infection via healthcare workers. Reports of absences are tabulated and examined for any possible connection to cases of nosocomial infection.

Monitoring the care environment is another aspect of infection surveillance. In many facilities, specimens from patient care areas are cultured monthly to identify any pathological bacteria growing in the care environment. The cultures are reported and tracked. When the presence of a significant infectious agent is identified, another specimen is cultured after the area has been cleaned to determine whether the area was sufficiently disinfected.

The cleanliness of food preparation and service areas is also tracked, and records are kept as documentation that all local and state regulations regarding safe food-handling procedures are being followed. The training and safety performance of food service staff are also documented.

Food temperatures and refrigerator temperatures are tracked daily, as are records of the cleaning of food preparation and service areas. Refrigerators containing medications are kept separate from refrigerators containing food, and temperature logs must be kept for medication refrigerators as well.

The infection control committee approves all substances used for cleaning in the facility. In many facilities, the infection control committee conducts monthly environmental rounds to look for areas of noncompliance with standards. The governing body may also review the results of the monthly rounds along with any actions for improvement suggested by the committee.

Step 3: Conduct educational and screening programs

An effective infection control program routinely evaluates all the means of transmission of infection throughout the facility and develops educational programs that promote disease prevention, such as hand-washing campaigns, influenza vaccination programs, hepatitis B vaccinations for high-risk employees, sterile technique in-services, and needle-stick prevention programs. Education on universal precautions is mandatory for all employees in most facilities.

Tracking exposures to blood-borne pathogens such as the human immunodeficiency virus (HIV) is required by most states and is outlined in Occupational Safety and Health Administration (OSHA) regulations. OSHA regulations require the monitoring of employees after exposure for at least one year, with frequent HIV testing. HIV testing and screening for employees who are known to have been exposed to HIV require the informed consent of individual employees. OSHA also mandates that specific education on the risks and outcomes of testing be provided to employees by a certified HIV instructor or physician.

When state law requires the facility to report positive test results to the state department of health, the employee involved must be notified ahead of time. Many state departments of health provide programs to test, treat, and educate employees and clients regarding the HIV disease process.

Most states require facilities to outline a tuberculosis prevention plan that involves the careful screening of employees and/or clients to identify those who suffer from the disease as well as those who carry the disease. Annual mandatory testing of workers is usually required by the states as an occupational safety measure for employees, but testing of patients and clients varies considerably across the state jurisdictions. Most often, the testing of patients and clients is required in long-term, rehabilitative settings. The tuberculosis plan for most facilities outlines the testing process, staff and client training and education, as well as required treatment interventions. Monthly reporting of the number of employees tested and the number of employees who convert to positive is required in many states.

Some states that have populations at high risk for tuberculosis are now requiring a two-step testing process. The two-step process involves an initial skin test for tuberculosis and then a second test seven days later to confirm a negative result. Positive results are followed up with a chest X ray. The state department of health can help any facility determine whether it serves clients who are at high risk for tuberculosis. Such facilities should institute two-step testing. Facilities that treat patients with active tuberculosis should also provide negative-pressure rooms specially designed for the treatment of tuberculosis to prevent the airborne transmission of the disease.

In summary, the management of infectious disease is an organizationwide performance issue that involves every area of the facility and affects every employee, patient, and visitor. The actual ability of individuals to perform their jobs may well depend on how carefully infection control is managed in the facility. The concept of wellness centers has been a positive outcome of the focus on infection control and prevention in many organizations. The effort focuses on creating centers that promote activities for health and wellness and limit exposures to debilitating infections.

Real-Life Example

At one time, Marilyn Nelson, RN, RHIA, worked as the nurse manager of the outpatient clinics at the Western States University Medical Center. She was responsible for managing performance improvement activities in the clinics, facilitating PI teams, and supporting PI activities with the various resources available to her. At that time, the medical center had recently embarked on a benchmarking program. **Benchmarking** is the systematic comparison of one organization's outcomes or processes with the outcomes or processes of similar organizations.

Marilyn and some of her colleagues began the benchmarking process by comparing the outcomes of the clinic's patients with published information on the outcomes of other organizations and with clinical trends apparent in the literature. In the course of examining pharmacy and therapeutics data, Marilyn and her clinical colleagues recognized that their organization appeared to be treating a significantly higher number of urinary tract infections (UTIs) than other similar organizations. To identify the reason for the apparent discrepancy, the team first examined the published literature on the frequency of urinary tract infections in ambulatory care practice. Next, they contacted clinicians at other ambulatory care centers in the country to gather information on their experiences. The team's investigations confirmed that the incidence of urinary tract infection was significantly higher at Western States than at any of the other medical centers contacted. The situation appeared to provide an excellent opportunity for performance improvement, the kind of improvement that clinicians would see as important and valuable to patients as well as one that had important cost implications for the organization.

Marilyn convened a performance improvement team to work on the improvement opportunity. The team included the director of the outpatient pharmacy, the director of the outpatient clinic laboratories, and leaders of the nursing teams from each of the ambulatory clinics in which patients with UTIs were commonly treated at Western States (internal medicine, family practice, obstetrics/gynecology, urology, general surgery, and pediatrics).

The team's initial discussion of the situation revealed the complexity of the processes in place to evaluate urinary tract function. Because the clinics are affiliated with a major university medical center, a number of caregivers might be involved in any patient's care. First, there were the attending physicians from a variety of specialties and areas of expertise. In addition, there were the nurses and medical assistants in each clinic. Because the medical center was a teaching facility, there were also any number of house staff rotating through the clinics on a monthly basis. Finally, there were the technicians who performed urinalysis procedures in the clinical laboratory. Where, when, and by whom a patient's urinalysis was performed could take any one of a number of paths in the organization.

Marilyn and her colleagues decided to develop flowcharts for the various care paths. (See figures 6.1 through 6.5.) They collected data on the outcomes of each of the paths to see whether they could identify the organization's true experience with urinary tract infection.

QI Toolbox Technique

The use of **flowcharts** allows a PI team to examine the process being investigated from all directions. The technique makes it possible for the team to gather the most important details so that everyone on the team can understand the process and its contributing subprocesses in the same way. When a flowchart is built well, few misconceptions can survive.

Flowcharts are used to represent standard functions within processes. Representative and commonly used **icons** are discussed below:

- *Process icons:* Process icons represent periods in the process when actions are being performed by human participants. It is important to break down the actions into their most detailed procedural bundles without adding as much detail as a narrative description would include. For example, in Marilyn Nelson's first flowchart, the first process icon reads: "Nurse triage of patient needs." The concept of triage is represented by the icon, but the description does not specify all of the steps that the nurse would have to go through in order to triage a patient.

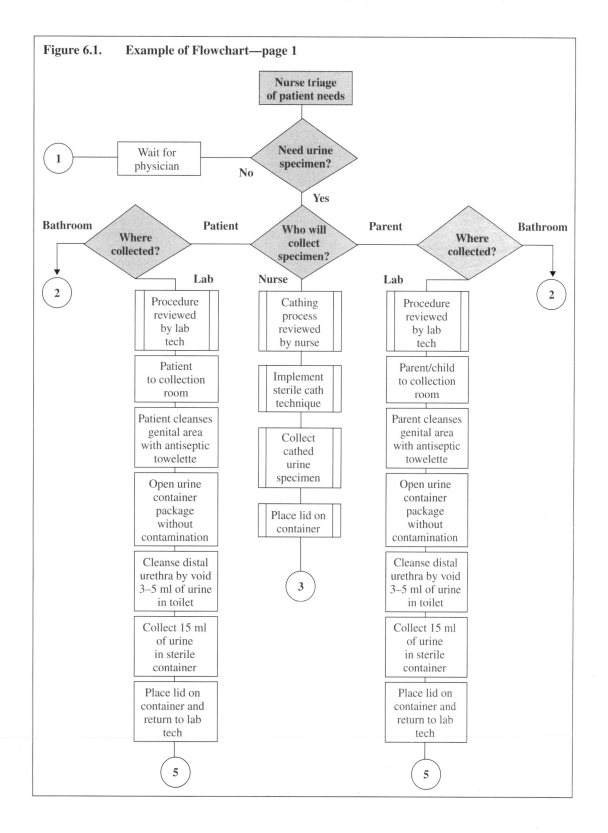

Figure 6.1.   Example of Flowchart—page 1

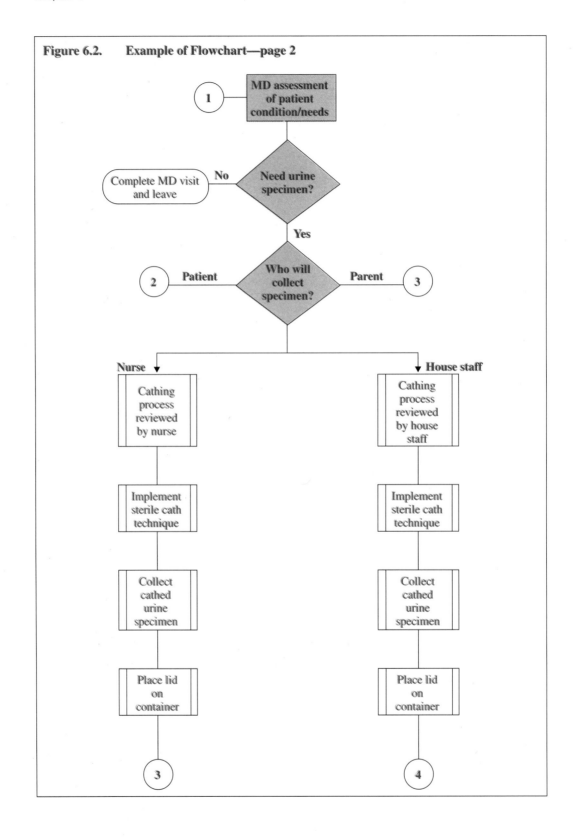

Figure 6.2.   Example of Flowchart—page 2

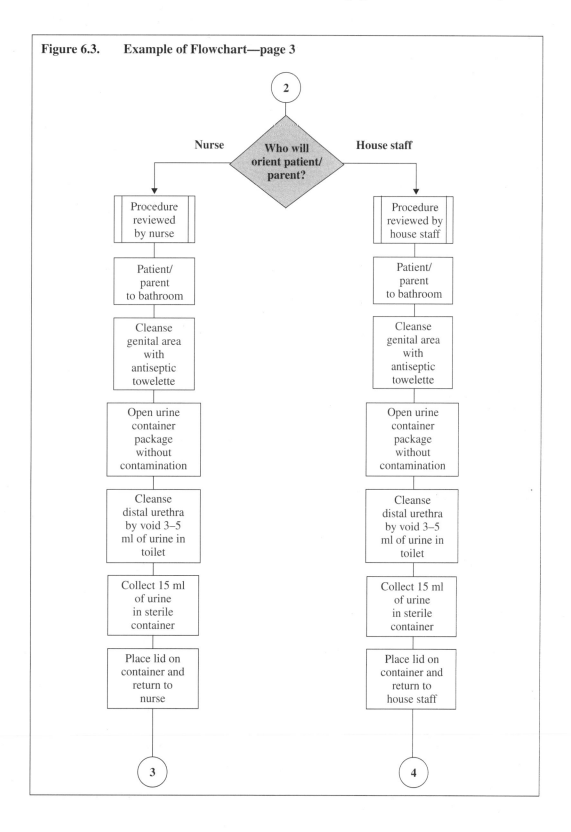

Figure 6.3.   Example of Flowchart—page 3

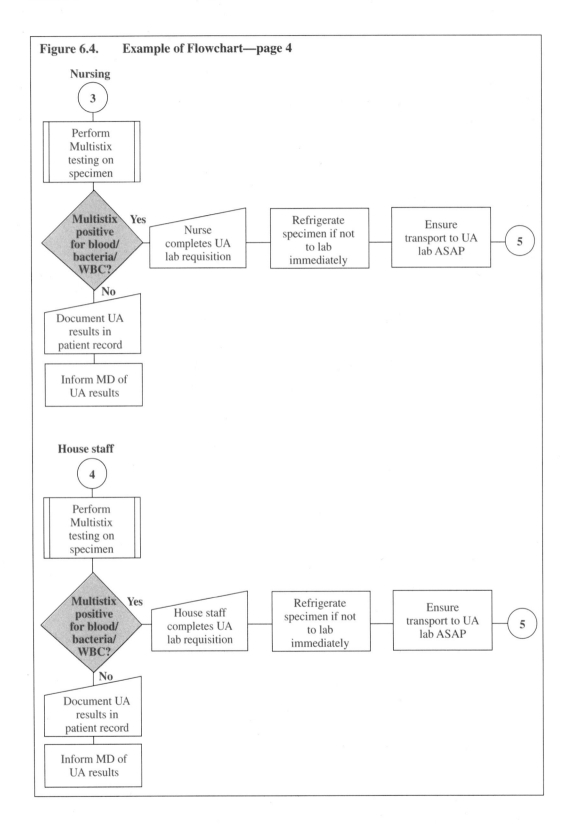

Figure 6.4.   Example of Flowchart—page 4

Figure 6.5.   Example of Flowchart—page 5

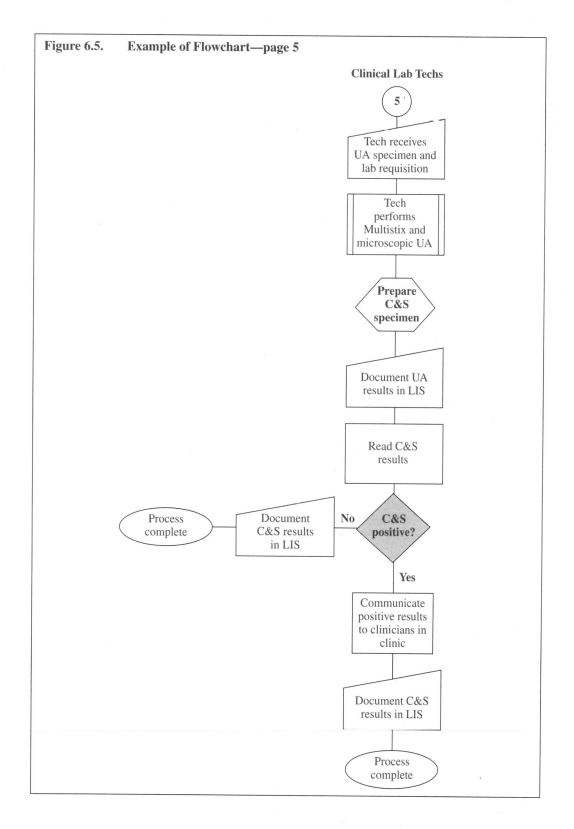

- *Predefined process icons:* Predefined process icons represent the formal procedures that participants are expected to carry out the same way every time. They are the kind of procedures that are formalized in procedure manuals. For example, in Marilyn's flowchart, one of the first predefined procedures is labeled, "Procedure reviewed by lab tech." The use of this icon at this point implies that the manner in which the lab tech explains the procedure to the patient is formalized. He or she must perform the explanation in the same way every time. Less formal steps in a process are indicated by process icons without screens or bars.

- *Decision icons:* Decision icons represent the points in the process at which participants must evaluate the status of the process. Depending on the outcome of the evaluation, the participant performs different subsequent courses of action. For example, in Marilyn's flowcharts, the first decision point asks, "Need urine specimen?" When the triage evaluation returns a "no" response to that question, the patient waits for his or her appointment with the physician. When the triage evaluation returns a "yes" response, then the alternative courses of action to obtain a urine specimen are undertaken.

- *Connector icons:* Connector icons represent points in the flowchart description of the process where the analysis skips to another common point of the process. Connector icons are most often used at the edges of a page, where there is insufficient page space for continuation of the description. For example, in Marilyn's flowchart (figure 6.1), a connector icon follows the process icon labeled "Wait for physician." The icon is labeled "1." Review of figure 6.2 reveals another connector icon labeled "1." At that point, the physician's process continues. Farther down in figure 6.1, two icons are labeled "2." Both of these icons refer to the continuation of the path of the flowchart in figure 6.3.

- *Terminator icons:* Terminator icons mark the end of a process. For example, in Marilyn's flowchart (figure 6.2), the patient leaves the clinic after seeing the physician when no urine specimen is needed. The process ends there.

- *Manual input icons:* Manual input icons represent points in the flowchart description of the process where the participants must record data in paper-based or computer-based formats. For example, Marilyn's flowchart (figure 6.4) includes a manual input icon labeled "Document UA results in patient record." The subprocess represented by the manual input icon follows the Dipstix analysis performed in the clinic by either a nurse or a member of the house staff. When the clinician performing the Dipstix does not find blood, bacteria, or white blood cells (WBCs) in the specimen, the analysis is complete, and only the documentation and communication of findings to the physician remain to be done.

- *Line connector icons:* Line icons direct the flow of the processes from one step to another from decision points to subprocesses.

Case Study

The case study for this chapter is a continuation of Marilyn Nelson's investigation of the urinary tract infection issue in the ambulatory clinics of the Western States University Medical Center.

After flowcharting the process for collecting urine specimens (depicted in figures 6.1 through 6.5), Marilyn and her colleagues recognized how complex the issue was within their organization. They decided to collect data from all of the process paths that were evident in the flowchart. Because so many people were involved in the processes and because significant delays could be involved, they also began to wonder what part contaminated specimens played in the situation.

Although it was an expensive project, the team designed an investigative study to collect data. Urine specimens were routinely tested by nursing personnel or house staff in the clinic to determine each specimen's pH and specific gravity and to classify each specimen according to its color, clarity, and presence of gross hematuria. Each specimen was then tested with Multistix to determine whether microscopic bacteria, red blood cells, or white blood cells were present. When a specimen failed any of the Multistix screens, it was referred to Clinical Laboratory Services for microscopic analysis, culture, and sensitivity analysis by a laboratory technician.

First, the team collected data about the time elapsed between the collection of the specimen, the point-of-care testing with Multistix, and receipt of the specimen in Clinical Laboratory Services. In addition, the team investigated the sequence of events that occurred in the interim. A summary of the data collected is provided in table 6.1.

Second, on a temporary and random basis, the team obtained urine specimens from each clinic immediately following collection and had a complete analysis performed on a stat basis in the clinic labs. This analysis identified pH, specific gravity, color, clarity, cell counts, and bacterial counts almost immediately after the specimen was delivered by the patient or collecting clinician. All specimens that showed microscopic bacteria either on Multistix or on microscopic analysis were cultured. A summary of the data collected is provided in table 6.2.

Table 6.1.	Average Time to Point-of-Care Screening with Confidence Intervals (in minutes)						
Point-of-Care Training & Processing	Internal Medicine Clinic	Pediatrics Clinic	General Surgery Clinic	Orthopedic Surgery Clinic	Obstetrics Clinic	Gynecology Clinic	Specialty Clinics
Nurse	5.0 (4.0, 6.0)	4.25 (3.0, 5.5)	6.25 (5.0, 7.5)	6.0 (5.0, 7.0)	3.25 (2.75, 3.75)	3.0 (2.0, 4.0)	3.0 (2.0, 4.0)
House staff	10.0 (7.0, 13.0)	8.0 (6.0, 10.0)	12.25 (10.0, 14.25)	11.0 (9.0, 13.0)	6.5 (4.0, 9.0)	6.0 (4.0, 8.0)	7.5 (5.5, 9.5)

Third, the team compared the incidence of urinary tract infection identified in the randomly collected specimens to incidence identified in specimens going through the usual process. A summary of the data collected is provided in table 6.3.

Questions for Case Study

1. Upon examination of the data sets, Marilyn and her colleagues identified several areas where the analysis revealed situations that were probably contributing to the clinic's high UTI rate. For instance, look at the UTI rate for children whose parents had collected the specimen versus the rate for children who had been catheterized by nursing personnel to collect the specimen. What do you see? What might be the reason for the higher rate in children whose parents had collected the specimen?

2. Are there any other areas in the data that reveal important aspects that may be contributing to the high UTI rates? What might be the reasons for these higher rates?

Table 6.2.	Random STAT Processing Clean Catch/Cath Urine Specimens (percentage of positive specimens for culture)						
Collector	**Internal Medicine Clinic**	**Pediatrics Clinic**	**General Surgery Clinic**	**Orthopedic Surgery Clinic**	**Obstetrics Clinic**	**Gynecology Clinic**	**Specialty Clinics**
Nurse or patient	5.6	13.2	4.2	3.4	7.0	3.9	5.7
House staff or patient	4.2	12.1	3.4	5.2	6.8	4.2	6.2
Parent	—	27.5	11.7	9.0	—	25.2	—

Table 6.3.	Routine Processing Clean Catch/Cath Specimens (percentage of positive specimens for culture)						
Collector	**Internal Medicine Clinic**	**Pediatrics Clinic**	**General Surgery Clinic**	**Orthopedic Surgery Clinic**	**Obstetrics Clinic**	**Gynecology Clinic**	**Specialty Clinics**
Nurse or patient	5.7	12.4	5.1	4.1	7.2	4.1	5.2
House staff or patient	36.8	25.6	10.2	8.7	10.0	9.2	14.2
Parent	—	25.6	12.2	8.0	—	23.0	—

Project Application

Students should consider using flowchart techniques in their projects.

Summary

The management of infectious disease is an organizationwide performance issue that involves every area of the facility and affects every employee, patient, and visitor. The ability of individuals to perform their jobs depends on how carefully infection control is managed in the facility. So does the ability of patients to recover as rapidly as possible without complications. Means by which the impact of infection is limited in healthcare organizations include use of universal precautions, infection surveillance procedures, appropriate treatment regimens, and staff and patient screening.

References

Benneyan, J. C. 1998. Statistical quality control methods in infection control and hospital epidemiology, part I: introduction and basic theory. *Infectious Control and Hospital Epidemiology* 19(3):194–214, March (review).

Boex, J. R., J. Cooksey, and T. Inui. 1998. Hospital participation in community partnerships to improve health. *Joint Commission Journal of Quality Improvement* 24(10):541–48, October.

Friedman, C., C. A. Baker, J. L. Mowry-Hanley, K. Vander Hyde, M. S. Stites, and R. J. Hanson. 1993. Use of the total quality process in an infection control program: a surprising customer-needs assessment. *American Journal of Infection Control* 21(3):155–59, June.

Howland, R., and M. D. Decker. 1992. Continuous quality improvement and hospital epidemiology: common themes. *Quality Management in Health Care* 1(1):9–12, fall.

Hurt, N. 1993. The role of the infection control nurse in quality management in the ambulatory care setting. *Journal of Healthcare Quality* 15(3):43–44, May–June.

Jhaveri, S. 1996. A total quality management approach to infection control. *Executive Housekeeping Today* 17(3):12, 14, March.

Lathrop, C. B. 1997. Using graphs to consolidate reports to the board. *Journal of Healthcare Quality* 19(1):26–33, January–February.

Seto, W. H. 1995. Training the work force: models for effective education in infection control. *Journal of Hospital Infections* 30 (suppl.):241–47, June.

Simmons, B. P., and S. B. Kritchevsky. 1995. Epidemiologic approaches to quality assessment. *Infection Control and Hospital Epidemiology* 16(2):101–4, February.

Welch, L., A. C. Teague, B. A. Knight, A. Kenney, and J. E. Hernandez. 1998. A quality management approach to optimizing delivery and administration of preoperative antibiotics. *Clinical Performance and Quality Health Care* 6(4):168–71, October–December.

Woomer, N., C. O. Long, C. Anderson, and E. A. Greenberg. 1999. Benchmarking in home health care: a collaborative approach. *Caring* 18(11):22–28, November.

Chapter 7
Decreasing Risk Exposure

Learning Objectives

- To understand the importance of managing risk exposure in the contemporary healthcare organization

- To understand the importance of the use of occurrence reporting in decreasing risk exposure

- To be able to define the concept of a sentinel event and discuss how sentinel events can point to important opportunities for improvement in healthcare organizations

- To be able to explain how risk managers use their skills in patient advocacy to lessen the impact that potentially compensable events can have on healthcare organizations

Background and Significance

For a variety of reasons and by the nature of their business, healthcare organizations are susceptible to claims of liability. Claims result for incidents that adversely affect customers and employees. Every day, employees in healthcare organizations work with equipment and substances that are dangerous even when used appropriately. Clinical laboratories perform analyses that use chemicals that can cause burns. Radiological instruments deliver high doses of radiation. Hospital pharmacies package and deliver medications that are poisonous to human beings when administered imprecisely.

Patients contribute to accidents when they refuse to wait for assistance before getting out of bed to go to the bathroom. Some patients do not like sleeping with the side rails up on their beds and risk dangerous falls. Belongings disappear due to theft or inadvertent circumstances. Patients pull out intravenous lines, thus exposing nursing staff to blood-borne pathogens. Response to therapy does not always go as planned. The surgeon's knife sometimes cuts through tissue more easily than expected and nicks contiguous structures. The possibility of unintended injury is everywhere in healthcare organizations.

In this atmosphere of complexity, danger, chance, and emotion, risk managers work to accomplish their professional objectives. Risk managers seek to manage the organization's risk exposure and improve its processes so that the threat of liability is minimized. **Risk** in this context is a formal insurance term denoting liability to compensate individuals for injuries sustained in the healthcare facility. Occurrences involving injury or property loss are called **potentially compensable events** (PCEs).

Patients and clients come to healthcare organizations expecting physical and emotional benefits for themselves and their family members. Employees come to work intending to provide the best-quality healthcare they can deliver. Because everyone's expectations are only for good, negative occurrences create situations that can be loaded with anger and guilt. Still, such occurrences also present opportunities for performance improvement.

Decreasing Risk Exposure: Steps to Success

Most people think of risk management as the process of working through a malpractice suit. Although that is sometimes the case, risk managers are more often trying to identify organizational conditions that increase risk exposure *before* occurrences involving injury happen. Identification before injury then allows the organization to improve care processes prior to incurring the exposure.

Step 1: Develop risk management policies and procedures

The risk manager leads the development of risk management policies and procedures for the organization. Policies and procedures in the risk management area include a policy describing the organization's insurance strategy, procedures outlining its claims tracking

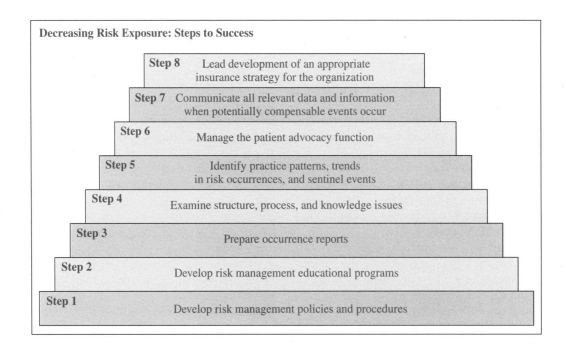

Decreasing Risk Exposure: Steps to Success

Step 8   Lead development of an appropriate insurance strategy for the organization

Step 7   Communicate all relevant data and information when potentially compensable events occur

Step 6   Manage the patient advocacy function

Step 5   Identify practice patterns, trends in risk occurrences, and sentinel events

Step 4   Examine structure, process, and knowledge issues

Step 3   Prepare occurrence reports

Step 2   Develop risk management educational programs

Step 1   Develop risk management policies and procedures

and negotiation system, and procedures outlining how its databases are maintained and risk management reports are developed. Risk managers also routinely review the operational policies and procedures of all departments to ensure that they have been designed in a way that reduces rather than increases the possibility of risk exposure. Risk management procedures also define completion requirements for occurrence reporting and reporting to insurers, licensing agencies, public health departments, governing bodies, the National Practitioner Data Bank, and other accrediting and regulatory agencies. In addition, risk managers review all policies and procedures approved in the organization to ensure that none include activities that expose the organization to risk.

Step 2: Develop risk management educational programs

Risk managers must lead educational activities for employees with respect to risk management issues. They do so in close cooperation with the managers responsible for the care environment and safety. (See chapter 9.) Program attendance must be documented in each employee's personnel file, and postprogram testing for comprehension and retention must be performed.

Step 3: Prepare occurrence reports

The risk manager's principal tool for capturing the facts about PCEs is the **occurrence report** (sometimes called the **incident report**). The most effective occurrence reports carefully structure the collection of data, information, and facts in a relatively simple format. An excellent example of an occurrence report is provided in figure 7.1. Note that the example captures information about the patient or other persons involved. It records information about the time of day, the day of the week, and the type of shift that the employees involved were working. Page 2 of the report gathers information about the witnesses to the incident and the results of contact with and examination by a physician or nurse practitioner Next, pages 3, 4, and 5 of this example gather information regarding specific aspects of the most common incidents that occur in healthcare. For example, in section 7, the report collects data on the type of burn. All data collected in these incident-specific sections are coded for easy check-off and entry into a database management system for incident tracking.

Following completion by individuals on the unit where the incident occurred, the occurrence report is sent to the risk managers. They review policy and procedure and other aspects of the occurrence and involve management and administrative staff as necessary. After the analysis for causes and revision of policy, the long-term follow-up of the incident is documented on page 6 of the report. For example, this would include action taken regarding policies and procedures, outcome to the injured individual, and contacts with manufacturers or retraining of personnel.

A second very important document for managing risk exposure is the patient's medical record. Everything that is done for a patient in response to an incident must also be documented in the medical record. If a case of injury should go on to become a malpractice suit or other legal action, the regular documentation in the medical record would become crucial. The clinicians involved in an incident must be certain that all appropriate clinical documentation regarding the occurrence is added to the medical record as well as being documented on the occurrence report. Another important consideration is the fact that occurrence reports are generally not open to view by the plaintiff's attorney. Thus, to

---

Figure 7.1.   Sample Occurrence Report

Med Rec # *00–05–45*
Name: *Jackson, Julia*
Date of Birth: *06–22–23*
Street: *6401 Fremont Ave*
City: *Western City, CA*

Risk Management use only_____

Patient ID/name of individual involved.
Use addressograph for patient.

INSTRUCTIONS: (1) Fill out the first page of the Incident Report Form. (2) Select the type of incident from the bottom of page 2. (3) Fill out all appropriate sections as directed. The report must be dated and filled out by the end of the shift in which the incident occurred or was discovered. **DO NOT COPY THIS FORM.** Please print, this report must be legible. **Please fill out all applicable parts of this form.** Upon completion of this form route it to your Nurse Manager or Supervisor. Do not leave this form in the patient's chart.

Date of incident: _05/ 29/ 00_   Time (2400 Clock): _1645_   Hospital Unit: _Med/Surg_

What day of the week did it occur on?				Did the incident occur during:		Employee involved worked a(n)	
Sun	[√]	Thurs	[ ]	Day 0701–1500	[ ]	8 Hour shift	[√]
Mon	[ ]	Fri	[ ]	Evening 1501–2300	[√]	10 Hour shift	[ ]
Tues	[ ]	Sat	[ ]	Night 2301–0700	[ ]	12 Hour shift	[ ]
Wed	[ ]					Double shift	[ ]
						Other_____	

Where did the incident occur? _patient room_

Description of incident. Include: follow-up care given, i.e., vital signs, X-Ray, laboratory tests, etc.
Pt. developed a macular rash over trunk and extremities after 10 mg
dose of Compazine given for postop nausea. Compazine stopped
and Benadryl given IM.

IMMEDIATE EFFECT OF THE INCIDENT: _Severe macular rash over trunk_
and extremities

Involved Person Data

Date of Admission _05 / 29 / 00_   Inpatient   [√]
What sex is the person?   Outpatient   [ ]
Male   [ ]   Student   [ ]
Female   [√]   Employee   [ ]
                                            Visitor   [ ]
What is the person's age? _76_   Volunteer   [ ]
                                            Other_____

Current Diagnosis/Reason for visit: _Bowel Obstruction_

Is the involved person aware of the incident?   Yes   [√]   No   [ ]
Is the family aware of incident?   Yes   [ ]   No   [√]
Did the incident involve equipment?   Yes   [ ]   No   [√]
If Yes, was Bioengineering notified?   Yes   [ ]   No   [ ]   N/A   [ ]

CONFIDENTIAL: This material is prepared pursuant to Code Annotated, §26-25-1, et seq., and 58-12-43(7, 8, and 9), for the purpose of evaluating health care rendered by hospitals or physicians and is NOT PART of the medical record.

Figure 7.1.   *(Continued)*

DO NOT COPY

****   PLEASE PRINT   ****

Person preparing report (Signature): *Gwen Nelson, R.N.* Print *Gwen Nelson, R.N.*

Name of individual witnessing incident (Print): *Bob Patterson, R.N.*

Dept/Address: *Med/Surg Team Leader*

Name of employee involved in incident: *Gwen Nelson, R.N.* Dept/Address *Med/Surg*

Name of employee discovering incident: *Gwen Nelson, R.N.* Dept/Address *Med/Surg*

**** STAFF TO NOTIFY ATTENDING PHYSICIAN AND/OR DESIGNATED RESIDENT/NURSE PRACTITIONER OF INCIDENT ****

I notified Dr./NP *Jeff Cook* at *1650* (time).

M.D./NP responded ☐ in person ☑ by phone at *1705* (time).

Was the attending physician notified?

Yes [√] Date: *05 / 29 / 00* Time: *1650*

No [ ] Why not? _____

Examining Physician/Nurse Practitioner statement regarding condition/outcome of person involved:

Pt. was examined by me at 1700 hours. Trunk and extremities show a macular rash on them. One dose of Benadryl given IM to pt. and rash began to subside. Compazine stopped.

Examining MD/NP signature: *Tom Lander, M.D. House Staff*

Examining MD/NP name (print): *Tom Lander, M.D.*

Date: *05 / 29 / 00* Time: *1700* Clinical Service: *Medicine*

CHOOSE THE TYPE OF INCIDENT YOU ARE REPORTING. Use the index below to locate the type of incident you are reporting, go to that section and mark the appropriate box(es). THERE MAY BE MORE THAN ONE ITEM APPLICABLE IN A SECTION. CHECK BOX(ES) IN APPROPRIATE SECTIONS.

Medication/IV Incident	Page 3, Section 1	Patient Behavioral Incident	Page 5, Section 6
Blood/Blood incident	Page 3, Section 2	Safety Incident	Page 5, Section 9
Burn	Page 5, Section 7	Security Incident	Page 5, Section 8
Equipment Incident	Page 5, Section 10	Surgery Incident	Page 5, Section 4
Fall	Page 4, Section 3	Treatment/Procedure Incident	Page 5, Section 5
Fire Incident	Page 5, Section 11		

(Continued on next page)

Figure 7.1. *(Continued)*

DO NOT COPY

SECTION 1 MEDICATION/IV INCIDENT

1A. TYPE OF MEDICATION

Fill in specific medication/solution on the adjacent line.

Analgesic _____
Anesthetic agent _____
Antibiotic _____
Anticoagulant _____
Anticonvulsant _____
Antidepressant _____
Antiemetic___*Compazine*_____
Antihistamine _____
Antineoplastic _____
Bronchodilator _____
Cardiovascular _____
Contrast media _____
Diuretic _____
Immunizations _____
Immunosuppressive _____
Insulin _____
Intralipids _____
Investigational drug _____
IV solution _____
Laxative_____
Narcotic_____
Oxytocics _____
Psychotherapeutic _____
Radionuclides _____
Sedative/tranquilizer_____
TPN _____
Vasodilator _____
Vasopressor _____
Vitamin _____
Other _____

1B. TYPE OF MEDICATION OR IV INCIDENT

Adverse reaction	[√]	1B01
Allergic/contraindication	[ ]	1B02
Delayed stat order	[ ]	1B03
Improper order (MD/NP)	[ ]	1B04
Incompatible additive	[ ]	1B05
Incorrect additive	[ ]	1B06
Incorrect dosage	[ ]	1B07
Incorrect drug	[ ]	1B08
Incorrect narcotic count	[ ]	1B09
Incorrect patient	[ ]	1B10
Incorrect rate of flow	[ ]	1B11
Incorrect route	[ ]	1B12
Incorrect schedule	[ ]	1B13
Incorrect solution/type	[ ]	1B14
Incorrect time	[ ]	1B15
Incorrect volume	[ ]	1B16
Infiltration	[ ]	1B17
Given before culture taken	[ ]	1B18
Medication given before lab results returned	[ ]	1B19
Medication missing from cart	[ ]	1B20
Not documented	[ ]	1B21
Not prescribed	[ ]	1B22
Omitted	[ ]	1B23
Outdated	[ ]	1B24
Out-of-sequence	[ ]	1B25
Patient took unprescribed medication	[ ]	1B26
Repeat administration	[ ]	1B27
Transcription error	[ ]	1B28
Other_____		1B29

1C. ROUTE OF MEDICATION ORDERED:

IM	[ ]	1C01
IV	[ ]	1C02
PO	[ ]	1C03
Other___*Suppository*_____	√	1C04

1D. MEDICATION DISPENSING INCIDENT

Meds not sent/delayed from pharmacy	[ ]	1C01
Incorrectly labeled	[ ]	1C02
Incorrect dose	[ ]	1C03
Incorrect drug sent	[ ]	1C04
Incorrect IV additive	[ ]	1C05
Incorrect IV fluid	[ ]	1C06
Incorrect route (IV, PO, IM, PR)	[ ]	1C07
Mislabeled	[ ]	1C08
Other_____		1C09

**SECTION 2
BLOOD/BLOOD COMPONENT INCIDENT**

2A. BLOOD/BLOOD COMPONENT TYPE

Albumin	[ ]	2A01
Cryoprecipitate	[ ]	2A02
Factor VIII (AHF)	[ ]	2A03
Factor IX (Konyne)	[ ]	2A04
Fresh frozen plasma	[ ]	2A05
Packed red blood cells (PRBC)	[ ]	2A06
Plasmanate	[ ]	2A07
Platelets	[ ]	2A08
Rhogam	[ ]	2A09
Washed red blood cells (WRBC)	[ ]	2A10
Whole blood	[ ]	2A11
Other_____		2A12

2B. TYPE OF BLOOD/BLOOD COMPONENT INCIDENT

Crossmatch problem	[ ]	2B01
Improper unit verification	[ ]	2B02
Inappropriate IV fluids administered with blood components	[ ]	2B03
Inappropriate documentation	[ ]	2B04
Inappropriate storage	[ ]	2B05
Incomplete patient ID	[ ]	2B06
Incorrect patient	[ ]	2B07
Incorrect rate	[ ]	2B08
Incorrect type	[ ]	2B09
Incorrect volume	[ ]	2B10
Patient refused	[ ]	2B11
Other_____		2B12

Figure 7.1. *(Continued)*

DO NOT COPY

SECTION 3
FALLS

3A. FALL CODE STATUS OF PATIENT
Attended [ ] 3A01
Unattended [ ] 3A02

3B. LOCATION OF FALL
Bathroom in patient's room [ ] 3B01
Bathroom (other location) [ ] 3B02
Elevator [ ] 3B03
Examining/treatment room [ ] 3B04
Hallway/corridor [ ] 3B05
Nursing station [ ] 3B06
Parking lot [ ] 3B07
Patient's room [ ] 3B08
Recreation area [ ] 3B09
Shower/tub room [ ] 3B10
Stairs [ ] 3B11
Waiting room [ ] 3B12
Walkway/sidewalk [ ] 3B13
Other_____ 3B14

3C. FALL OCCURRED IN CONJUNCTION WITH:
Bedside commode [ ] 3C01
Chair [ ] 3C02
Due to toy [ ] 3C03
During transfer [ ] 3C04
Exam table [ ] 3C05
Fainting/dizzy [ ] 3C06
Fall/slip [ ] 3C07
From bed [ ] 3C08
Improperly locked device [ ] 3C09
Recreational activity [ ] 3C10
Scales [ ] 3C11
Stretcher [ ] 3C12
Table [ ] 3C13
Tripped [ ] 3C14
While ambulating unattended [ ] 3C15
While ambulating with assist [ ] 3C16
While entering or leaving bed [ ] 3C17
While using ambulatory device [ ] 3C18
Other_____ 3C19

3D. PATIENT ACTIVITY PRIVILEGES
(As per medical order)
Ambulate with assistance [ ] 3D01
Ambulate with walker [ ] 3D02
Ambulate without assistance [ ] 3D03
Bathroom privileges with assistance [ ] 3D04
Bathroom privileges without assistance [ ] 3D05
Bedrest [ ] 3D06
Up Ad lib [ ] 3D07
Up in chair/wheelchair [ ] 3D08
Other_____ 3D09

3E. PATIENT MENTAL CONDITION AT THE TIME OF THE FALL
Confused/poor judgment [ ] 3E01
Language barrier [ ] 3E02
Oriented [ ] 3E03
Unconscious [ ] 3E04
Uncooperative [ ] 3E05
Unresponsive/medicated [ ] 3E06
Other_____

3F. PATIENT'S CALL LIGHT WAS:
On [ ] 3F01
Off [ ] 3F02
Not within reach [ ] 3F03
Patient unable to use [ ] 3F04
Not applicable [ ] 3F05

3G. POSITION OF BED
High [ ] 3G01
Low [ ] 3G02
Intermediate [ ] 3G03
Not applicable [ ] 3G04

3H. BED ALARM
On [ ] 3H01
Off [ ] 3H02
Not applicable [ ] 3H03

3I. POSITION OF SIDE RAILS
(At the time of the fall)

Half Rails	[ ] 3E01	Full Rails	[ ] 3E06
1 Up	[ ] 3E02	1 Up	[ ] 3E07
2 Up	[ ] 3E03	2 Up	[ ] 3E08
3 Up	[ ] 3E04		
4 Up	[ ] 3E05		

Not applicable [ ] 3E09

3J. PATIENT RESTRAINTS
Removed by patient [ ] 3J01
Restraints intact [ ] 3J02
Not applicable [ ] 3J03
Other_____ 3J04

3K. CONDITION OF AREA WHERE FALL OCCURRED
Normal/dry [ ] 3K01
Wet floor [ ] 3K02
Ice condition [ ] 3K03
Other_____ 3K04

3L. FALLS IN CONJUNCTION WITH MEDICATION
Narcotic or sedative received by patient
in the past 12 hours? [ ] 3L01
When was the last dose? _____ 3L02
What was the drug? _____ 3L03
What was the route of administration?_____ 3L04

CONFIDENTIAL: This material is prepared pursuant to Code Annotated, §26-25-1, et seq., and 58-12-43(7, 8, and 9), for the purpose of evaluating health care rendered by hospitals or physicians and is NOT PART of the medical record.

(Continued on next page)

Figure 7.1. *(Continued)*

DO NOT COPY

SECTION 4
SURGERY INCIDENT

Anesthesia occurrence	[ ] 0401
Contamination	[ ] 0402
Incorrect needle count	[ ] 0403
Incorrect sponge count	[ ] 0404
Informed consent absent	[ ] 0405
Informed consent incorrect	[ ] 0406
Instrument lost/broken	[ ] 0407
Retained foreign body	[ ] 0408
Other_____	0409

SECTION 5
TREATMENT/PROCEDURE INCIDENT

Adverse reaction	[ ] 0501
Allergic response	[ ] 0502
Application/removal of cast/splint	[ ] 0503
Cancellation of procedures	[ ] 0504
Catheter or tube related	[ ] 0505
Delay	[ ] 0506
Dietary problem	[ ] 0507
Dressing/wound occurrence	[ ] 0508
Informed consent absent	[ ] 0509
Informed consent incorrect	[ ] 0510
Injection site	[ ] 0511
Invasive procedure/placement	[ ] 0512
Mislabeled specimen	[ ] 0513
Missing specimen	[ ] 0514
Not documented	[ ] 0515
Omitted	[ ] 0516
Patient/site identification	[ ] 0517
Positioning	[ ] 0518
Prep problem	[ ] 0519
Repeat procedure	[ ] 0520
Reporting of test results	[ ] 0521
Thermoregulation problem	[ ] 0522
Transcription error	[ ] 0523
Transfer/moving of patient	[ ] 0524
Other_____	0525

SECTION 6
PATIENT BEHAVIORAL INCIDENT

Attempted AWOL	[ ] 0601
AWOL	[ ] 0602
Inappropriate sexual behavior	[ ] 0603
Injured by other patient	[ ] 0604
Patient altercation	[ ] 0605
Self-inflicted injury	[ ] 0606
Suicide gesture	[ ] 0607
Other_____	0608

SECTION 7
BURNS

Chemical	[ ] 0701
Electrical	[ ] 0702
Inhalation	[ ] 0703
Radioactive	[ ] 0704
Thermal	[ ] 0705

SECTION 8
SECURITY INCIDENTS

Bomb threat	[ ] 0801
Breaking and entering	[ ] 0802
Drug theft	[ ] 0803
Secure area key loss/missing	[ ] 0804
Major theft (over $250)	[ ] 0805
Amount:_____	
Minor theft	[ ] 0806
Amount:_____	
Personal property damage/loss	[ ] 0807
Amount:_____	
Hospital property damage	[ ] 0809
Amount:_____	
Other_____	

SECTION 9
SAFETY INCIDENTS (patients and visitors only)

Body fluid exposure	[ ] 0901
Chemical exposure	[ ] 0902
Chemotherapy spill	[ ] 0903
Drug exposure	[ ] 0904
Hazardous material spill	[ ] 0905
Needlestick	[ ] 0906
Other_____	0907

SECTION 10
EQUIPMENT INCIDENT

Disconnected	[ ] 1001
Electrical problem	[ ] 1002
Improper use	[ ] 1003
Malfunction/defect	[ ] 1004
Mechanical problem	[ ] 1005
Not available	[ ] 1006
Electrical shock	[ ] 1007
Electrical spark	[ ] 1008
Struck by	[ ] 1009
Wrong equipment	[ ] 1010
Tampered with	
By patient	[ ] 1011
Non-patient	[ ] 1012
Other_____	1013

SECTION 11
FIRE INCIDENT

Equipment caused	[ ] 1101
Cigarette caused	[ ] 1102
Laser caused	[ ] 1103
Other_____	1104

CONFIDENTIAL: This material is prepared pursuant to Code Annotated, §26-25-1, et seq., and 58-12-43(7, 8, and 9), for the purpose of evaluating health care rendered by hospitals or physicians and is NOT PART of the medical record.

Figure 7.1. *(Continued)*

DO NOT COPY

EMPLOYEES DO NOT COMPLETE BELOW,
FOR NURSE MANAGER/SUPERVISOR USE ONLY.

Recommendations and/or corrective actions based on review of report and discussion with employee:

NURSE MANAGER/SUPERVISOR Follow-Up [Check appropriate box(es)]/Corrective action]

Policy/Procedure:

Evaluate	[ ] 1201	**Discussed with:**	
Recommend change	[ ] 1202	Physician	[ ] 1209
Changed	[ ] 1203	Staff	[ ] 1210
No action taken	[ ] 1204	Patient	[ ] 1211
Non-compliance	[ ] 1205	Other	[ ] 1212
Inadequate	[ ] 1206		
Needs enforcement	[ ] 1207	Date: _____	
Review with involved individual(s) . . .	[ ] 1208	Time: _____	

Describe specific follow-up actions taken (if applicable include names of depts) _____
_____
_____

SIGN AND DATE: (Indicates review of report)

1. Quality Management/Risk Management_____ ___/___/____

2. Nurse Manager/Supervisor (as applicable) _____ ___/___/____

3. Department Head/DON (As applicable) _____ ___/___/____

4. QM Coordinator (As applicable)_____ ___/___/____

5. Other: Title_____ Name _____ ___/___/____

BIOENGINEERING USE ONLY

Manufacturer contacted	[ ] 1301
Manufacturer instructions followed	[ ] 1302
Needs enforcement of policy/procedure	[ ] 1303
Include instructions in staff education and training	[ ] 1304
Preventative maintenance or biomedical evaluation of equipment ordered	[ ] 1305
Recommend repair or replacement	[ ] 1306
Removed from service	[ ] 1307
Other _____	1308

RISK MANAGEMENT USE ONLY

IMMEDIATE EFFECT OF THE INCIDENT

Alteration in skin integrity	[ ] 1401	Patient discomfort/inconvenience	[ ] 1411
Birth related injury	[ ] 1402	Psycho/social trauma.	[ ] 1412
Breach of confidentiality	[ ] 1403	Reproductive injury or loss	[ ] 1413
Death	[ ] 1404	Sensory impairment.	[ ] 1414
Disability	[ ] 1405	Severe internal injuries	[ ] 1415
Disfigurement.	[ ] 1406	Substantial disability	[ ] 1416
Drug/blood reaction	[ ] 1407	Unanticipated neuro deficit	[ ] 1417
Fluid imbalance	[ ] 1408	Unanticipated systemic deficit.	[ ] 1418
Neuro deficit	[ ] 1409	Indeterminate	[ ] 1419
Orthopedic injury	[ ] 1410	None	[ ] 1420
		Other_____	1421

Description_____

CONFIDENTIAL: This material is prepared pursuant to Code Annotated, §26-25-1, et seq., and 58-12-43(7, 8, and 9), for the purpose of evaluating health care rendered by hospitals or physicians and is NOT PART of the medical record.

communicate the care given the patient in its entirety, and especially regarding an occurrence, the record must be documented carefully because it will be used to portray the events to the public. A careful balance must be developed by the risk manager overseeing the documentation of a potentially compensable event. Complete details on all persons involved, actions taken, condition and responses of the patient should be recorded on the occurrence record. However, in the patient's medical record, the details should be limited to those documenting the care given the patient. No details about how the occurrence came about or what contributed to it should be recorded there. No mention should be made in the patient's medical record of an incident or occurrence report having been completed. The documentation of a medication error in the sample occurrence report (figure 7.2) is a good example.

Step 4: Examine structure, process, and knowledge issues

As department members and process improvement teams begin to identify customers and review performance, issues in organizational structures, processes, or knowledge may become apparent. Commonly, these issues are documented in department or team communications to a performance improvement council. (See the discussion of documentation recommendations in chapter 12.) Risk managers are usually members of the council and routinely review communications from the departments and teams for this purpose. Issues in turn should be documented in the risk management databases so that corrective action may be initiated if and when they meet a performance threshold (a level above which the occurrence is not occurring by chance and cannot be tolerated). If it becomes apparent that members of the organization do not have appropriate background in procedure or policy, the risk manager may have to initiate educational sessions to develop staff background regarding the issue.

Step 5: Identify practice patterns, trends in risk occurrences, and sentinel events

Another important performance improvement activity that contributes to the risk manager's databases are those related to the credentialing of physicians and the validation of nurses' and therapists' licenses to practice. (See chapter 10.) Standardized reviews of clinicians' practice patterns and outcomes are conducted by committees of the medical staff and hospital administration. Documentation of these reviews is analyzed by the risk manager to identify clinicians who can benefit from additional education regarding policy and procedure or the current standard of practice in the region where the healthcare organization does business.

Using aggregate data summarized from the occurrence report discussed in step 1, the risk manager attempts to identify trends in risk occurrences in the organization. For instance, if there were an increase in blood transfusion reactions, the manager might request a focused review by blood bank personnel to be sure that typing and grouping procedures are being followed appropriately. If there were an increase in occurrence reports documenting patients' falls on a particular nursing unit, the risk manager might ask the nurse manager on that unit to be sure that staff know how to identify a patient at risk of falling and are taking appropriate preventive measures with those patients.

Most important, in this area, risk managers thoroughly investigate occurrences that are classified as **sentinel events.** Sentinel events involve injuries to patients, staff, or other

Figure 7.2.   Sample Progress Note in Patient's Record

PROGRESS NOTES	Med Rec # 00-05-45 Jackson, Julia

DATE & TIME	NOTES MUST BE DATED AND TIMED
5/29/00 1650	Patient developed a macular rash over entire trunk and extremities after 10 mg of Compazine given for nausea. Dr. Cook and house staff notified. *Gwen Nelson, R.N*
5/29/00 1700	Called to pt. for rash on trunk & extremities. Pt. examined, adverse reaction to Compazine most likely. Patient to receive 20 mg of Benadryl IM now. If nausea continues, Dramamine 50 mg IV prn. *J. Lander, MD*
5/29/00 1700	Dr. Lander examined patient and ordered Benadryl 10 mg IM. Patient injected IM 10 mg of Benadryl. *Gwen Nelson, R.N*
5/29/00 1810	Rash is subsiding and nausea less. *Gwen Nelson, R.N*

PROGRESS NOTES

individuals that are life-threatening or that result in serious compromise of the individual's physiologic functioning or physical health. Sentinel events also include occurrences that might have led to injury if anyone had been near enough to the event at the time of occurrence. This latter type of incident would include occurrences such as explosions in laboratories or unintended fires anywhere in the facility.

Sentinel events are reportable to the Joint Commission on Accreditation of Healthcare Organizations (JCAHO). The JCAHO requires that an in-depth investigation of such events be carried out to find the root cause of the occurrence so that it is unlikely to happen again. (See the real-life example and QI toolbox discussions later in this chapter.)

Step 6: Manage the patient advocacy function

The first major objective of risk management is to minimize the organization's exposure to risk. The second major objective of risk management is to minimize the likelihood that a legal action will be filed once a potentially compensable event has occurred. This objective is a function of risk management responsibilities known as patient advocacy.

The objective of the patient advocacy is to support the patient through difficult interactions with the healthcare organization as a bureaucracy. All businesses have a bureaucratic component, and healthcare organizations are no different. Add the confusion, complexity, danger, and chance of potentially compensable events, and the customer may feel shunned and isolated by the organization at a time of great personal anger. The customer needs to express the anger to lessen it, and he or she needs someone in the organization to validate his or her right to feel it.

At the same time, the risk manager as patient advocate must be sure that the customer knows the facts associated with the occurrence. The risk manager must accept responsibility for the occurrence in the customer's eyes when the organization's employees were responsible for the situation during which the incident occurred. Negotiation may even require monetary settlement of a claim against the organization by the customer. If the organization's employees were not responsible for the situation, but the customer believes that they were, the risk manager must carefully explain the facts of the situation. The hope is that the risk manager will be able to shed light on the situation and persuade the customer that an inadvertent outcome resulted even though clinicians and other staff followed standard procedures.

Step 7: Communicate all relevant data and information when potentially compensable events occur

Inevitably, some claims of liability do go on to involve formal legal action. The facility's attorneys, the representatives of the facility's insurance company, and the plaintiff's attorneys then become involved.

The risk manager should continue to function as the "face" of the organization in such legal environments. He or she coordinates all requests for information by subpoena *duces tecum* from attorneys or from the courts. He or she explains the organization's perspective to attorneys regarding the completion of interrogatories and coordinates the appearance of employees at depositions or at trial. He or she remains open to negotiation of an appropriate settlement to conclude the action before it goes to trial.

The risk manager is responsible for communicating all relevant data and information to the organization's insurer as soon as possible after a potentially compensable event is recognized. The risk management department routinely provides the organization's insurance company with copies of the occurrence reports for all potentially compensable events. The timeliness and efficiency of such communications are extremely important if potentially compensable events are to be resolved rapidly and without litigation. Subsequently, the risk manager must keep the insurer apprised of important communications with the customer or the customer's attorneys. Insurance company representatives must have complete information in order to make appropriate resolution decisions.

Step 8: Lead development of an appropriate insurance strategy for the organization

In addition to the transmission of information regarding PCEs, the risk manager also takes the lead in designing an insurance strategy that meets the needs of the healthcare organization. To be effective in this area, the risk manager must have an in-depth knowledge of the organization's services, facilities, equipment, procedures, and staff capabilities.

The insurance strategy is developed with reference to the healthcare service lines of the organization. For example, perinatal services is one of the service lines that has the greatest inherent risk of liability. Numerous complications can occur during a woman's pregnancy, labor, and the delivery. And many of these complications cannot be foreseen. Many result in serious injury to the infant or mother. The fact that the organization provides perinatal services would be taken into consideration by the organization's management and insurer.

Real-Life Example

Dr. Low, an obstetrician, delivered Mrs. Yu's infant with relatively little difficulty. However, when the placenta was delivered, a rush of blood appeared at the patient's cervical os. Dr. Low attempted to explore the patient's uterus to see whether there were still some pieces of the placenta inside that were causing the bleeding, but there was so much blood that she could not explore the uterus adequately. After some minutes of trying to deal with the situation, she realized that the bleeding did not appear to be abating even though the uterus was contracting appropriately. Dr. Low decided to take Mrs. Yu to surgery to perform an exploratory laparotomy and possible emergency hysterectomy. The physician knew that if she could not stop the bleeding, the patient's life would be in danger. She packed the uterus as tightly as possible, instructed nursing staff to find blood for a transfusion, covered the patient with a sheet, placed the patient on oxygen, and began wheeling the patient's gurney to the elevator.

Community Hospital of the West is a major tertiary care facility in a major American city. It had always provided obstetrical delivery and neonatal services in the north wing of the second floor of the facility. Delivery rooms were developed in this wing. Surgical services and the operating rooms were developed on the third floor in the north wing. When patients required cesarean section deliveries or other surgical treatment, they had to be transferred from the delivery rooms on the second floor to the operating rooms on the third floor.

Dr. Low and the obstetrical nurse assisting her waited about a minute for an elevator to arrive. Most of the staff of the hospital believed that the elevators were the slowest elevators known to man and had commented as much many times over the years. Dr. Low, the nurse, and the patient on the gurney arrived in about another minute and half on the third floor and they rushed into an operating room. Crash induction of anesthesia was begun. As the operating room staff tried to get a line in to start the blood transfusion and Dr. Low began to remove the packing from the uterus, a massive amount of blood gushed from the organ. The patient's heart went into ventricular fibrillation, and despite emergency resuscitative efforts, Mrs. Yu died. She was 25 years old.

Because the death occurred during a surgical procedure, it was reportable to the county coroner's office. The coroner accepted the case and performed an autopsy. Mrs. Yu was found to have an anomalous uterine artery that had been opened upon delivery of the placenta. Mrs. Yu had bled to death.

QI Toolbox Techniques

The death of a patient in a situation like that discussed in the real-life example is always classified as a sentinel event. For such cases, the JCAHO requires the organization to do a **root-cause analysis** of the event to discover what processes in the organization led to the occurrence. The human body always presents a possibility for unusual and unexpected situations to occur. No one could really have known that Mrs. Yu's uterus was anomalous in its blood supply. Does that mean that Mrs. Yu's death was truly inadvertent? Could the death of this patient have been averted despite the anomaly in her anatomy?

The toolbox technique that is used most in root-cause analysis is the **cause-and-effect, or fishbone, diagram.** This technique structures the root-cause inquiry and helps the investigators to be sure that they have examined the situation from all perspectives. As figure 7.3 shows, the "fishbones" delineate the causes of the situation (the effect is at the head of the fish) as classified in four categories. In the structure shown, the categories all begin with the letter M. This design was intended to make it easier to remember the categories as "the 4 Ms." Other approaches use other names for the categories, such as equipment, procedures, people, and policies.

The manpower category examines influences of the human worker on the situation. In the case of the death of Mrs. Yu, a human worker influence was the obstetrics nurses' lack of training in surgical procedures. This lack of training meant that surgical procedures could not be performed in the delivery rooms.

The materiel category examines the influences of supplies and equipment on the situation. In the case of the death of Mrs. Yu, surgical supplies and equipment were not available to Dr. Low in the delivery room, and so she could not perform the necessary exploratory procedure there.

The methods category examines influences of policies and procedures on the situation. In the case of the death of Mrs. Yu, it was the policy of the institution to take all obstetrical cases requiring surgical delivery or other surgical procedures to the operating room on an entirely different floor of the hospital. This policy caused a fairly long period of time to elapse during transport and in this situation led to the patient's death from blood loss.

The machinery category examines influences of machines or other major pieces of equipment on the situation. In the case of the death of Mrs. Yu, the slowness of the elevator in the hospital contributed to the delay in effective treatment.

In root-cause analysis, it is important to continue to ask the question *why?* until the absolute root cause has been discovered. Omachonu discusses proximate versus root

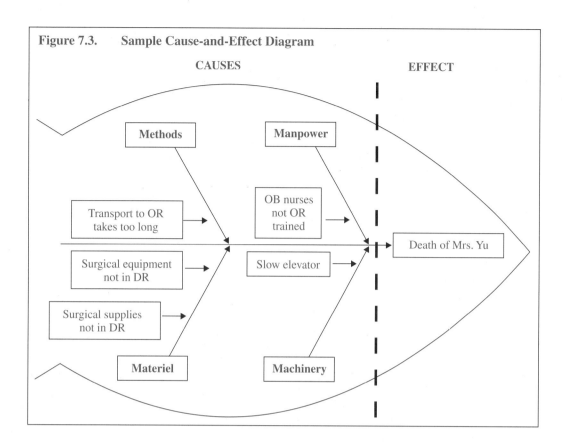

Figure 7.3.   Sample Cause-and-Effect Diagram

causes (Omachonu, 1999). Proximate causes are those that can be pointed to relatively directly. In the real-life example, a proximate cause was the inability of the obstetrical nurses to assist in emergency surgical procedures. However, that proximate cause has, in turn, many underlying causes, some of which may be the root cause of the sentinel event. Those underlying causes must be identified, because the existence of those underlying causes is what really allowed the sentinel event to happen.

Investigators of Mrs. Yu's death had to ask *why?* many times to get to the root causes of all the aspects contributing to that occurrence. With respect to the lack of expertise in surgical procedures of obstetrical nursing staff, asking *why?* uncovered significant negative attitudes on the part of all involved. Obstetrical nurses were reluctant to take on new responsibilities. Nursing administration was unwilling to commit the funds to develop new expertise in the nurses. Obstetrical physicians were skeptical that acceptable levels of competence could be developed in the obstetrical nurses. The institution's administration recognized that significant remodeling of the delivery suites would be required to provide the surgical services there. If root-cause analysis had not been performed, all of these contributing factors would have remained under the surface and would not have been dealt with.

In any situation, several levels of proximate causes must be identified and worked through to finally uncover the root causes. Asking *why?* repeatedly helps the investigators to get to the root causes. (See figure 7.4.)

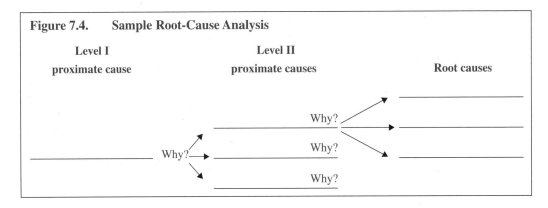

Figure 7.4.   Sample Root-Cause Analysis

Following investigation and root-cause analysis of the factors that contributed to Mrs. Yu's death, administrators at Community Hospital of the West recognized that the current configuration of the delivery suite in the facility had directly contributed to a patient's death. In a situation where her anomalous uterine anatomy presented the care team with dangerous and unexpected consequences, she need not have died. If the exploratory laparotomy and possible emergency hysterectomy procedures could have been performed in the delivery room, Mrs. Yu's life probably could have been saved.

The administrators recognized that every transport of a patient from the delivery room to the operating rooms exposed the patient to unnecessary risk. The time wasted in transport in this case had proved fatal. The administrators undertook reconfiguration of the system to prevent the reoccurrence of this situation. The delivery rooms were rapidly remodeled and equipped with all the supplies and equipment necessary to support the performance of surgical procedures in the delivery rooms. Obstetrics nurses were retrained to assist on surgical procedures performed in the delivery room as they would be performed in the operating rooms. Following that episode, all cesarean sections and other emergency procedures were performed without requiring that the patient be transported to an operating room.

Case Study

Derek Johnson, M.D., had been an anesthesiologist at Community Hospital of the West for 15 years. He was 45 years of age. The physician was board certified to perform all kinds of anesthesia procedures, including all types of surgical procedures and obstetrical anesthetic procedures. His colleagues had noticed for some time that he was becoming more and more haggard looking, visibly older, but they ascribed this to the hectic work schedule that anesthesiologists often must maintain: up early in the morning to be prepared for a day of surgeries; at the hospital late at night tending to new mothers delivering babies. Then, one day, Derek Johnson, M.D., was admitted to the intensive care unit at Community Hospital of the West.

The news spread through the organization quickly. No one was supposed to be talking about it, but everyone was. Derek Johnson, M.D., was suffering from compromise of his immune system and was close to dying from septicemia. Could he possibly have AIDS?

No, some of the OR nurses chatted at the supper table. It was unlikely that he had AIDS because he was not gay. They speculated that it was more likely that Dr. Johnson was a drug addict. The anesthesiologists provided morphine to patients from a lockbox to which only they had keys. The anesthesiologists were not required to account for narcotics beyond signing out dosages from the lockbox on a clipboard that hung beside it. Some of the OR nurses had noticed over the past six months to a year that Dr. Johnson's patients invariably received morphine for pain as recorded on the clipboard. In many cases, the patients clearly did not need it. For most, there was no documentation in their medical charts of the morphine administration.

One of the nurses reported that she had even cornered the chief of the Anesthesia Service and told him of Dr. Johnson's narcotics irregularities three months previously. Not wanting to challenge or accuse a fellow physician, the chief said indignantly that there must be some other explanation and terminated the conversation. The nurse went nowhere else to discuss the problem—not to the director of surgical services, not to the chief of surgery, not to the director of nursing, not to an administrator.

Case Study Questions

1. Besides basic human weakness, what other reasons are evident for Dr. Johnson's narcotics problem?

2. Does Community Hospital of the West bear any responsibility for Dr. Johnson's predicament?

3. What are the root causes of this situation? Build a cause-and-effect diagram on the basis of the findings in this case study.

4. What is the likely response of the hospital's governing body to this situation?

Project Application

Students should consider using a cause-and-effect diagram and root-cause analysis in their projects.

Summary

Healthcare facilities are dangerous places. Employees in healthcare organizations must be continuously aware of situations that might result in injury to staff or patients. To help manage the dangerous work setting, healthcare organizations use occurrence reporting systems that track and document incidents. Risk managers carefully review the organization's policies and procedures and assess the staff's ability to carry them out. Risk managers maintain open communications channels with any person injured in the facility until a satisfactory resolution of the claim or litigation has been reached. Finally, risk managers provide information to the organization's insurers and represent the organization at all formal meetings and legal proceedings related to injury claims.

References

Joint Commission on Accreditation of Healthcare Organizations. 1998. Sentinel events: approaches to error reduction and prevention. *Joint Commission Journal of Quality Improvement* 24(4):175–86.

Omachonu, Vincent K. 1999. *Healthcare Performance Improvement,* pp. 146–52. Norcross, Ga.: Engineering and Management Press.

Spath, Patrice L., editor. 2000. *Error Reduction in Health Care.* San Francisco: Jossey-Bass Publishers.

Troyer, Glenn T., and Steven L. Salman. 1986. *Handbook of Health Care Risk Management.* Rockville, Md.: Aspen Publications.

Wakefield, D. S., et al. 1999. Understanding why medication administration errors may not be reported. *American Journal of Medical Quality* 14(2):81–88.

Youngberg, Barbara J., editor. 1999. *Essentials of Hospital Risk Management.* Gaithersburg, Md.: Aspen Publishers.

Chapter 8
Optimizing Patient Care

Learning Objectives

- To recognize the common means by which healthcare organizations monitor and improve the quality of patient care

- To understand the expectation that healthcare will be individualized across the care continuum

- To understand the roles that clinical practice guidelines and evidence-based medicine play in standardizing patient care

- To be able to explain the contribution that the long-term care Minimum Data Set and the Health Plan Employer Data and Information Set can make to improving the quality of patient care

Background and Significance

The preceding chapters discussed the performance improvement model, its goals, and some of the factors involved in working with performance improvement processes. This chapter focuses on a systematized approach to process improvement that can ultimately benefit the patient.

Even the individual medical requirements of a single patient can initiate the cycle of performance improvement. The critical factor in optimizing the care of patients is the organization's ability to improve the patients' understanding of their health, their ability to care for themselves, their independence, and their quality of life. The hub in the cycle of performance improvement in healthcare is a unique and individual human being. The goal of performance improvement in healthcare is to design and implement systems that provide consistency and quality in all of the patient care processes performed to improve each individual patient's health.

The standards of the Joint Commission on Accreditation of Healthcare Organizations (JCAHO) describe the goal of patient care as providing "individualized, planned, and appropriate interventions." These interventions may be in the form of care, services, treatment, habilitation, or rehabilitation. Performance improvement efforts provide a process for evaluating every service, provider, setting, and outcome. The cornerstone of patient care is the establishment of a treatment plan that is specific, individualized, and based on a thorough assessment of the patient's physical, emotional, social, cognitive, and cultural needs.

Treatment/Care Plans

In today's healthcare settings, the treatment/care plan for an individual patient is often completed by a multidisciplinary team using data developed through team assessment processes. The assessment process may be as simple as having a patient complete a questionnaire in a physician's office. It may be as complicated as having physicians, radiologists, and nurses take part in a medical triage assessment in a hospital emergency department.

The goals of the treatment/care plan are broad in scope and set the overall direction for care. The plan defines the specific treatment and its timing and frequency. Many healthcare facilities use a system of care based on established national clinical standards for treatment interventions.

Risser and his colleagues (2000) advocate the use of team approaches in every care process. They identify the team approaches as significant contributions to improving patient care and to decreasing the number of patient care errors. The teamwork approach:

> teaches team members to actively coordinate and support each other in the course of clinical task execution using the structure of work teams. Teams and teamwork behaviors do not replace clinical skills but rather serve to ensure that clinical activities are properly integrated and executed to deliver effective . . . care. Teamwork is a management tool to expedite care delivery to patients, a mechanism to give caregivers increased control over their constantly changing environments, and a safety net to help protect both patients and caregivers from inevitable human failings and their consequences. . . . The goal of each core team is to deliver high-quality clinical care to the set of patients assigned to it. To achieve this goal, team members coordinate directly and repeatedly with each other to ensure proper and timely clinical task execution and to detect and help overloaded teammates. Each team member works to maintain a clear understanding (a common situation awareness) of the care status and care plan for each patient assigned to the team and the workload status of each team member. Teams hold brief meetings to make team decisions, assign/reassign responsibilities and tasks, establish/reestablish situation awareness, and learn lessons. The team oversees and directly manages the use of all care resources needed by the patient assigned to the team (Risser and others, 2000, pp. 241–42).

Regulatory and licensing agencies usually define the items required in an assessment at any particular healthcare or medical site. Many agencies also define the degree and experience required of team members to perform an adequate assessment. One of the key requirements is that only caregivers educated, trained, and appropriately licensed and deemed competent are allowed to perform patient assessment. The team and the patient establish priorities for treatment. Some treatment issues may be delayed or postponed on the basis of the urgency or immediacy of care needs. For example, a patient admitted to an emergency department with an actively bleeding injury and diabetes may undergo treatment for the acute injury first and an evaluation of the diabetes later. Goals and interventions are developed by the team to address the patient's need for services and to evaluate clinical improvement.

Once the treatment/care plan has been developed, implementation of the plan is undertaken. The patient's status is continuously monitored for signs of stabilization or improvement. Revisions of the care plan and treatment interventions are developed in response to changes in the patient's status.

Most treatment/care teams meet on a regular basis to evaluate patient data, interventions, and improvement. The flow of patient care is from assessment to treatment planning; from treatment planning to care or service; from care or service to reassessment; from reassessment to continuation of care when improvement is demonstrated; or from reassessment to new interventions when improvement is not demonstrated. As the patient's care proceeds, some key care processes are implemented. These key care processes include such services as laboratory tests, radiological examinations, pharmacy products, dietary intake, nursing care, and physical therapy.

The eventual outcome of this flow of care is discharge to the patient's home or to a different care setting. (See figure 8.1.) The coordination of patient services and care is often discussed among care team members. Patients should be involved in this process and should be actively encouraged to take part in the planning of their own care. The strengths and limitations of the patient should be considered in the development of the treatment plan. Family members and other significant persons should be encouraged to become involved and should be educated about the patient's treatment process.

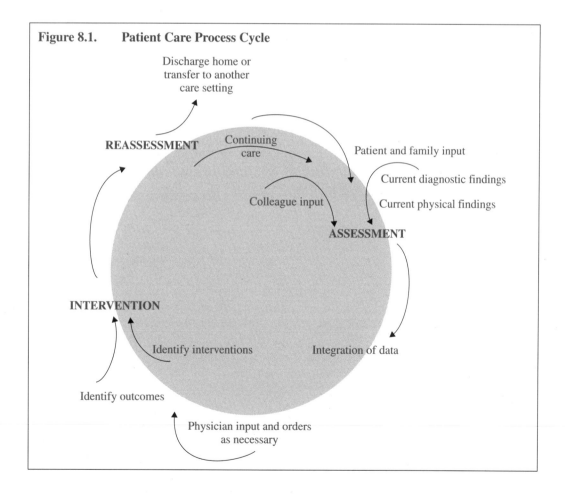

Figure 8.1.   Patient Care Process Cycle

Optimizing Patient Care: Steps to Success

The treatment and care of patients in a healthcare system can be measured in many different ways. The different measures can be used to identify problems, to demonstrate compliance with regulations, or to reflect improvement in patient care processes. Some problems, however, are more easily measured than others. For example, it is easier to measure the number of patients who receive a presurgical dose of antibiotics to prevent postoperative wound infection than it is to measure that particular intervention's effect on the occurrence of infection in an individual. Different people have different responses to medication interventions. Such differences create variations in the overall response to medication. The focus of improvement processes, therefore, must be tied to patient-specific data about the care processes being provided at any given facility.

Several common improvement processes are discussed in the following steps.

Step 1: Conduct evaluations of the organization's medication systems and processes

Medication systems and processes should be evaluated to ensure the safe and effective use of medications in any facility that provides medications to patients. Methods for prescribing, ordering, and securing medications should be defined in policy and procedure and monitored for compliance. Patient and family education regarding medication use, contraindication, and side effects are other areas for monitoring.

Pharmacy and therapeutics (P and T) committees monitor the preparation, dispensing, and storage of medications. The committees also administer the organization's **formulary,** which specifies the drugs approved for use in the organization. The selection of items to be included in the formulary is based on objective evaluations of their relative therapeutic merits, safety, and cost. The committee minimizes duplication of the same basic drug type, drug entity, or drug product. The kinds of medication that are monitored depend on the care setting and type of services provided.

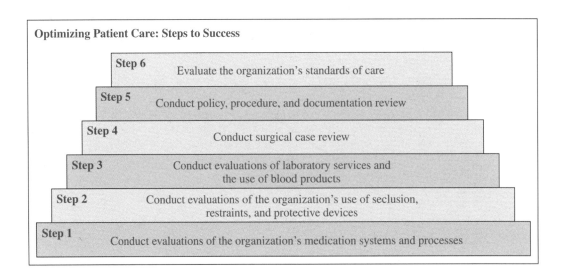

Optimizing Patient Care: Steps to Success

Step 6 — Evaluate the organization's standards of care

Step 5 — Conduct policy, procedure, and documentation review

Step 4 — Conduct surgical case review

Step 3 — Conduct evaluations of laboratory services and the use of blood products

Step 2 — Conduct evaluations of the organization's use of seclusion, restraints, and protective devices

Step 1 — Conduct evaluations of the organization's medication systems and processes

The P and T committee plays an advisory role for the medical staff and recommends policies related to medication and other therapies. Its recommendations have far-reaching therapeutic and economic effects for the healthcare organization. The committee is the organizational link between the medical staff and the pharmacy department. In addition, the committee develops educational programs on issues related to medications and medication use to meet the needs of the professional staff—physicians, nurses, pharmacists, and other healthcare practitioners.

The composition of the P and T committee varies from organization to organization. Membership, however, usually consists of physicians, nurses, an administrator, and pharmacists. The committee should meet regularly (at least six times per year), and its minutes should be maintained in a permanent record. The functions and scope of this committee have been described by the American Society of Health-System Pharmacists (ASHP). According to the ASHP, the committee's functions include the following:

- Serving in an advisory capacity to the medical staff and administration in all matters pertaining to the use of drugs (including investigational drugs)

- Developing a formulary of drugs accepted for use in the organization and providing for its constant revision

- Establishing programs and procedures that help ensure cost-effective drug therapy

- Establishing or planning suitable educational programs for the organization's professional staff on matters related to drug use

- Participating in PI activities related to the distribution, administration, and use of medications, including the handling of medication errors and patient or staff complaints

- Reviewing all adverse drug reactions

- Initiating or directing drug use review programs or studies and reviewing the results of such activities

- Advising the pharmacy in the implementation of effective drug distribution and control procedures

- Making recommendations to determine which drugs should be stocked in the facility's patient care areas

Developing an effective formulary is a significant responsibility. With the number of drugs available, every organization should have a program for objectively evaluating and selecting the drugs to be included in its formulary. Limiting the number of drugs routinely available from the pharmacy produces substantial financial and patient care benefits. Because of the changing nature of healthcare delivery, the P and T committee can serve as an effective bridge between the clinical factors and economic consequences related to drug therapy.

The pharmacy and therapeutics program of Western States University Hospitals and Clinics has two major components. The first component is the drug usage evaluation (DUE), and the second is its therapeutic interchange program.

The DUE is a systematic, criteria-based, ongoing function of the medical staff. It evaluates how drugs are used at the University Hospital in four key areas:

- Medication ordering, including appropriate indications and dosing
- Medication preparation and dispensing
- Medication administration
- Monitoring of the effects of medications and their therapeutic outcomes

Drug use evaluation projects can be either disease focused or drug specific. Projects are usually selected on the basis of the following criteria:

- The drug is less effective than another drug that can be used to treat the same condition; the physician and pharmacist may identify a more effective drug therapy.
- The drug is considered high risk or problem prone; drugs may fall into this category because they have an adverse reaction profile or because certain populations have additional risk.
- The drug is frequently prescribed.
- The drug is costly.

The DUE subcommittee at the Western States University Hospitals and Clinics uses several screening mechanisms to monitor drug use and identify issues that may require additional evaluation. These mechanisms include the following:

- Receiving information from other performance improvement activities including the infection committee, critical care committee, and risk management committee
- Reviewing incident reports and medication errors
- Reviewing all nonformulary drug requests
- Reviewing all adverse drug reactions reported
- Reviewing drug purchases
- Maintaining the hospital formulary

The major component of the P and T performance improvement program at Western States is the investigation of **adverse drug reactions** (ADRs) to improve the use of drugs and prevent adverse reactions. An ADR is a detrimental response to a medication that is undesired, unintended, or unexpected in dosages recognized in accepted medical practice. Adverse reactions that should be reported to the P and T committee include those that prolong the length of a patient's hospital stay, cause discontinuation of drug therapy, or provoke a change in drug therapy requiring corrective measures such as antidotes. Mild reactions that do not require drug discontinuation, antidotes, or prolonged hospital stays are not reported.

The committee is also interested in **medication error** rates. The committee monitors the frequency with which clinicians administer medications to the wrong patient. It also monitors food–medication or medication–medication interactions that produce symptoms in patients.

For example, an ambulatory care clinic might choose to monitor the side effects from high-dose antibiotics used on repeat urinary tract infections. The hypothesis identified might be that repeat urinary tract infections are occurring because patients are not completing their medications as prescribed. A literature search might confirm that this is a reasonable assumption. Data from random patient responses might also confirm this assumption. Patients might not complete the medication as prescribed because of unpleasant side effects such as diarrhea and stomach pain. When the data suggest that this assumption is correct, a plan can be implemented to correct the side effects and promote completion of medication regimens. The result should be a reduction in the number of repeat infections. Completion of medications would also help prevent the development of resistant strains of bacteria as well as decrease the cost of treatment through more effective management of care.

In managing the facility's formulary, the Western States P and T committee implemented a program known as therapeutic interchange. Therapeutic interchange is the authorized exchange of therapeutic alternatives in accordance with previously established and approved guidelines or protocols within a formulary system. The following activities summarize the therapeutic interchange process.

The P and T committee designates a group of drugs as therapeutically equivalent and appropriate for therapeutic interchange after seeking feedback from the medical staff. The committee approves guidelines for interchanging the drugs. The pharmacy then evaluates the cost of using each drug and determines which drug will be the drug of choice. The factors weighed in these analyses include the cost of the drug, any special contract price incentives, and other costs associated with using the drug.

Drugs included on the interchange program are listed in the computerized formulary, and notations are made to indicate the drug of choice for a given group of drugs. When the pharmacy receives an order for any drug in the group, the pharmacist substitutes the selected formulary agent according to the guidelines established by the P and T committee. Prescribers are notified of the change in drug by interchange. Prescribers may order an alternative agent within the group and document a reason why the patient cannot receive the selected agent through interchange.

Step 2: Conduct evaluations of the organization's use of seclusion, restraints, and protective devices

The use of seclusion, restraints, and protective devices requires intensive performance monitoring. Protective devices include wrist restraints, jacket restraints, chairs with restraining tables, restraints to stabilize a patient's body during surgery, and side rails on hospital beds. Protective devices prevent something from happening. One example is the use of head stabilization devices for dental procedures. The JCAHO refers to the use of any of these devices as **special treatment procedures** (STPs).

The use of special treatment procedures involves legal risk. Monitoring should assess compliance with physician's orders; mandated maximum time limits of two hours for children and two to four hours for adolescents and adults; physical assessment during STPs every two hours; and assessment by a physician within one hour of initiation of the order. The appropriateness of the use of STPs must be evaluated. Patients must be checked every fifteen minutes during the procedure and must remain in the direct line of sight of supervising clinicians.

Independent licensed practitioners should be credentialed for applying for STPs. Continued training and documentation of staff competency for special treatment procedures and protective devices must be documented. It is also very important to document leadership education and commitment to the reduction of the use of STPs facilitywide. The JCAHO wants to reduce the frequency of STPs across all facilities. The JCAHO is particularly concerned about the use of special treatment procedures and protective devices in long-term care and rehabilitation settings because the procedures may impinge on patients' rights.

Step 3: Conduct evaluations of laboratory services and the use of blood products

The organization's compliance with established standards related to the use of laboratory equipment and the handling of laboratory specimens must be monitored. Laboratory services are regulated by established protocols from the Clinical Laboratory Improvement Amendments (CLIA) and the Centers for Disease Control. Equipment calibration and other parameters of laboratory values must be monitored daily.

The handling of blood and blood products for transfusions is also regulated and monitored. Measuring, assessing, and improving the ordering, typing, matching, dispensing, and administering of blood and blood products are a standard part of continuous monitoring for most clinic and hospital settings. The review process seeks to validate the need for transfusion, the use of the appropriate type of blood product, and effective procedures for blood product administration.

The cause of every **transfusion reaction** must be investigated. The JCAHO now considers hemolytic transfusion reactions to be sentinel events, and as such they require in-depth analysis, data collection, and a written communication to the JCAHO concerning actions taken to prevent such occurrences in the future.

Step 4: Conduct surgical case review

Facilities that perform operative and diagnostic procedures must monitor their performance because of the inherently hazardous nature of many procedures. The procedures are monitored to look for trends or patterns of professional practice that vary from established standards. The clinical professionals conducting case review also examine procedures prone to problems. Surgical case monitoring examines preoperative and postoperative diagnoses, outcome, variances in procedure technique, safety compliance, and adherence to protocols. The review seeks to validate the need for surgery, appropriate diagnosis prior to surgery, appropriate surgical technique, and documentation of disease on pathological analysis. The reviewing panel of physicians and other clinicians may make important recommendations to the organization's administration on improvements that could be made in surgical services.

Anesthesia use is monitored closely because of its potential for costly negative outcomes and because it involves the use of powerful and high-risk medications. (See the QI toolbox technique later in this chapter for an example of a surgical case review format.)

Step 5: Conduct policy, procedure, and documentation review

The development of policies on standard practices in the facility should be multidisciplinary in nature and design. Most facilities operate within a standard set of policies that have been developed by a multidisciplinary team of clinical and administrative professionals who meet regularly. Updates and revisions of policies are undertaken as national standards of care change. The governing board and leadership of an organization hold the ultimate responsibility for the services provided in the facility and generally recommend changes and set time frames for the review of every policy and procedure to be followed. Some facilities operate with a separate policy and procedure committee.

A key quality performance concern is the adequate and reliable documentation of care. Poor documentation leads to the largest number of risk management and legal situations in the industry. Accreditation and licensing agencies have standards on the documentation of patient care and expect that a sample of clinical documentation will be reviewed regularly as part of an organization's performance improvement activities. The expectation is that all records are complete in terms of authentication and necessary reports and that they appropriately document the condition and treatment of the patient.

Step 6: Evaluate the organization's standards of care

A healthcare organization's ability to define optimal care begins with the clear establishment of **standards of care** and care policies. Some healthcare organizations have moved from a policy and procedure format to a **clinical practice standards** model. This model defines practice based on diagnosis. The flow of treatment interventions and the patient's progress are evaluated on the basis of nationally accepted standards of care for the diagnosis. As each standard is developed and approved, a baseline for performance in the healthcare setting develops. Variations from the standards of care, sentinel events, and high-risk, problem-prone activities must be examined. Action plans are then developed to improve care in areas identified through the monitoring process. A decline in performance or a lack of improvement may require further evaluation of the processes and redesign of care processes.

Ongoing Developments

It is important to recognize at this point that the PI processes discussed in the preceding section are part of a continuum of development in the evaluation of patient care. This continuum of development began, effectively, with the initiation of accreditation and standardization programs decades ago. It will continue in the future.

The principal reason for this long continuum of development is that the evaluation of patient care across all settings is extremely difficult. The expectation is that healthcare will be individualized, because what works well for one patient may not work well for another.

Some healthcare researchers, particularly those working in the federal government, have spent millions of dollars and years of research in developing **clinical guidelines** that attempt to standardize the care of a single condition across the entire country. Many clinical practitioners, however, find the guidelines difficult to implement or even contraindicated in some cases because of comorbid conditions or social ramifications in a patient's clinical presentation. (The use of **clinical paths** was discussed in more detail in chapter 5.)

Other healthcare researchers have developed the concept of **evidence-based medicine.** Evidence-based medicine attempts to identify the care processes or interventions that achieve the best outcomes in different types of medical practice. Researchers perform large, population-based studies. Such studies, however, are difficult to do without a well-developed information infrastructure to provide data for analysis. The United States does not yet have a well-developed information infrastructure.

Another group of researchers developed the concept of **indicators** to point healthcare organizations toward areas where improvement is necessary. (This concept was first introduced in chapter 5.) One example of this approach is the JCAHO's Oryx program. In this approach, JCAHO staff attempted to define indicators for all of the care situations commonly encountered in U.S. healthcare. The JCAHO then mandated that healthcare organizations participate in some kind of aggregate indicator comparison program so that data could be drawn from multiple organizations across the country. The JCAHO hopes that this approach will facilitate the identification of effective patterns of care over the next decade.

The National Committee for Quality Assurance (NCQA) began accrediting managed care organizations in 1991 in response to the need for standardized, objective information about the quality of the services provided by managed care organizations. The NCQA introduced the Health Plan Employer Data and Information Set (HEDIS) in the early 1990s as a means of gathering information about care, outcomes, and member satisfaction with managed care organizations and other health plans. HEDIS gathers a significant amount of information about the ambulatory care experiences of millions of health plan members from across the country. Specifically, HEDIS gathers data in the following areas:

- Measures of quality, such as immunization, cholesterol screening, mammography, and prenatal care

- Measures of access, with at least one visit to a provider within three years used as an indicator of assessment of healthcare need

- Measures of membership, with particular attention to disenrollment as an indicator of dissatisfaction

- Measures of utilization, including factors such as high-occurrence, high-cost diagnosis-related groups; frequency of procedures; general hospital acute care; outpatient and emergency visits; cesarean section rates; complicated neonatal care; and outpatient drug utilization

- Measures of financial performance, such as cost per member, cost for member plus dependents, and indicators of financial stability

The NCQA then reports its findings to employers, who use the information in making decisions about contracts with health plans. In this way, the NCQA influences the kind of care offered by managed care plans and provides consumers with information about which plans have superior healthcare offerings.

Another new approach to monitoring care and identifying opportunities for improvement for healthcare organizations has recently been demonstrated in the long-term care setting. Beginning in June 1998, the federal government has mandated the use of the long-term care **Minimum Data Set** (MDS) to plan the care of long-term care residents. This data set structures the assessment of long-term care residents in the areas of cognitive patterns, communication and hearing patterns, vision patterns, physical functioning and structural problems, continence, psychosocial well-being, mood and behavior patterns, activity pursuit patterns, disease diagnoses, other health conditions, oral/nutritional status, oral/dental status, skin condition, medication use, and treatments and procedures.

The federal government requires that long-term care facilities receiving Medicare or Medicaid funding transmit the patient-specific data to the state departments of health for processing and use in the long-term care certification and survey review process. The certification and survey review process is carried out by the state departments of health on behalf of the federal government to certify that facilities receiving Medicare or Medicaid funds are complying with federal regulations. The departments of health pay special attention to data on the occurrence of decubitus ulcers in low-risk patients (those who can ambulate, can turn over in bed, are not cognitively impaired, and so on), dehydration, and fecal impaction.

On the basis of the data gathered via the MDS, the facility is provided a **facility quality indicator profile** that shows what proportion of the facility's residents have deficits in each area of assessment during the reporting period and specifically which residents have which deficits. The profile also provides data comparing the facility's current experience with its preestablished comparison group. Data from the facility quality indicator profile are also forwarded to the Health Care Financing Administration. An example of a facility quality indicator profile is provided in figure 8.2.

In 2000, efforts to develop a minimum data set and quality indicator profiles for home care services were under way.

Real-Life Example

A typical example of an improvement effort might begin with an assessment of an overweight adolescent who is being treated for psychosis with the antipsychotic drug Zyprexia. One side effect of Zyprexia is a decrease in satiety factors in the brain, which creates a sense of hunger even when adequate food is provided. National standards for height and weight based on age are available. The adolescent's height and weight could be compared to the height and weight of other adolescents in his age group. The assessment process might then identify the patient as being in a high-risk category for obesity. An evaluation of the causative factors might reveal a heredity (genetic) component, a disease component, medication side effects, poor personal habits, and knowledge deficit regarding healthy nutrition. A multilayered action plan could be initiated after an investigation of all aspects of the contributing factors. A nutritional consult coupled with a dietary regimen and medication evaluation might result in weight loss and a significant change in the patient's health and well-being. A psychiatric consult to gauge the patient's compliance with medication and diet might be required to help initiate a treatment plan with which the patient would comply. Data could be collected to determine whether the interventions have had a continued positive effect on the patient's health. At some point in the process, an activity therapist might be consulted to direct physical exercise as an intervention to increase and support muscle strengthening as weight is lost. This example of the performance improvement process demonstrates how the process may be individualized for a patient.

Figure 8.2.   **Example of a Long-Term Care Facility Quality Improvement Profile**

Facility Characteristics

Run Date: 2/1/00   12:36:15 p.m.   **Report Period:** 8/1/99 to 1/31/00
Facility: Western Gardens   **Date Submitted:** 1/31/00
Comparison Group Used: **Facility Login ID:** AT 4763
  All State Facilities,
  October–December 1998

Resident Population	Number of Residents	Facility Percentage*	Comparison Group Percentage*
Gender			
Male	19	28.8	33.7
Female	47	71.2	66.2
Age			
<25 years	1	1.5	0.5
25–54 years	4	6.1	7.5
55–64 years	2	3.0	6.5
65–74 years	13	19.7	14.8
75–84 years	23	34.8	32.7
84+ years	23	34.8	38.0
Payment source (all that apply)			
Medicaid per diem	48	72.7	45.1
Medicare per diem	11	16.7	22.1
Medicare ancillary part A	18	27.3	19.2
Medicare ancillary part B	6	9.1	5.8
Self-pay/family-pay per diem	4	6.1	16.3
Medicaid resident liability or Medicare copayment	1	1.5	6.1
Private insurance per diem	3	4.5	8.1
All other per diem	1	1.5	2.6
Diagnostic characteristics			
Psychiatric diagnosis	8	12.1	9.7
Mental retardation	2	3.0	2.5
Hospice	0	0.0	0.7
Type of assessment			
Admission	12	18.2	34.0
Annual	7	10.6	11.0
Significant change in status	0	0.0	4.6
Significant correction of prior full assessment	1	1.5	0.5
Quarterly	42	63.6	49.7
Significant correction of prior quarterly	4	6.1	0.2
All other	0	0.0	0.0
Stability of conditions			
Conditions/disease make resident unstable	5	7.6	35.6
Acute episode or chronic flare-up	2	3.0	4.6
End-stage disease, ≤6 months to live	2	3.0	1.3
Discharge potential			
None	44	66.7	56.6
Within 30 days	2	3.0	15.3
Within 31–90 days	5	7.6	3.9
Uncertain	14	21.2	21.6

Figure 8.2.   (*Continued*)

Facility Quality Indicator Profile

Run Date: 2/1/00   12:36:15 p.m.   **Report Period:** 8/1/00 to 1/31/00
Facility: Western Gardens   **Date Submitted:** 1/31/00
Comparison Group Used: **Facility Login ID:** AT 4763
  All State Facilities,
  October–December 1999

Domain/Quality Indicator	Number in Numerator	Number in Denominator	Facility Percentage*	Comparison Group Percentage*	Percentile
Accidents					
1. Incidence of new fractures	0	53	0.0	1.1	0
2. Prevalence of falls	1	54	1.9	14.4	0
Behavioral/emotional patterns					
3. Prevalence of behavioral symptoms affecting others	13	54	24.1	28.2	41
High risk	10	40	25.0	32.7	34
Low risk	3	14	21.4	16.9	70
4. Prevalence of symptoms of depression	8	54	14.8	21.1	42
5. Prevalence of symptoms of depression without antidepressant therapy	1	54	1.9	8.7	18
Clinical management					
6. Use of nine or more medications	21	54	38.9	37.7	56
Cognitive patterns					
7. Incidence of cognitive impairment	1	14	7.1	12.5	41
Elimination/incontinence					
8. Prevalence of bladder or bowel incontinence	27	51	52.9	52.0	51
High risk	13	13	100.0	88.6	100
Low risk	14	38	36.8	39.9	38
9. Prevalence of occasional or frequent bladder or bowel incontinence without a toileting plan	9	18	50.0	55.7	40
10. Prevalence of indwelling catheter	3	54	5.6	4.9	60
11. Prevalence of fecal impaction	0	54	0.0	0.7	0
Infection control					
12. Prevalence of urinary tract infection	0	54	0.0	0.7	0
Nutrition/eating					
13. Prevalence of weight loss	1	54	1.9	2.5	54
14. Prevalence of tube feeding	1	54	1.9	2.5	54
15. Prevalence of dehydration	0	54	0.0	0.9	0
Physical functioning					
16. Prevalence of bedfast residents	1	54	1.9	6.1	29
17. Incidence of decline in late-loss activities of daily living	3	43	7.0	14.7	23
18. Incidence of decline in range of motion	7	47	14.9	9.8	79

(*Continued on next page*)

Figure 8.2.   (*Continued*)

Domain/Quality Indicator	Number in Numerator	Number in Denominator	Facility Percentage*	Comparison Group Percentage*	Percentile
Psychotropic drug use					
19. Prevalence of antipsychotic drug use in the absence of psychosis or related conditions	8	50	16.0	18.7	46
High risk	4	9	44.4	35.4	75
Low risk	4	41	9.8	13.9	38
20. Prevalence of antianxiety/hypnotic use	9	50	18.0	18.6	61
21. Prevalence of hypnotic use more than two times in past week	1	54	1.9	3.4	50
Quality of life					
22. Prevalence of daily physical restraints	11	54	20.4	9.4	91
23. Prevalence of little or no activity	33	54	61.1	36.1	86
Skin care					
24. Prevalence of stage 1–4 pressure ulcers	4	54	7.4	7.9	65
High risk	4	23	17.4	13.5	81
Low risk	0	31	0.0	2.8	0

*Percentages may not total 100 owing to missing data.

Note: Original form designed by the Center for Health Systems Research and Analysis at the University of Wisconsin–Madison.

A systemwide performance improvement measure could be instituted in a care setting in regard to the problem of obesity in adolescents. If treating physicians noted significant weight increase over a brief period of time in many adolescent patients started on medications with the side effect of promoting weight gain, they might standardize their case management. Baseline evaluations of weight and height could be mandated for all patients and for all patients started on this type of medication. Significant weight gains could be tracked, and interventions could be instituted for the most effective outcomes. The outcomes may lead to a resulting change in treatment that would lead physicians to order dietary consults and weight monitoring on all patients on this medication. Other preventive measures could be instituted early in treatment to prevent excessive weight gain and alleviate the patient's risk of cardiac disease related to obesity. The potential outcome from this performance improvement process could lead to healthier patients who require fewer medical services in the future.

QI Toolbox Technique

A common toolbox technique applicable to the improvement of patient care is the surgical case review criteria set. Criteria sets are used to review the appropriateness, processes, and outcomes of surgical procedures in healthcare facilities with respect to procedures that are commonly performed and/or problem prone. The criteria are used to help identify opportunities for improvement with respect to the performance of the procedures. (See the preceding discussion of surgical case review.)

An example of a criteria set is provided in figure 8.3. *CPT-4* or *ICD-9-CM* procedure codes can be used to identify the cases for review, or cases can be reviewed on the basis

---

Figure 8.3.   Sample Criteria Set

CYSTOSCOPY/CYSTOURETHROSCOPY, WITH OR WITHOUT ENDOSCOPIC SURGERY (EXCLUDING EXCISION OR DESTRUCTION)

Indications for Surgical Procedure

1. Urinary tract inflammation, neoplasm, trauma, foreign body, congenital abnormality
2. Hematuria
3. Urinary incontinence, obstruction, or abnormal bladder function
4. Evaluation of vesical or extravesical lesion
5. Follow-up to rule out recurrent tumor in asymptomatic patient

Instructions to Nonphysician Reviewers

1. Indications of abnormal bladder function are frequency of urination, pain, bladder spasms

Required Procedure-Specific Ancillary Studies

1. Urinalysis

Optional Procedure-Specific Ancillary Studies

1. IVP
2. Creatinine
3. BUN
4. Culture and sensitivity
5. Ultrasound of abdomen

of admission diagnosis and expected surgical procedure. The indications section identifies the diagnoses or presenting symptoms that should be present for the procedure to be performed. The instructions to nonphysician reviewers section further specifies factors that must to be taken into consideration in the review. The required procedure-specific ancillary studies section identifies diagnostic studies that should be performed prior to the procedure. Other optional diagnostic studies are listed in the optional section.

Case Study

Students should think of a personal healthcare experience in any setting (dentist's office, nursing home, or hospital, for example). Then they should identify the key processes in relationship to the areas discussed in this chapter (for example, pharmacy, medication administration, nutritional assessment, or special procedure).

Case Study Questions

1. How might one monitor the processes? What types of data would be useful? Describe variations and possible causes of variations in the care processes.

2. What was working and what was not working in the processes? Consider interviewing healthcare professionals to discuss the issues.

Project Application

Students should consider using a standardized criteria set in evaluating customer satisfaction for the student project.

Summary

The application of performance improvement processes to patient care is a varied, multifaceted approach to quality. Opportunities for improvement can be identified at many levels, and organizations are limited only by constraints on their creativity and resources. Typical activities focusing on improvement of care include assessment of pharmacy and therapeutics usage; blood products usage; policy, procedure, and documentation; surgical case review; and special treatment procedures. There is also important work being done at the national level in the areas of clinical practice guidelines, clinical paths, evidence-based medicine, indicator monitoring, and data set analysis.

References

Allison, J. J., et al. 2000. The art and science of chart review. *Joint Commission Journal of Quality Improvement* 6(3):173–81.

American Society of Health-Systems Pharmacists. 1999–2000. *Best Practices for Health-System Pharmacy: Position and Practice Standards of the ASHP.*

Ashton, C. M., et al. 1999. An empirical assessment of the validity of explicit and implicit process-of-care criteria for quality assessment. *Medical Care* 37(8):798–808.

Bodenheimer, Thomas. 1999. The American health care system: the movement for improved quality in health care. *The New England Journal of Medicine* 340(6):488–92, February 11.

Brook, Robert H., Elizabeth A. McGlynn, and Paul D. Cleary. 1996. Measuring quality of care. *The New England Journal of Medicine* 335(13):966–70, September 26.

Chassin, M. R. 1993. Improving quality of care with practice guidelines. *Frontiers of Health Services Management* 10(1):40–44.

Cohen, M. R., J. Senders, and N. M. Davis. 1994. Failure mode and effects analysis: a novel approach to avoiding dangerous medication errors and accidents. *Hospital Pharmacy* 29(4):319–30.

Cook, Deborah J., et al. 1997. The relation between systematic reviews and practice guidelines. *Annals of Internal Medicine* 127(3):210–16, August 1.

DeBruin, A. F., et al. 1994. The sickness impact profile: SIP68, a short generic version. *Journal of Clinical Epidemiology* 47(8):863–71.

Dreachslin, J. L., P. L. Hunt, and E. Sprainer. 1999. Communication patterns and group composition: implications for patient-centered care team effectiveness. *Journal of Healthcare Management* 44(4):252–66, July.

Eddy, David M. 1998. Performance measurement: problems and solutions. *Health Affairs* 17(4), July.

Feinstein, Alvin R. 1995. Meta-analysis: statistical alchemy for the 21st century. *Journal of Clinical Epidemiology* 48(1):71–79.

Freund, Deborah, et al. 1999. Patient outcomes research teams: contribution to outcomes and effectiveness research. *Annual Review of Public Health* 20:337–59.

Greenfield, Sheldon, and Eugene C. Nelson. 1992. Recent developments and future issues in the use of health status assessment measures in clinical settings. *Medical Care* 30(suppl.), May.

Grimshaw, Jeremy M., and Ian T. Russell. 1993. Effect of clinical guidelines on medical practice: a systematic review of rigorous evaluations. *The Lancet* 342:1317–22, November 27.

Guyatt, Gordon, and the Evidence-Based Medicine Working Group. 1992. Evidence-based medicine. *JAMA* 268(17):2420–25, November 4.

Iezzoni, Lisa I. 1995. Risk adjustment for medical effectiveness research: an overview of conceptual and methodological considerations. *Journal of Investigative Medicine* 43(2):136–50, April.

Iezzoni, Lisa I. 1997. The risks of risk adjustment. *JAMA* 278(19):1600–1607.

Johr, J. J., et al. 1996. Improving health care: clinical benchmarking for best patient care. *Joint Commission Journal of Quality Improvement* 22(9):599–616.

Keller, R. B., D. E. Wennberg, and D. N. Soule. 1997. Changing physician behavior: the Maine Medical Assessment Foundation. *Quality Management in Health Care* 5(4):1–11.

Laupacis, Andreas, Nandita Sekar, and Ian G. Stiell. 1997. Clinical prediction rules: a review and suggested modifications of methodological standards. *JAMA* 277(6):488–94, February 12.

Lomas, Jonathon, et al. 1989. Do practice guidelines guide practice? *The New England Journal of Medicine* 321(19):1306–11, November 9.

Longo, Daniel R. 1993. Patient practice variation. *Medical Care* 30(5, suppl.).

McHorney, Colleen. 1999. Health status assessment. *Annual Review of Public Health* 20:309–35.

Mosser, G. 1996. Clinical process improvement: engage first, measure later. *Quality Management in Health Care* 4(4):11–20.

Risser, Daniel T., et al. 2000. A structured teamwork system to reduce clinical errors. In *Error Reduction in Health Care,* P. L. Spath, editor. San Francisco: Jossey-Bass Publishers.

Chapter 9
Improving the Care Environment and Safety

Learning Objectives

- To recognize the importance of environment of care and safety issues

- To recognize the seven most important areas in managing the care environment and safety

- To understand the means by which safety monitoring is carried out

- To understand the importance of posteducation assessment and occurrence reporting in documenting performance improvement activities involving the care environment and safety management

Background and Significance

As discussed in chapter 7, healthcare organizations are dangerous places. They house complex equipment, chemicals, and hazardous instruments and materials that can injure patients, visitors, and staff when they are used inappropriately. Because of the potential danger in the patient care environment, healthcare organizations must continuously monitor and evaluate their performance with respect to the quality of the patient environment and the safety of the individuals receiving or providing care services.

Improving the Care Environment and Safety: Steps to Success

The monitoring and improvement of the patient care environment and its safety involve the continuous examination and evaluation of activities in seven important areas:

- Security management

- Hazardous materials and waste management

- Emergency preparedness
- Life safety (fire prevention) program
- Medical equipment management
- Utility management
- Safety program

This chapter discusses each area in terms of its scope, goals, and objectives; its education, orientation, and training considerations; its roles and responsibilities; and its annual evaluation.

Step 1: Monitor and improve the security management program

The security management program accords highest priority to the following activities:

- Addressing security concerns affecting patients, visitors, employees, medical staff, and volunteers, particularly in the event of a security incident or failure or as necessary to maintain the privacy of VIPs

- Providing personal and role identification, as appropriate, for patients, visitors, employees, medical staff, and volunteers

- Controlling access, as appropriate, to security-sensitive areas such as cashier's offices and pharmacy services, where access to money, monetary instruments, or drugs must be restricted

- Controlling vehicular access around emergency services areas or during disasters

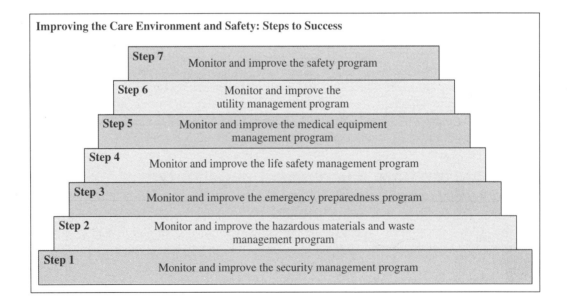

Improving the Care Environment and Safety: Steps to Success

Step 7 — Monitor and improve the safety program

Step 6 — Monitor and improve the utility management program

Step 5 — Monitor and improve the medical equipment management program

Step 4 — Monitor and improve the life safety management program

Step 3 — Monitor and improve the emergency preparedness program

Step 2 — Monitor and improve the hazardous materials and waste management program

Step 1 — Monitor and improve the security management program

Security management activities primarily concern ensuring that employees are able to follow established security procedures. Employees must understand the processes in place for minimizing security risks and handling breaches of security. Occurrence reports should also be tracked carefully to identify incidents in which security policy and procedures were ineffective.

Step 2: Monitor and improve the hazardous materials and waste management program

The hazardous materials and waste management program should be designed to identify all types of materials and waste that require special handling to minimize the risk of injury to patients, visitors, employees, medical staff, and volunteers. The program should accord highest priority to the following activities:

- Selecting, handling, storing, using, and disposing of hazardous materials appropriately and safely

- Identifying, evaluating, and maintaining an inventory of hazardous materials and waste used or generated by the departments of the organization

- Managing chemical, chemotherapeutic, radioactive, body fluid, and infectious waste, including sharps

- Monitoring and disposing of hazardous gases and vapors

- Providing adequate and appropriate housing and equipment for the safe handling and storage of hazardous materials and wastes

The hazardous materials and waste management program must provide an integrated and coordinated effort that complies with state statutes and meets the standards of the Joint Commission on Accreditation of Healthcare Organizations (JCAHO), National Fire and Protection Allocation, Life Safety Code, and Occupational Safety and Health Administration (OSHA). The program must work effectively to eliminate risk exposure and maximize loss prevention related to the numerous hazardous materials used in healthcare organizations.

Activities in the hazardous materials and waste management area primarily concern the employees' knowledge of and ability to perform appropriate procedures. Because different materials are inventoried, used, and disposed of in many different areas of healthcare organizations, department managers must take a leading role in ensuring their employees' compliance with procedures.

Any equipment used in conjunction with hazardous materials and waste management must be inspected, maintained, and tested at regular intervals to ensure proper operation.

Occurrence reports should be tracked carefully to identify incidents in which hazardous material and waste management policy and procedures were not followed.

Most important, all employees must know the procedures to follow in the event of an actual or suspected exposure to hazardous materials or waste. They must recognize the health hazards of mishandling hazardous materials and understand the reporting procedures that should be performed when an exposure occurs. Employees must understand what should be done to clear spilled material from exposed individuals. They must also know whether protective equipment or special precautions must be taken in the course of cleaning up and disposing of spilled materials.

As backup for employee training, department managers must maintain a **material safety data sheet** (MSDS) on every hazardous material used in their departments. Material safety data sheets should include the following information:

- Identification of the material, including its common and chemical names, family name, and product codes

- Risks associated with the material, including overall health risk, flammability, reactivity with other chemicals, and effects at the site of contact

- Descriptions of the protective equipment and clothing that should be used to handle the material

- Precautionary labeling that must appear on containers or storage units

- Physical characteristics of the material, including its boiling and melting points, specific gravity, solubility, appearance and odor, vapor pressure and density, evaporation rate, and physical state

- Information on potential fire and explosion hazards, including the material's flash point and autoignition temperature as well as unusual explosion hazards or toxic gases associated with the material

- Information on appropriate fire-extinguishing media and special fire-fighting procedures needed for the material

- Information on specific health hazards associated with the material, including the toxicity of components, carcinogenicity, reproductive effects, effects of overexposure, target organs, medical conditions aggravated by exposure, and routes of entry

- Information on emergency first-aid procedures

- Reactivity data, including storage and use conditions to avoid and other materials with which the material is incompatible

- Instructions on the disposal of spilled material

- Industrial protective equipment needed, such as ventilation hoods and respiratory protective devices

- Storage and handling precautions

- Procedures and precautions to be followed when the material is being transported

See figure 9.1 for an example of an MSDS.

Figure 9.1. Example of an MSDS

J.T. Baker Inc.
222 Red School Lane
Phillipsburg, NJ 08865

24-Hour Emergency Telephone 908-859-2151
National Response Center 800-424-8802
Chemtrec 800-424-9300

| National Response in Canada CANUTEC 613-996-6666 |
| Outside U.S. and Canada Chemtrec 202-483-7616 |

MATERIAL SAFETY DATA SHEET

| FICHE SIGNALETIQUE | HOJAS DE DATOS DE SEGURIDAD |

NOTE: CHEMTREC, CANUTEC and National Response Center emergency numbers are to be used only in the event of chemical emergencies involving a spill, leak, fire, exposure or accident involving chemicals. All non-emergency questions should be directed to Customer Service (1-800-JTBAKER) for assistance.

C5874 –02
Effective: 03/09/92

Cupric Nitrate, n-Hydrate

FOR FURTHER INFO
CALL WSU SAFETY OFFICER
626-7233

Page: 1
Issued: 11/02/93

J.T.BAKER INC., 222 Red School Lane, Phillipsburg, NJ 08865

```
================================================================
                SECTION I - PRODUCT IDENTIFICATION
================================================================
```

Product Name: Cupric Nitrate, n-Hydrate
Common Synonyms: Copper (II) Nitrate; Copper Dinitrate
Chemical Family: Copper Compounds
Formula: $Cu(NO_3)_2 \, nH_2O$

Formula Wt.:   N/A
CAS No.:   3251-23-8
NIOSH/RTECS No.:   GL7875000
Product Use: Laboratory Reagent
Product Codes: 1800,1803

```
================================================================
                     PRECAUTIONARY LABELING
================================================================
```

BAKER SAF-T-DATA* System

HEALTH	FLAMMABILITY	REACTIVITY	CONTACT
1	**0**	**3**	**2**
SLIGHT	NONE	SEVERE	MODERATE

Laboratory Protective Equipment

GOGGLES   LAB COAT

U.S. Precautionary Labeling

DANGER!

STRONG OXIDIZER. CONTACT WITH COMBUSTIBLE MATERIALS, FLAMMABLE MATERIALS, OR POWDERED METALS CAN CAUSE FIRE OR EXPLOSION. HARMFUL IF SWALLOWED. CAUSES IRRITATION.
Keep from contact with clothing and other combustible materials. Do not store near combustible materials. Avoid contact with eyes, skin, clothing. Keep in tightly closed container. Wash thoroughly after handling. In case of fire, soak with water. In case of spill, sweep up and remove. Flush spill area with water.

(Continued on next page)

Figure 9.1.   (Continued)

J.T. Baker Inc.
222 Red School Lane
Phillipsburg, NJ 08865

24-Hour Emergency Telephone 908-859-2151
National Response Center 800-424-8802
Chemtrec 800-424-9300

National Response in Canada
CANUTEC 613-996-6666
Outside U.S. and Canada
Chemtrec 202-483-7616

NOTE: CHEMTREC, CANUTEC and National Response Center emergency numbers are to be used only in the event of chemical emergencies involving a spill, leak, fire, exposure or accident involving chemicals. All non-emergency questions should be directed to Customer Service (1-800-JTBAKER) for assistance.

MATERIAL SAFETY DATA SHEET
FICHE   HOJAS DE DATOS
SIGNALETIQUE   DE SEGURIDAD

```
===================================================================
          PRECAUTIONARY LABELING (CONTINUED)
===================================================================
```

International Labeling

Avoid contact with eyes. After contact with skin, wash immediately with plenty of water. Keep container tightly closed.

SAF-T-DATA* Storage Color Code: Yellow (reactive)

```
===================================================================
               SECTION II - COMPONENTS
===================================================================
```

Component	CAS No.	Weight %	OSHA/PEL	ACGIH/TLV
Cupric Nitrate, n-Hydrate	N/A	90-100	N/E	N/E

```
===================================================================
             SECTION III - PHYSICAL DATA
===================================================================
```

Boiling Point: N/A   Vapor Pressure (mmHg): N/A

Melting Point: 115°C (239°F)   Vapor Density (air=1): 8.3
  (at 760 mm Hg)

Specific Gravity: 2.32   Evaporation Rate: N/A
  (H_2O=1)

Solubility(H_2O): Appreciable (>10%)   % Volatiles by Volume: 0
                                              (21°C)

pH: N/A

Odor Threshold (ppm): N/A   Physical State: Solid

Coefficient Water/Oil Distribution: N/A

Appearance & Odor: Blue-green crystals. Odorless.

Figure 9.1.   *(Continued)*

J.T. Baker Inc.
222 Red School Lane
Phillipsburg, NJ 08865
24-Hour Emergency Telephone 908-859-2151
National Response Center 800-424-8802
Chemtrec 800-424-9300

National Response in Canada
CANUTEC 613-996-6666
Outside U.S. and Canada
Chemtrec 202-483-7616
NOTE: CHEMTREC, CANUTEC and National Response Center emergency numbers are to be used only in the event of chemical emergencies involving a spill, leak, fire, exposure or accident involving chemicals. All non-emergency questions should be directed to Customer Service (1-800-JTBAKER) for assistance.

MATERIAL SAFETY DATA SHEET
FICHE   HOJAS DE DATOS
SIGNALETIQUE   DE SEGURIDAD

C5874 –02   Cupric Nitrate, n-Hydrate   Page: 3
Effective: 03/09/92   Issued: 11/02/93

==
                  SECTION IV - FIRE AND EXPLOSION HAZARD DATA
==

Flash Point (Closed Cup): N/A   NFPA 704M Rating: 0-0-0 OXY

Autoignition Temperature: N/A

Flammable Limits: Upper - N/A   Lower - N/A

Fire Extinguishing Media
    Use water spray.

Special Fire-Fighting Procedures
    Firefighters should wear proper protective equipment and self-contained
    breathing apparatus with full facepiece operated in positive pressure
    mode. Move containers from fire area if it can be done without risk. Use
    water to keep fire-exposed containers cool.

Unusual Fire & Explosion Hazards
    Strong oxidizer. Contact with combustible materials, flammable materials,
    or powdered metals can cause fire or explosion. When exposed to heat,
    closed containers may explode; may also give off highly toxic or
    irritating fumes.

Toxic Gases Produced
    oxides of nitrogen

Explosion Data-Sensitivity to Mechanical Impact
    None identified.

Explosion Data-Sensitivity to Static Discharge
    None identified.

==
                        SECTION V - HEALTH HAZARD DATA
==

Threshold Limit Value (TLV/TWA): Not Established

Short-Term Exposure Limit (STEL): Not Established

Permissible Exposure Limit (PEL): Not Established

Toxicity of components

Oral Rat LD_{50} for Cupric Nitrate, n-Hydrate   940 mg/kg

(Continued on next page)

Figure 9.1. *(Continued)*

J.T. Baker Inc. 222 Red School Lane Phillipsburg, NJ 08865 24-Hour Emergency Telephone 908-859-2151 National Response Center 800-424-8802 Chemtrec 800-424-9300	National Response in Canada CANUTEC 613-996-6666 Outside U.S. and Canada Chemtrec 202-483-7616 NOTE: CHEMTREC, CANUTEC and National Response Center emergency numbers are to be used only in the event of chemical emergencies involving a spill, leak, fire, exposure or accident involving chemicals. All non-emergency questions should be directed to Customer Service (1-800-JTBAKER) for assistance.	**MATERIAL SAFETY DATA SHEET** FICHE HOJAS DE DATOS SIGNALETIQUE DE SEGURIDAD

```
C5874 -02                   Cupric Nitrate, n-Hydrate            Page: 4
Effective:  03/09/92                                      Issued: 11/02/93
```

```
========================================================================
                SECTION V - HEALTH HAZARD DATA (CONTINUED)
========================================================================
```

Carcinogenicity: NTP: No   IARC: No   Z List: No   OSHA Reg: No

Carcinogenicity
    None identified.

Reproductive Effects
    None identified.

Effects of Overexposure

    INHALATION: irritation of nose and throat, headache, coughing,
                      dizziness, difficult breathing

    SKIN CONTACT: irritation

    EYE CONTACT: irritation

    SKIN ABSORPTION: none identified

    INGESTION: nausea, vomiting, unconsciousness

    CHRONIC EFFECTS: none identified

Target Organs
    none identified

Medical Conditions Generally Aggravated by Exposure
    none identified

Primary Routes of Entry
    inhalation, ingestion, skin contact, eye contact

Emergency and First Aid Procedures

    INGESTION: CALL A PHYSICIAN. If swallowed, if conscious, immediately
                  induce vomiting.

    INHALATION: If inhaled, remove to fresh air. If not breathing, give
                  artificial respiration. If breathing is difficult, give
                  oxygen.

    SKIN CONTACT: In case of contact, flush skin with water.

    EYE CONTACT: In case of eye contact, immediately flush with plenty of
                  water for at least 15 minutes.

Figure 9.1. *(Continued)*

J.T. Baker Inc.
222 Red School Lane
Phillipsburg, NJ 08865
24-Hour Emergency Telephone 908-859-2151
National Response Center 800-424-8802
Chemtrec 800-424-9300

National Response in Canada
CANUTEC 613-996-6666
Outside U.S. and Canada
Chemtrec 202-483-7616
NOTE: CHEMTREC, CANUTEC and National Response Center emergency numbers are to be used only in the event of chemical emergencies involving a spill, leak, fire, exposure or accident involving chemicals. All non-emergency questions should be directed to Customer Service (1-800-JTBAKER) for assistance.

MATERIAL SAFETY DATA SHEET
FICHE   HOJAS DE DATOS
SIGNALETIQUE   DE SEGURIDAD

```
C5874 -02                 Cupric Nitrate, n-Hydrate              Page: 5
Effective:  03/09/92                              Issued: 11/02/93
```

===
SECTION V - HEALTH HAZARD DATA (CONTINUED)
===

SARA/TITLE III HAZARD CATEGORIES and LISTS

Acute: Yes Chronic: Yes Flammability: Yes Pressure: No Reactivity: No

Extremely Hazardous Substance: No
CERCLA Hazardous Substance: Yes Contains Cupric Nitrate (RQ = 100 LBS)
SARA 313 Toxic Chemicals: Yes Contains Copper
     Generic Class: Generic Class Removed from CFR: 7/1/91
TSCA Inventory: Yes

===
SECTION VI - REACTIVITY DATA
===

Stability: Stable   Hazardous Polymerization: Will not occur

Conditions to Avoid: heat, shock, friction

Incompatibles: combustible materials, organic materials, strong
                        reducing agents

Decomposition Products: oxides of nitrogen

===
SECTION VII - SPILL & DISPOSAL PROCEDURES
===

Steps to be Taken in the Event of a Spill or Discharge
    Wear self-contained breathing apparatus and full protective clothing. Keep
    combustibles (wood, paper, oil, etc.) away from spilled material. With
    clean shovel, carefully place material into clean, dry container and
    cover; remove from area. Flush spill area with water.

Disposal Procedure
    Dispose in accordance with all applicable federal, state, and local
    environmental regulations.

EPA Hazardous Waste Number: D001 (Ignitable Waste)

(Continued on next page)

Figure 9.1. *(Continued)*

J.T. Baker Inc.
222 Red School Lane
Phillipsburg, NJ 08865
24-Hour Emergency Telephone 908-859-2151
National Response Center 800-424-8802
Chemtrec 800-424-9300

National Response in Canada
CANUTEC 613-996-6666
Outside U.S. and Canada
Chemtrec 202-483-7616

MATERIAL SAFETY DATA SHEET
FICHE   HOJAS DE DATOS
SIGNALETIQUE   DE SEGURIDAD

NOTE: CHEMTREC, CANUTEC and National Response Center emergency numbers are to be used only in the event of chemical emergencies involving a spill, leak, fire, exposure or accident involving chemicals. All non-emergency questions should be directed to Customer Service (1-800-JTBAKER) for assistance.

```
C5874 -02                  Cupric Nitrate, n-Hydrate             Page: 6
Effective:   03/09/92                                   Issued: 11/02/93
```

```
==============================================================================
            SECTION VIII - INDUSTRIAL PROTECTIVE EQUIPMENT
==============================================================================
```

Ventilation: Use adequate general or local exhaust ventilation to
                        keep fume or dust levels as low as possible.

Respiratory Protection: None required where adequate ventilation conditions
                        exist. If airborne concentration is high, use an
                        appropriate respirator or dust mask.

Eye/Skin Protection: Safety goggles, uniform, proper gloves are
                        recommended.

```
==============================================================================
             SECTION IX - STORAGE AND HANDLING PRECAUTIONS
==============================================================================
```

SAF-T-DATA* Storage Color Code: Yellow (reactive)

Storage Requirements
    Keep container tightly closed. Store separately and away from flammable
    and combustible materials.

```
==============================================================================
          SECTION X - TRANSPORTATION DATA AND ADDITIONAL INFORMATION
==============================================================================
```

Domestic (D.O.T.)

Proper Shipping Name: NITRATES, INORGANIC, N.O.S. (Cupric Nitrate, N-Hydrate)
Hazard Class: 5.1
UN/NA: UN1477   Reportable Quantity: 100   LBS.   Packaging Group: II
Labels: 5.1 OXIDIZER
Regulatory References: 49CFR 172.101

International (I.M.O.)

Proper Shipping Name: Nitrates, inorganic, n.o.s. (Cupric Nitrate, n-Hydrate)
Hazard Class: 5.1   I.M.O. Page: 5162
UN: UN1477   Marine Pollutants: No   Packaging Group: II
Labels: OXIDIZING AGENT
Regulatory References: 49CFR PART 176; IMDG Code

AIR (I.C.A.O.)

Proper Shipping Name: Nitrates, inorganic, n.o.s. (Cupric Nitrate, n-Hydrate)
Hazard Class: 5.1
UN: UN1477   Packaging Group: II

Figure 9.1. *(Continued)*

J.T. Baker Inc.
222 Red School Lane
Phillipsburg, NJ 08865
24-Hour Emergency Telephone 908-859-2151
National Response Center 800-424-8802
Chemtrec 800-424-9300

| National Response in Canada CANUTEC 613-996-6666 |
| Outside U.S. and Canada Chemtrec 202-483-7616 |

NOTE: CHEMTREC, CANUTEC and National Response Center emergency numbers are to be used only in the event of chemical emergencies involving a spill, leak, fire, exposure or accident involving chemicals. All non-emergency questions should be directed to Customer Service (1-800-JTBAKER) for assistance.

MATERIAL SAFETY DATA SHEET

| FICHE SIGNALETIQUE | HOJAS DE DATOS DE SEGURIDAD |

C5874 –02   Cupric Nitrate, n-Hydrate   Page: 7
Effective: 03/09/92   Issued: 11/02/93

```
=======================================================================
      SECTION X - TRANSPORTATION DATA AND ADDITIONAL INFORMATION (CONTINUED)
=======================================================================
```

Labels: OXIDIZER
Regulatory References: 49CFR PART 175; ICAO=== We believe the transportation
                       data and references contained herein to be factual and
                       the opinion of qualified experts. The data is meant as
                       a guide to the overall classification of the product
                       and is not package size specific, nor should it be
                       taken as a warranty or representation for which the
                       company assumes legal responsibility.=== The
                       information is offered solely for your consideration,
                       investigation, and verification. Any use of the
                       information must be determined by the user to be in
                       accordance with applicable Federal, State, and Local
                       laws and regulations. See shipper requirements 49CFR
                       171.2, Certification 172.204, and employee training 49
                       CFR 173.1(b).

U.S. Customs Harmonization Number: 28342900005

```
=======================================================================
=======================================================================
```

NOTE: When handling liquid products, secondary protective containers must be
used for carrying.
-N/A = Not Applicable, or not Available;
N/E = Not Established.-
The information in this Material Safety Data Sheet meets the
requirements of the United States OCCUPATIONAL SAFETY AND HEALTH ACT and
regulations promulgated thereunder (29 CFR 1910.1200 et. seq.) and the
Canadian WORKPLACE HAZARDOUS MATERIALS INFORMATION SYSTEM. This document
is intended only as a guide to the appropriate precautionary handling of
the material by a person trained in, or supervised by a person trained
in, chemical handling. The user is responsible for determining the
precautions and dangers of this chemical for his or her particular
application. Depending on usage, protective clothing including eye and
face guards and respirators must be used to avoid contact with material
or breathing chemical vapors/fumes.
Exposure to this product may have serious adverse health effects. This
chemical may interact with other substances. Since the potential uses
are so varied, Baker cannot warn of all of the potential dangers of use
or interaction with other chemicals or materials. Baker warrants that
the chemical meets the specifications set forth on the label.
BAKER DISCLAIMS ANY OTHER WARRANTIES, EXPRESSED OR IMPLIED WITH REGARD
TO THE PRODUCT SUPPLIED HEREUNDER, ITS MERCHANTABILITY OR ITS FITNESS
FOR A PARTICULAR PURPOSE.
The user should recognize that this product can cause severe injury and
even death, especially if improperly handled or the known dangers of use
are not heeded. READ ALL PRECAUTIONARY INFORMATION. As new documented

(Continued on next page)

Figure 9.1.   *(Continued)*

| J.T. Baker Inc.
222 Red School Lane
Phillipsburg, NJ 08865

24-Hour Emergency Telephone 908-859-2151
National Response Center 800-424-8802
Chemtrec 800-424-9300 | National Response in Canada
CANUTEC 613-996-6666
Outside U.S. and Canada
Chemtrec 202-483-7616
NOTE: CHEMTREC, CANUTEC and National Response Center emergency numbers are to be used only in the event of chemical emergencies involving a spill, leak, fire, exposure or accident involving chemicals. All non-emergency questions should be directed to Customer Service (1-800-JTBAKER) for assistance. | **MATERIAL SAFETY DATA SHEET**
FICHE   HOJAS DE DATOS
SIGNALÉTIQUE   DE SEGURIDAD |

C5874 -02   Cupric Nitrate, n-Hydrate   Page: 8
Effective: 03/09/92   Issued: 11/02/93

==

general safety information becomes available, Baker will periodically
revise this Material Safety Data Sheet.
Note: CHEMTREC, CANUTEC, and NATIONAL RESPONSE CENTER emergency telephone
numbers are to be used ONLY in the event of CHEMICAL EMERGENCIES involving
a spill, leak, fire, exposure, or accident involving chemicals. All
non-emergency questions should be directed to Customer Service
(1-800-JTBAKER) for assistance.

COPYRIGHT 1993 J.T.BAKER INC.
* TRADEMARKS OF J.T.BAKER INC.
===
Approved by Quality Assurance Department.

Step 3: Monitor and improve the emergency preparedness program

The emergency preparedness program provides a concise, preestablished plan to be implemented during an internal or external disaster or other emergency. The goal of the program is to ensure the continuity of patient care during emergencies. The types of disasters and emergencies sometimes encountered by healthcare organizations include bomb threats, civil disturbances, loss of communication networks, evacuation of industrial or other sites, internal fires, severe weather conditions, loss of utilities such as electricity and water, and major transportation systems accidents (train derailments, freeway pileups, and airplane crashes). The organization's emergency preparedness plan is usually part of a regional plan carried out by multiple institutions, because the inflow of patients from a major disaster would not be handled by one institution alone.

The emergency preparedness plan outlines the following information:

- Procedures to be followed in response to a variety of internal and external disasters

- Preparation, staffing, organization, activation, and operation of organizational response in the event of a communitywide disaster

- Means for minimizing suffering, loss of life, personal injury, and damage to property

- Triage system for handling incoming injured persons to identify the appropriate level of treatment

- Resource utilization procedures to prevent or minimize the consequences of hazardous or emergency situations

- Organization's emergency management plans in support of county and statewide operations

- Procedures for notifying the proper authorities within and outside the organization

- Procedures for notifying the organization's staff that the disaster plan is to be implemented and for defining staff roles and responsibilities

- Internal and external emergency communications and information systems

- Procedures for the partial or total evacuation of the facility

- Management of patients, including schedule modification or discontinuation of services; release of information regarding patients; and admission, transfer, or discharge of patients

Monitoring activities for emergency preparedness primarily concern maintaining employees' knowledge of and ability to perform appropriate procedures to handle emergencies. Disaster drills must be carried out regularly so that employees have an opportunity to practice the processes they would need to put into effect in the event of a real disaster. They must also know how to coordinate efforts with other institutions and regional disaster management agencies and what communication paths are available in this kind of situation. Regular educational sessions should be held, and the abilities of each participant should be assessed after the training is complete.

Step 4: Monitor and improve the life safety management program

The life safety management program focuses on protecting patients, visitors, staff, and property from fire and the products of combustion (smoke). The program includes the following activities:

- Inspection, testing, and maintenance of fire detection and alarm systems

- Management of portable fire extinguishers and their identification, placement, and use

- Plans for proposed acquisition of bedding, window coverings, furnishings, room decorations, wastebaskets, and equipment in the context of fire safety

The other major function of the life safety program is fire safety training. All employees and clinical staff must be able to demonstrate their knowledge of and ability to perform fire alarm transmission, physical containment of smoke and fire, transfer of patients and those injured to areas of refuge, extinguishing of fire, preparation for evacuation of buildings, and location and use of equipment for evacuating and transporting patients.

Monitoring activities in the life safety preparedness area primarily concern maintaining employees' knowledge of and ability to perform appropriate procedures to handle fire emergencies. Fire drills must be carried out regularly so that employees have an opportunity to practice the processes they would need to put into effect in the event of a real fire.

Step 5: Monitor and improve the medical equipment management program

The medical equipment management program focuses on ensuring that all of the equipment used within the healthcare organization is functioning properly. It also ensures that employees know how to properly use the equipment necessary to their job duties as well as the equipment's capabilities, limitations, and special applications. Users must know the emergency procedures to be instituted in case of equipment failure.

The program must include the following information:

- Criteria for identifying and evaluating medical equipment and performing inventories of medical equipment

- Appropriate procedures for monitoring the equipment's function and providing maintenance when necessary

- Tracking systems for all occurrences associated with each piece of equipment that resulted in increased exposure to risk of injury to patients or personnel

In addition, **recall logs** must be maintained for each piece of medical equipment to document communications from manufacturers regarding problems with the equipment.

The program must be carried out in conjunction with biomedical engineering staff. The program can be staffed by regular, full-time employees or by contractors from an outside agency.

It is important to recognize that most individual departments also perform quality assurance activities on a regular basis to ensure the proper performance of equipment. For example, in the clinical laboratories, all of the instruments are calibrated at least daily to ensure that the equipment is performing well and providing accurate reports. Each piece of equipment is tested with calibrating reagents of known control values to be certain that the instrument can achieve results within acceptable limits. This type of testing is mandated by the federal government for all FDA-approved analyzers and is codified in the Clinical Laboratory Improvement Amendments (CLIA), regulations to which clinical laboratories must adhere. In addition, both the JCAHO and the College of American Pathologists publish additional standards regarding the calibration and maintenance of laboratory analyzers.

Other areas of healthcare organizations have the same kinds of issues. Each runs its own set of calibration routines. Two other important examples are the studies performed on the equipment in critical care areas and the studies performed on radiological imaging equipment. In both areas, equipment malfunctions can lead to severe patient injury or death. The appropriate maintenance of equipment is therefore extremely important in direct patient care areas.

Step 6: Monitor and improve the utility management program

The utility management program focuses on ensuring that all utility resources used within the organization are functioning properly and that, when disruptions occur, employees are prepared to perform appropriate procedures to manage both the disruption and its effects on patient services. Utility resources include electricity, natural gas, water, sewer, and telecommunications services provided from outside the organization by community utilities companies.

Physical facilities within the organization where utilities are turned on or off or are otherwise monitored are called **control areas.** Control areas for each of the utility resources must be adequately labeled so that employees know how to shut down the utility when necessary in an emergency. These systems must also be routinely monitored for proper functioning and necessary preventive maintenance. Failures and user errors must be identified through the occurrence reporting system.

An important component of the utility management program is the requirement that the organization be able to provide a source of emergency power should electrical service be interrupted in the community. Engineering services must routinely inspect, test, and maintain emergency power generators to provide electricity to critical areas at any time the community's electrical service is interrupted. Common critical areas include alarm systems, exit illumination, elevators, emergency communication systems, blood/bone/tissue storage units, medical/surgical vacuum systems, air compressors and ventilators, postoperative recovery rooms, and special care units.

The organization must also meet state statutes and regulations from other entities, including OSHA, the National Fire Protection Association, and the Life Safety Code as well as the JCAHO.

Step 7: Monitor and improve the safety program

The safety program focuses on ensuring that all employees are aware of the safety risks encountered in the patient care environment and that they understand and can initiate the occurrence reporting system for risk management. Employees also must be able to take action to prevent, eliminate, or minimize safety risks. Each employee is provided department- and job-specific safety training that is documented in each employee's personnel file.

Real-Life Example

Patrick Baggs is the director of environment of care and safety services at Ogden Regional Medical Center in Ogden, Utah. He provided this real-life example to show the importance of environment of care issues.

One Saturday morning in April 1997, a third-party construction company was laying cable under the street about a quarter of a mile north of the hospital. The workers were using an auger to drill under the roadway so that they would not need to tear up the street. The gas lines and electric cables in the area had been marked with blue stakes, but the construction crew laying the cable did not pay attention to the stakes. The workers inadvertently damaged the main telephone cable under the street. Communications in and out of the hospital and other businesses in the area were cut off.

Because they were not able to receive or make calls, the staff at the hospital faced a major problem in communicating with physicians and providing care support for patients in the emergency department. The staff had to find a solution rapidly. They decided to use the cellular telephones that various employees happened to be carrying with them. One pay phone was still working for an unknown reason. Crews from the telephone company worked all day to restore service, which was reestablished at around 7:30 that evening.

Because the organization had not been prepared for this type of emergency, the hospital's safety council met later to initiate the following steps:

- Purchase a cellular telephone to be kept by the telephone operator.

- Establish a telephone directory of employees who carry hospital-owned cellular telephones.

- Ask employees on a volunteer basis to allow the hospital staff to use their cellular phones when there is a communications emergency. (The hospital's telephone operator now keeps a regularly updated list of the cellular phone numbers that were offered by employees.)

QI Toolbox Technique

Postprogram assessments are the most common method used to evaluate employees' knowledge about issues in the environment of care and safety areas. The assessments are given to employees after each training session. Every employee must attend training in each of the areas at least annually. Human resource systems track each employee's training attendance and record the attendance in the employee's personnel file. Figure 9.2 shows an example of a posttraining assessment tool used at the Community Hospital of the West.

Figure 9.2.   Example of a Posttraining Assessment Tool

Exposure to Blood-Borne Pathogens

1. Universal precautions means:
   A. All employees must be trained in the same safety procedures.
   B. Wearing protective personal equipment is not necessary when handling organic tissue, alive or dead.
   C. All blood and other potentially infectious body fluids are treated as though they were infected with blood-borne pathogens.

2. The following conditions must be present for you to catch an infectious disease:
   A. Port of entry
   B. Contact with contaminated blood or other body fluids
   C. None of the above
   D. A and B

3. The exposure control plan is:
   A. OSHA's standards regarding procedures for handling exposures to HIV and HBV
   B. Our organization's written plan to help employees eliminate or minimize exposure to blood-borne pathogens
   C. A policy on how to deal with infectious exposure to HIV and HBV

4. Hand washing is required:
   A. After removing gloves, before eating, but not before gloving
   B. Before eating, before gloving, but not before leaving the workplace
   C. Before leaving the workplace, after touching potentially contaminated surfaces, but not after every patient
   D. Before gloving, after each patient, before eating, and before leaving the workplace

5. Healthcare workers have developed AIDS following exposure to contaminated blood and body fluids through:
   A. Needlesticks
   B. Open cuts and wounds
   C. Mucous membranes
   D. All of the above

6. Following are some symptoms of hepatitis B infection:
   A. Extreme fatigue, excessive thirst, red eyes
   B. Nausea, learning difficulties, anorexia
   C. Dark urine, jaundice, abdominal pain
   D. Abdominal pain, rash, swelling limbs

7. When an exposure occurs:
   A. You should report the exposure to your supervisor immediately.
   B. When possible and with consent, the source individual is tested to determine whether he or she is infected with HIV or HBV.
   C. You will be provided medical evaluation, treatment, and counseling.
   D. All of the above.

(Continued on next page)

Figure 9.2.   *(Continued)*

Codes: Fires and Disasters

8. What does the PBX operator announce for fire?
   A. Code yellow
   B. Code blue
   C. Code green
   D. Code red

9. What does the PBX operator announce for internal and external disasters (check two)?
   A. Code red
   B. Attention, disaster #
   C. Attention, please, disaster and location
   D. Code yellow

10. In a hospital emergency, you dial the following number to get help:
   A. 911
   B. 5000
   C. O (Operator)
   D. 411

Security

11. The employee parking lot is located:
   A. In front of the hospital
   B. By the emergency department
   C. In front of the professional building
   D. West of the hospital

Chemical Hazcom

12. You need to know about the chemicals in your workplace because:
   A. This will test your knowledge.
   B. You will find it interesting.
   C. You may not be aware of the type of hazards for each chemical.

13. Your rights to know about hazardous chemicals are contained in:
   A. The Hazardous Communication manual
   B. Personnel memos
   C. Letter to supervisors only

14. Chemical hazard labels:
   A. Give you quick information
   B. Are in blue
   C. Are not required

15. Chemical material safety data sheets:
   A. Are available only for supervisors
   B. Replace the need for labels
   C. Give detailed information about hazardous materials

16. The hazard communications program includes training on:
   A. Stress control
   B. How chemicals can enter the body
   C. Lifting techniques

17. A safe work environment is:
   A. Not always possible
   B. Up to you
   C. A responsibility shared by employers and employees

Figure 9.2. *(Continued)*

Fire Extinguisher

18. Portable fire extinguishers are effective if you:
    A. Know how to use them and act fast
    B. Wait for instructions
    C. Use more than one

19. The "fire triangle" includes:
    A. Small, medium, and large
    B. You, supervisor, and firefighter
    C. Fuel, air, and heat

20. Multipurpose dry chemical extinguishers are effective on:
    A. Class A, B, and C fires
    B. Class A fires only
    C. Class B and C fires only

21. In case of fire, top priority is:
    A. PATE (patient, alarm, telephone, extinguish)
    B. Whatever you decide
    C. Going on a break

22. If a fire becomes larger:
    A. Get more extinguishers
    B. Get closer
    C. Get out and close doors

23. If the contents of a fire extinguisher are partially used:
    A. Put it back
    B. Report it; get it replaced
    C. Throw it out

Body Mechanics

24. Good body mechanics includes all of the following except:
    A. Twisting at the waist
    B. Tightening stomach muscles when you lift
    C. Lifting with your legs
    D. Holding the load close to the body

25. Basic prevention of back injury involves all of the following principles of lifting except:
    A. Using the squat position
    B. Bending at the waist
    C. Using the heavy muscles of the legs
    D. Maintaining the normal arch of the lower back

26. When a job requires staying in the same posture or position for long periods of time, you should:
    A. Twist at the waist occasionally to improve circulation
    B. Listen to the radio to take your mind off the pain
    C. Change positions as often as possible
    D. Just tough it out even when your feet get numb

27. Conditions that lead to low back pain include which of the following:
    A. Poor posture
    B. Lack of exercise
    C. Long exposure to sunlight
    D. Overeating

Case Study

Students should search the Internet for information issues related to patient care environments and safety. Information can be obtained on clinical laboratory safety, disposal of biohazardous waste, disaster planning and preparation, and other current issues within the geographic area. Suggested places to search are state licensure regulations, Medicare/ Medicaid Conditions of Participation, OSHA standards, and laboratory standards.

Project Application

Students should identify existing environmental and safety guidelines or regulations that have implications for their projects. If the student project recommends training people better to improve their performance, participants should consider how they would assess the outcomes of training to determine whether individuals retained important aspects of the training.

Summary

The significant challenge in performance improvement activities for environment of care and safety is maintaining the knowledge and abilities of employees. Every employee must be able to perform appropriate procedures in the event of an emergency. Appropriate emergency response is crucial to minimizing risk to other employees, patients, and medical staff. Therefore, performance improvement activity is organized around training and retraining personnel so that emergency procedures are initiated without question or hesitation when necessary. The abilities of individual employees must also be consistently and frequently assessed to ensure that their knowledge base is adequate at all times. Equipment maintenance and security management are also critical areas for performance improvement.

Reference

Hinckley, C. M. 1997. Defining the best quality control system by design and inspection. *Clinical Chemistry* 43(5):873–79.

Chapter 10
Developing Staff and Human Resources

Learning Objectives

- To recognize the importance of human resources to the functioning of healthcare organizations

- To understand the tools commonly used to manage the acquisition and retention of human resources

- To be able to describe the credentialing process for independent practitioners and employed clinical staff

Background and Significance

The environment in which healthcare organizations manage their human resources is dictated in large part by state and federal employment laws, regulatory agencies, and market trends. The organization also develops and maintains internal human resources policies. Variations in the way healthcare is delivered also affect the organization's recruitment, training, retention, and termination practices. Potential legal actions undertaken by employees against healthcare organizations must also be considered. This chapter blends information on laws, regulations, and shifting market trends with common factors in organizational policy to demonstrate some of the processes and tools used to manage people in today's healthcare environment.

During the twentieth century, inequitable and unsafe employment practices were a driving force in the passage of legislation intended to improve the working environment of Americans. Legislation addressed wages and hours (the Equal Employment Opportunity Act of 1972); working conditions (the Occupational Safety and Health Act of 1970); and discrimination on the basis of race, ethnic origin, color, gender, age, disability, military experience, religion, and pregnancy. The result is standardization of employment practices in healthcare today. Other employment guidelines and standards of practice in the areas of state licensure and outside accrediting agencies have evolved to direct the employer–employee relationship.

An organization's employees are its most important resource. Machines and robots cannot provide high-quality patient care. Only experienced clinical professionals can evaluate patient status and design individualized care. Therefore, competent healthcare professionals must be recruited and retained by the organization. Nonclinical healthcare workers offer healthcare-specific skills to support the provision of healthcare services. The organization's leadership must ensure that it employs a highly competent staff through appropriate human resources processes.

Effective leadership is defined by external agencies as how well an organization's leaders plan, direct, integrate, and coordinate services and how well they create a culture that focuses on continually improving performance. These key leadership functions are demonstrated in the management of human resources in the following ways:

- By defining the qualifications and performance expectations for all staff positions

- By providing adequate numbers of staff

- By ensuring that the staff's qualifications are consistent with their job responsibilities

- By continually assessing, demonstrating, and improving staff competence

Today's cutting-edge work environment encourages and empowers employees to take responsibility for improving the environment in which they work, no matter what their position in the organization structure is. **Continuous quality improvement** (CQI) can be a powerful concept when woven into the culture of an organization. Organizations that embrace continuous quality improvement rely on their leaders to foster a culture of staff self-development and lifelong learning. The competitive advantage for healthcare organizations today lies in their intellectual capital and organizational effectiveness. This style of motivating and developing employees is grounded in the ability of leaders to create, communicate, and model strategic vision, direction, priorities, and values.

Steps to Success: Developing Staff and Human Resources

Healthcare organizations take several factors into consideration when they determine staffing needs. Relevant factors include the mix of patients served, the degree and complexity of the care required, and the technology used to provide care. The expectations of consumers and independent medical staff are also an important factor. An organization's ability to provide for its patients' needs is directly related to its ability to employ qualified, competent staff.

Step 1: Manage the recruitment process

A well-defined recruitment process provides both the organization and the applicant for employment with an opportunity to evaluate and determine their potential compatibility. The recruitment process is usually initiated to fill a vacant position, to fill a newly created position, to staff a newly instituted service, or to support increases in patient acuity and/or census. Organizations sometimes retain the services of outside recruitment agencies when vacancies are difficult to fill because of shortages in qualified applicants or the organization's remote geographic location.

Position requisitions, position (job) descriptions, and employment applications are the tools used in the recruitment process. Position requisitions begin the formal communication between human resources staff and the department or service area initiating the recruitment process. (See figure 10.1.) A detailed position requisition provides human resources staff with the information they need to prepare advertisements for open positions. Position requisitions include information such as the position's title, the qualifications and experience required, the work schedule, and the salary. Position requisitions can also be used to monitor the appropriateness of personnel requests. For example, a non-budgeted position or a new position request may require additional documentation (administrative approval) before recruitment can begin.

Position (job) descriptions define the responsibilities of the job and the qualifications needed to fulfill those responsibilities. Qualifications may define the education; licensure, certification, or registration status; and experience required. Qualifications may also include specific experience requirements, for example, training or experience in working with children and adolescents.

In healthcare organizations, **credentials** and **licenses** are qualifications of paramount importance. Every clinical professional (nurses, occupational therapists, physical therapists, respiratory therapists, and others) and most ancillary services professionals (radiology technicians, laboratory technicians and scientists, health information managers, and others) are required to hold a credential or license to practice their professions.

Credentials are usually conferred by national professional organizations dedicated to a specific area of healthcare practice. Licenses are conferred by state regulatory agencies. Credentialing and licensing processes usually require an applicant to pass an examination to obtain the credential or license initially and then to maintain the credential or license through continuing education activities thereafter.

Job responsibilities describe the major tasks of the position. The responsibilities should be stated in measurable terms. (This measurability is the standard in healthcare today.) A clinical position, for example, may describe a position responsibility as "completing a nursing assessment on each admission within the time frame defined by policy."

Developing Staff and Human Resources: Steps to Success

Step 5 Monitor and manage independent practitioners

Step 4 Manage the retention process

Step 3 Manage the performance appraisal process

Step 2 Conduct new employee orientation and training

Step 1 Manage the recruitment process

Figure 10.1.   **Sample Position Requisition**

PERSONNEL REQUISITION

JOB TITLE	DATE OF REQUEST	DATE REQUIRED

DEPARTMENT

☐ Replacement for:

☐ Additional Personnel	Budgeted: ☐ Yes ☐ No

☐ Temporary: End Date _____	☐ Full-Time	☐ Part-Time	☐ Exempt	☐ PRN	☐ Per-Diem

Shift: Hours per week:	Suggested Pay Grade:

Qualifications needed: education, experience, training, duties, physical fitness		Actual:	Budgeted:	Prior Year:
	YTD FTE's			
	MH / STAT			
	SAL $/STAT			
	Reason for additional personnel or new position:			

APPROVALS (must be obtained prior to offering position)

DIRECTOR / MANAGER: DATE:	CEO: DATE:
CFO: DATE:	HUMAN RESOURCES: DATE:

NEW PERSONNEL

To be completed by human resources		Date Required
Employee's Name	Department	Employee Number
Address	Social Security Number	
Telephone Number	Birthdate	
Date of Hire	Temporary Date of Termination	

☐ New Hire	☐ Rehire	☐ Full-Time	☐ Part-Time	☐ PRN	☐ Per-Diem	☐ Exempt	☐ Temp.

RATE/HOUR	BIWEEKLY RATE	RACE	EEO CAT.	TAX EXEMP.	POS CODE

COMMENTS OR SPECIAL INSTRUCTIONS:

In general, position descriptions provide guidance to human resources staff by defining the initial selection criteria for potential candidates. Position descriptions are also used to provide the applicant or new employee with information about the position. With the support of human resources specialists, managers generally maintain position descriptions that reflect local market and current position requirements.

The employment application is provided to interested candidates who contact the organization in response to an advertised position. A review of the completed application and the applicant's resume provides human resources and the requesting department or service area manager with enough information to determine whether the applicant meets the minimum position requirements. (See the example in figure 10.2.) Applicants who meet the initial position requirements are invited to interview for the position

The interview gives the applicant and the organization an opportunity to exchange information not listed on the employment application or in the position advertisement. The organization may have additional questions specific to experience, skills, and qualifications not covered in the application. The candidate, in turn, may have questions related to salary, benefits, or the organization's history. The interview provides an excellent opportunity for the interviewer to evaluate the applicant's communication skills, general personality, and demeanor.

Several types of interviews can be used to screen applicants. A structured interview is conducted using a set of standard questions that are asked of all job applicants. The purpose of a structured interview is to gather comparative data. The unstructured interview uses general questions from which other questions are developed over the course of the conversation. The purpose of the unstructured interview is to prompt the interviewee to speak openly.

Any of the following general areas might be discussed during an interview:

- Tell us about your previous position. In general, what kinds of duties did you perform?

- Tell us about your personal understanding of the need for maintaining the patient's rights to confidentiality.

The stress interview uses specific questions to determine how the interviewee responds under pressure. Questions in this type of interview set up specific scenarios and ask the interviewee how he or she would handle the situation. For example:

- If a newspaper reporter came to you and wanted you to reveal information from a prominent person's medical record, how would you respond?

- If an attorney came onto your nursing unit and wanted to review her client's medical record, what would you do?

Some types of questions should not be asked at all during an interview. Asking questions that might be interpreted as attempts to learn personal information about the applicant (such as his or her age, marital status, or family status) are prohibited by federal regulations. Figure 10.3 provides examples of questions that are not related to employment and would be considered discriminatory.

Figure 10.2.   Sample Employment Application

INSTRUCTIONS TO THE APPLICANT:

Please complete the application in full. You can send a resume with your completed application.

Please apply for a specific position(s) and include that position's job title(s) on the application.

APPLICANT: The federal government requires employers to collect statistical information on job applicants. Providing this information is voluntary. The information is used for statistical purposes only and will not be included in your application file. Information will be maintained and utilized in accordance with applicable laws and regulations. Refusal to provide the information below will not subject you to any adverse treatment or affect the application process in any way.

1. SEX   __ Male   __ Female

2. RACE/ETHNIC BACKGROUND (check only one):

    ___ Asian or Pacific Islander (O)
    ___ American Indian/Native American (A)
    ___ Black (not of Hispanic Origin) (B)
    ___White (not of Hispanic Origin) (C)
    ___ Hispanic (a person whose cultural or linguistic origins are Spanish or Latin American, regardless
         of race, for example, Mexican, Puerto Rican, Cuban, Central or South American) (S)

3. DISABLED OR VETERAN STATUS (check all that apply):

    ___ Disabled, but not a veteran (I)
    ___ Veteran of Vietnam era (V)
    ___ Disabled Veteran (D)
    ___ None of the above

___ I do not wish to provide this information.

PLEASE CONTINUE ON THE NEXT PAGE

Figure 10.2. *(Continued)*

_____ App#

APPLICATION FOR EMPLOYMENT

All applicants selected for employment must satisfactorily pass a preemployment drug screen and criminal background check to be eligible for employment.
CHW is an Equal Opportunity and Affirmative Action Employer.
CHW hires only individuals who are authorized to work in the United States.
This application is subject to the conditions set forth in the Certification and Agreement section on the last page.

PLEASE COMPLETE APPLICATION IN FULL
DATE OF APPLICATION _____
LAST NAME _____ FIRST NAME _____ MIDDLE INITIAL _____
CURRENT ADDRESS _____ CITY _____ COUNTY _____
STATE _____ ZIP CODE_____
SOCIAL SECURITY # _____ HOME PHONE (___) _____ WORK PHONE (___) _____

SOURCE OF REFERRAL
RECRUITING METHOD: (Please check one)
__ (60) Student Work Experience   __ (05) Walk-in   __ (10) Internal Referral _____
__ (30) Newspaper   __ (80) Past Experience   __ (06) Temp Employment Agency, Temp-to-hire
__ (13) Internet   __ (15) Job Line   __ (85) Community Based Organization
__ (07) Job Service   __ (20) Professional Journal __ (52) Job Elimination
__ (90) School Organization Referral

Have you ever been convicted of a felony or a misdemeanor, or have you ever plead no contest to any criminal charges?   __ Yes   __ No
Provide date, city, state and an explanation for any yes responses: _____
Criminal conviction is not an absolute bar to employment but will be considered in relation to specific job requirements.

Can you perform the functions of the job for which you are applying, either with or without a reasonable accommodation?   __ Yes   __ No
Do you have any relatives employed by Community Hospital of the West?   __ Yes   __ No
If yes, Where/Relationship _____
Have you ever been employed by or are you currently employed by Community Hospital of the West?   __ Yes   __ No
If yes, Where? _____ When? _____
Why did you leave? _____

POSITION(S) DESIRED (only two positions per application please)
TITLE: _____ Job Number:_____
TITLE: _____ Job Number:_____

WORK AVAILABILITY
MARK ALL THAT APPLY
Type of Employment   Work Schedule/Shift   Weekends __ Yes __ No   No Rotating Weekends __ Yes __ No
__ Full-Time   __ Days
__ Part-Time   __ Evenings
__ Temporary   __ Nights
__ On-Call   Hours Available _____
Current Salary: $ _____   Minimum Salary Requirement $ _____   Date Available to Work _____

JOB SKILLS
Check all that you have experience with: PC Graphics __ Yes __ No   Word Processor __ Yes __ No
Desktop Publishing __ Yes __ No   PC __ Yes __ No   Spreadsheet __ Yes __ No
LAN __ Yes __ No   Database __ Yes __ No   Windows __ Yes __ No
AS/400 __ Yes __ No   Tandem __ Yes __ No   Medical Terminology __ Yes __ No
List specific software programs used: _____
Typing Speed: _____ WPM   10-Key by Touch __ Yes __ No   _____ SPM

(Continued on next page)

Figure 10.2.   (Continued)

EDUCATION

Have you graduated from High School or completed the GED equivalent? __ Yes __ No

List all degrees that you have received. List your HIGHEST DEGREE FIRST. Do NOT list degrees that you are currently working toward (see below)

MAJOR	DEGREE	SCHOOL	GRADUATION DATE

Are you currently enrolled? __ YES __ NO   Last year attended: _____   Major: _____
Check last level of school completed:
Years completed: Undergraduate: __ Freshman   __ Sophomore   __ Junior   __ Senior
                           Graduate: __ 1st year   __ 2nd year   __ 3rd year   __ 4th year

LICENSURE/REGISTRATION/CERTIFICATION

List all professional licenses, registrations, and certifications

Lic/Reg/Cert Type	License #	State	Expiration Date

Do you have any pending restrictions and/or suspensions on your current professional license/registration that would restrain you from performing in this position? __ YES __ NO

Have you ever been refused professional licensure, or had a license/registration suspended or revoked? __ YES __ NO
If Yes, please explain: _____

List any trade or professional organizations of which you are a member, include offices held: _____
_____

List any special skills: _____

EMPLOYMENT HISTORY

Start with your most recent employment, give a complete record of all employment and reasons for periods of unemployment.

How many years of experience do you have related to this position? _____

MAY WE CONTACT YOUR CURRENT EMPLOYER? __ YES __ NO   If no, why? _____
_____

NOTE: If your current or most recent employer is not contacted before an offer of employment is made, then any offer of employment that is made will be subject to CHW subsequently contacting such employer, and may be withdrawn based on the information received from such employer.

COMPANY NAME	ADDRESS	CITY	STATE	ZIP CODE	AREA CODE PHONE
					(____) _____

TYPE OF BUSINESS   SUPERVISOR'S NAME, TITLE & PHONE NUMBER:

_____   _____

DATE EMPLOYED: MO _____   YR _____   DATE LEFT: MO _____   YR_____

TITLE AND DUTIES: _____

REASON FOR LEAVING: _____

IF YOUR EMPLOYMENT RECORDS EXIST UNDER ANOTHER NAME, PLEASE SPECIFY: _____

FINAL SALARY: $_____

Figure 10.2. *(Continued)*

COMPANY NAME	ADDRESS	CITY	STATE	ZIP CODE	AREA CODE PHONE
_____	_____	_____	_____	_____	(____) _____

TYPE OF BUSINESS   SUPERVISOR'S NAME, TITLE & PHONE NUMBER:

_____   _____

DATE EMPLOYED: MO _____ YR _____   DATE LEFT: MO _____ YR_____
TITLE AND DUTIES: _____
REASON FOR LEAVING: _____
IF YOUR EMPLOYMENT RECORDS EXIST UNDER ANOTHER NAME, PLEASE SPECIFY: _____
FINAL SALARY: $_____

COMPANY NAME	ADDRESS	CITY	STATE	ZIP CODE	AREA CODE PHONE
_____	_____	_____	_____	_____	(____) _____

TYPE OF BUSINESS   SUPERVISOR'S NAME, TITLE & PHONE NUMBER:

_____   _____

DATE EMPLOYED: MO _____ YR _____   DATE LEFT: MO _____ YR_____
TITLE AND DUTIES: _____
REASON FOR LEAVING: _____
IF YOUR EMPLOYMENT RECORDS EXIST UNDER ANOTHER NAME, PLEASE SPECIFY: _____
FINAL SALARY: $_____

GIVE THREE ADDITIONAL WORK-RELATED REFERENCES

Name	Occupation or Title	Firm Name and Address (include city, state and zip)	Phone
_____	_____	_____	_____
_____	_____	_____	_____
_____	_____	_____	_____

CERTIFICATION AND AGREEMENT

I certify that the information I provided in this application is complete and accurate to the best of my knowledge. I understand that any misrepresentation or omission of facts in this application disqualifies me from further consideration, or, if I am employed, is sufficient cause for dismissal. I understand that any alteration of this application in content or form may be considered cause for disqualification and/or termination.

I authorize investigation of all statements contained in this application and understand that I may be required to provide verification (diploma, license, transcripts, type tests, etc.) of information contained in this application.

I authorize any and all persons, companies or agencies to release to CHW any and all information they may have which is relevant to the application process. I also release all such parties from any liability that may result from furnishing information to CHW.

I understand that to be considered as a formal applicant, the position for which I am applying must be specifically identified as open, and recruitment for the position going on at the time this application is received by the Human Resources Department.

I understand that if I am employed with CHW, my employment will be at-will. As such, it can be terminated by me or by CHW with or without advance notice, at any time, and for any reason not prohibited by law. I agree that if I am employed by CHW, I will review the information contained in CHW's General Information Handbook.

I understand that any employment offer is contingent upon the following: (1) producing documents establishing my eligibility to work in the United States; (2) satisfactorily passing the preemployment drug screen, criminal background and reference checks; and (3) complying with CHW's preemployment application procedures.

By either writing or typing my name and submitting this application to CHW, I acknowledge that I have read the certification and agreement and agree to abide by its terms.

NAME: _____   DATE : _____

Community Hospital of the West is an Equal Employment Opportunity/Affirmative Action Employer.

Whatever interview approach or combination of approaches is used, the information collected at this point in the recruitment process should be enough to determine who will advance to the next stage of the selection process. Reference checks and criminal background checks and verifications of licensure, training, and educational requirements should all be documented before any applicant is offered a position. In the past, checking past employment references sometimes yielded important new information about a candidate. Today, however, most organizations release only general information regarding an employee's past work performance, such as dates of employment and whether the applicant is eligible for rehire.

Step 2: Conduct new employee orientation and training

Orientation to the organization as a whole should be provided to every new employee and then annually for all employees thereafter. Upper- and middle-level managers assigned as

---

Figure 10.3.   Appropriate and Inappropriate Interview Questions

Examples of Appropriate Job-Related Questions

- How does your education and work experience relate to the position we are discussing?
- What courses did you take in school?
- What was your grade point average?
- Are you willing to work on weekends?
- Are you willing to work overtime?
- What kind of work have you done in your previous positions?
- What kind of work do you enjoy the most? The least?
- What areas of your work skills would you like to improve?
- How do you perform under pressure?
- How many people were you responsible for supervising in your previous positions?
- Why did you leave your last position?
- How do you explain the gaps in your employment history?
- Would you require any additional training to perform this position?
- What are your career goals?
- What is your understanding of this area of the healthcare industry?
- What was your attendance record like in your previous positions?
- How long have you lived in this area?
- Are you able to work the hours required for this position?

Examples of Inappropriate Questions Unrelated to the Job

- Where were you born?
- What race are you?
- What does your husband (or father) do for a living?
- Are you married?
- Do you plan to get married?
- How old are you?
- Do you have any children? How many? What are their ages?
- Do you plan to have children?
- Is your husband likely to be transferred?
- Who cares for your children while you are at work?
- Are you involved in any church groups?
- Where do you live?
- Do you own or rent the place where you live?
- What organizations do you belong to?
- Have you ever been arrested?

expert resources conduct organizationwide orientation programs. Topics may include information on the organization's mission, vision, and values; strategic goals; performance improvement model; and environmental safety practices.

Orientation to the patient care and service area is specific to the area in which an individual is going to work. This orientation should be conducted as part of the hiring process and annual review and should be directly linked to the performance expectations and required competencies noted in the employee's position description.

Testing to verify the competency of a clinical staff member might include having the employee insert a catheter, draw blood, or use a piece of medical equipment. This type of training and orientation may include having the new employee shadow a seasoned employee for a specified period of time, complete a self-directed study course, or attend classroom instruction and then demonstrate his or her competency.

Policies and procedures facilitate the education and training of staff and form the basis for individual accountability. Policies and procedures should clearly represent and communicate the required functions and tasks the employee is expected to perform.

Some organizations use a training checklist to document employee orientation. The checklist documents the names of the trainee and trainer(s), orientation dates, tasks, and demonstrated competencies. The tool can be used in the performance appraisal process to monitor whether training and competency requirements have been met. Aggregate data can also be compiled from training checklists to monitor organizationwide and care- or service-specific orientation and competency requirements.

Step 3: Manage the performance appraisal process

The employee performance appraisal process should include individual appraisals conducted at predetermined intervals. Ideally, the appraisal should include a one-on-one discussion between the employee and the supervisor or manager along with a written appraisal that provides room for employee response. The employee and supervisor or manager should work together to develop new performance goals and modify or enhance performance standards. The manager or supervisor should follow up with the employee to monitor his or her progress in meeting goals and performance standards through frequent informal assessments as well as periodic formal appraisals. At a minimum, the periodic assessment should address each of the following areas of the employee's performance:

- Strengths and weaknesses

- Attitudes and relationships

- Potential and limitations

- Productivity and creativity

- Morale and motivation

- Degree of compliance with written standards of performance

- Participation in ongoing performance improvement activities

- Findings from staff development activities

The performance criteria used in the appraisal process should be directly linked to the employee's current position description and to the organization's mission. This process should also verify that the employee has maintained his or her credentials or licenses as appropriate.

Organizations that have successfully implemented continuous quality improvement philosophies have expanded the appraisal process to include team performance in combination with individual performance. Teams may include a clinical treatment team, an administrative or leadership team, or a single department as a team. The appraisal process includes the team's definition of performance expectations and goals and a periodic assessment of its performance as a team rather than as individuals.

Ideally, organizationwide performance measures should be referenced and incorporated into the employee and team appraisal process. Provider- or employee-specific variance information derived from risk management databases or other quality-monitoring activities may identify staff development needs. This same information reported in aggregate may identify trends in care that support the need for changes in staffing patterns, skill sets, or the environment where care is delivered.

Other ongoing measures frequently monitored by an organization's leadership include the following:

- Organizationwide, service-specific, and discipline-specific turnover rates

- Results of exit interviews that quantify the reason(s) why employees leave the organization

- Results of organizationwide performance appraisal reviews, which note corrective actions to be taken for employees with less than acceptable performance ratings

- Periodic provider and employee satisfaction surveys, which provide valuable information about customer service when tracked over time

- Organization's experience with work-related injuries

- Staff education and training needs

- Comparison of salary and benefits packages across staff categories

These data, along with other performance measures, should be reviewed in preparation for the organization's annual strategic planning process.

Step 4: Manage the retention process

Commitment to the development and retention of human resources is of strategic importance to every healthcare organization. High retention rates communicate a strong message about the organization's values to existing and potential employees. Beyond traditional in-house orientation programs, many organizations offer tuition and professional education reimbursement as an incentive for ongoing staff development and retention. Maintaining a competitive salary and benefits package continues to be a primary leverage point in recruitment and retention programs. Organizations that go beyond traditional incentives look to employee input for the creation of reward structures in promoting employee retention. Incentives such as profit-sharing, job-sharing, sign-on bonuses, shared leadership, and cutting-edge technology resources are a few of the trends.

Certainly the most compelling link to employee retention is the creation of a work environment in which organizational and personal values mesh and a natural synergy develops. Teams working together with a common vision begin with a self-directed, motivated workforce.

Step 5: Monitor and manage independent practitioners

An *independent practitioner,* by definition, is any individual permitted by law to provide healthcare services without direction or supervision, within the scope of the individual's license as conferred by state regulatory agencies. Professional practice may also include *clinical privileges* individually granted by a healthcare organization. Physicians, dentists, and podiatrists are the most common licensed independent practitioners. However, certified nurse anesthetists, physician's assistants, nurse practitioners, registered nurse–midwives, speech pathologists, dieticians, clinical psychologists, and clinical social workers may be considered part of this category as well. Independent practitioners may work as employees of a hospital or physician group, or they may work under contract to provide designated patient services in a healthcare organization.

Like full-time employees, licensed independent practitioners must go through the credentialing process. This process is defined by the medical staff bylaws and usually includes initial staff appointment, the delineation of clinical privileges, and the periodic reappraisal and reappointment of clinical staff members. The main purpose of the credentials process is to ensure that any individual who wishes to provide patient care services within a healthcare facility is qualified and competent to do so. The credentials process applies to all individuals seeking clinical privileges, whether they are applicants for medical staff membership, for clinical privileges without medical staff membership, or for clinical privileges as contractual practitioners.

The credentialing process is generally initiated with the completion of an application for membership and privileges. The information submitted by the applicant should include the following:

- Education (undergraduate and postgraduate with names of educational institutions)

- Training (residencies and fellowships)

- Previous and current healthcare affiliations (hospitals practiced in, private office locations)

- Specialty board certifications

- Current state licenses

- Drug enforcement administration (DEA) registration number with expiration dates

- Professional references who have personal knowledge of the applicant's *recent* professional performance and experience

- Information on current health status

- Professional liability insurance coverage

- Past and present professional litigation and liability history
- Clinical privileges being requested (what services the practitioner wants to provide)

An applicant status checklist should be used in processing the application to confirm and document areas requiring written source verification. State licenses, postgraduate degrees, residency and fellowship training, specialty board status, professional liability insurance coverage, and other healthcare affiliations should all be source verified. Source verification involves contacting other organizations to confirm the accuracy of the information provided by the candidate for privileges. The references submitted by the applicant should also be sent a letter asking specific questions about the applicant's qualifications.

Healthcare organizations are required by law to query two additional sources of information on candidates for clinical privileges: the **National Practitioner Data Bank** (NPDB) and the **Healthcare Integrity and Protection Data Bank** (HIPDB). The NPDB maintains reports on medical malpractice settlements, clinical privilege actions, and professional society membership actions against licensed healthcare providers. The HIPDB maintains reports on civil judgments and criminal convictions of licensed healthcare providers.

The delineation of clinical privileges should be based on the practitioner's training, experience, and proven clinical competence. Individual privilege delineation is intended to protect the patient, the medical staff, and the healthcare facility. The privilege lists sent out to applicants or used for reappointment should be associated with the applicant's type of practice and limited to hospital-specific privileges. For example, privileges for cardiac surgery should not be listed when that service is not specific to the applicant's practice or is not offered by the healthcare organization.

Once the applicant information has been source verified and references and data bank queries have been returned, the application and supporting documentation are reviewed by the organization's credentials and/or medical executive committee. Individual appointment and privilege delineation recommendations are then forwarded to the organization's governing board for final determination. When the application is approved, the appointment period is generally for two years. A provisional period is generally required (the medical staff bylaws should specify a time limit) for all new staff members. The performance of new staff members should be observed and monitored by an assigned proctor during the provisional period.

The reappraisal and reappointment process generally occurs every two years and includes a review of current licenses, DEA registration, professional liability coverage, information related to claims and litigation, health, and changes in outside affiliations. Training, education, and certification as well as the frequency with which a clinical privilege has been exercised should show evidence of continuing proficiency for the privileges requested. An assessment of the provider's profile since the last staff appointment to verify peer review activities provides the final basis for supporting reappointment or repriviliging.

An ongoing provider profile includes both administrative aspects of staff membership (for example, meeting attendance statistics, medical record delinquency status, medical staff committee appointments, and practice volume statistics) and clinical performance data (for example, clinical outcome statistics, committee or department citations, peer review, and performance monitoring reviews and actions). Again, the NPDB and HIPDB should be queried to determine whether any adverse information has been reported during the previous period of appointment.

Following review of the reappointment application information and provider profile information, the chief of staff or clinical department chairperson provides a written recommendation on reappointment and reprivileging to the credentials and/or executive committee of the medical staff. These bodies then make their own recommendation and forward it to the governing body for a final decision. When a recommendation for continuing privileges is not made, the applicant must be offered due process. **Due process** provides for fair treatment through a hearing procedure that is generally outlined in the healthcare organization's medical staff bylaws. The procedure stipulates the means by which the applicant's application and supporting materials will be reviewed by an impartial panel to ensure objective assessment.

Real-Life Example

Western States University Medical Center recently completed a national search and recruitment effort to fill its chief clinical officer (CCO) position. The position had been vacant for six months and had experienced rapid turnover of two previous CCOs within the past two years. The members of the search team invited to participate in the recruitment effort included the chief executive medical director, the chief financial officer, the human resources director, the medical staff president, and the nurse managers from each clinical care area.

The search team followed internal policy requirements related to the recruitment process. The position description was reviewed and updated, and from it minimum position requirements were identified and included in the advertisement posted internally and published in the local newspaper and a national nursing journal. The search team also retained the services of a national recruitment firm in an effort to fasttrack the recruitment process because the organization was less than a year away from its triennial survey with the Joint Commission on Accreditation of Healthcare Organizations.

The search generated about fifteen applicants. The team screened the applicants and narrowed the list down to the six that seemed to meet the minimum position requirements. These six applicants (five of whom were out-of-state candidates) were interviewed via conference call. The selection was then narrowed to two candidates, who were invited to fly in and meet with the search team.

Of primary importance to this search team's recruitment charge was finding a chief clinical officer who had a clinical background and experience that paralleled the services provided at Western States. The candidate's experience, strong knowledge of accreditation and licensure requirements, educational background with a master's degree, past employment patterns, personal demeanor, communication style, leadership philosophy, and availability were important factors in the selection. The final candidate selected by the search team met the important criteria and minimum position requirements. Reference checks and source documents verifying licensure confirmed the search team's decision to hire the final candidate as the CCO.

Five months into the new CCO's tenure and six weeks before the triennial survey, Western States' director of risk and quality management resigned. Because the risk and quality position reported to the CCO, the new CCO was asked to facilitate survey preparations.

Within days of this decision, the CCO requested that the leadership team recruit a local consulting group to assist in survey coordination efforts. Just two weeks before the anticipated survey, the CCO resigned.

Several factors resulted in the CCO's resignation. First, the source documents confirming the CCO's graduate education were not in her human resource file. As personnel files were being reviewed in preparation for survey inspection, it was noted that the written verification of the CCO's graduate degree was incomplete. When the graduate program was contacted, it was revealed that the CCO had never completed the master's program. Second, although the CCO's curriculum vitae and references confirmed that she had twenty plus years of experience in nursing administration and JCAHO survey work, she was unable to assume a leadership role in facilitating the nursing component of the JCAHO survey preparation process.

Western States University Medical Center has since defined what information it source verifies (verbal and written) when confirming education, experience, and licensure. It has also implemented a check-off list to be used by human resources to ensure that key action items are completed in the recruitment process. Western States University Medical Center has also developed sets of interview questions that better evaluate key competencies and skill sets.

QI Toolbox Technique

Summary profiles of physician performance provide the credentials committee with significant data about specific physicians scheduled for reappointment to the medical staff. With this information, the credentials committee has the information needed to make a sound decision on the performance of members of the hospital's medical staff.

The type of data captured on a physician profile summary should be unique to the healthcare organization's specific needs. The sample form in figure 10.4 is designed for a physician in the specialty area of obstetrics. It includes data about the physician's cesarean section rate, the number of vaginal births after a C-section, types of medications used, transfusion usage, record completion delinquency rates, risk management issues, and attendance at medical staff meetings. It also allows documentation of any disciplinary action that has taken place since the last credentialing process for the physician.

Case Study

The physician performance data for the Obstetric Service at Community Hospital of the West are provided in figure 10.4. The physician profile for Dr. Jones is provided in figure 10.5. The physician index summary for Dr. Doe, an OB/GYN physician on the medical staff, are provided in figure 10.6. Using the physician index summary, students should complete as much of the information as possible on the blank physician profile (figure 10.7) for Dr. Doe. They should identify which information cannot be obtained from the physician index. Then they should determine what other sources of hospital data would have to be accessed in order to complete the physician profile for Dr. Doe. Finally, they should compare Dr. Doe's performance to the performance of the rest of the physicians on the Obstetric Service in the areas for which data are available. (See figure 10.4.)

Figure 10.4.   Physician Profile for OB/GYN Group

COMMUNITY HOSPITAL OF THE WEST
PHYSICIAN PERFORMANCE REVIEW SUMMARY FOR REAPPOINTMENT

		Profile Timeframe:	
SERVICE	*OB/GYN*	**From:**	1/1/
CATEGORY	*Active*	**To:**	12/31/

UTILIZATION:

Admissions	*1,400*	Procedures	*598*	
Patient Days	*9,143*	V-BAC s	*154*	
Deliveries	*1,187*	Blood Given	*25*	
C-Sections	*137*			

OUTCOMES:

Category	#	%	Comments:
C-Section Rate	*137*	*11.5%*	
V-BAC Rate	*154*	*11%*	
Nosocomial Inf Rate	*21*	*1.5%*	
Surgical Wound Inf Rate	*5*	*0.36%*	
Mortality Rate	*1*	*0.07%*	

PERFORMANCE REVIEW:

Category	# Reviewed	# Appropriate/%	Comments:
Surgical/Inv/Non-Invasive Procedures	*60*	*58/96.7%*	
Medication Use	*140*	*139/99.3%*	
Blood Use	*25*	*25/100%*	
Utilization Management	*140*	*135/95.7%*	
Other Peer Review	*140*	*130/92.8%*	*Clinical Pert.*

DATA QUALITY

Data Quality Monitoring			Comments:
Delinquency (>21 days)	*15*	*7.7%*	
Suspensions	*5*	*2.6%*	

RISK/SAFETY MANAGEMENT

Incidents reported by other professionals/ administration	*2*	*2/100%*	Comments:
Litigation	*1*	*0.07%*	

MEETING ATTENDANCE

Medical Staff Meetings	*26*	*93%*	Comments:
Committee Meetings	*40*	*85%*	

Figure 10.5.　　Physician Profile for Dr. Jones

COMMUNITY HOSPITAL OF THE WEST
PHYSICIAN PERFORMANCE REVIEW SUMMARY FOR REAPPOINTMENT

PHYSICIAN	Bob Jones, MD	Profile Timeframe:	
SERVICE	OB/GYN	From:	1/1
CATEGORY	Active	To:	12/31

UTILIZATION:

Admissions	175	Procedures	53	
Patient Days	540	V-BAC's	28	
Deliveries	145	Blood Given	2	
C-Sections	22			

OUTCOMES:

Category	#	%	Comments:
C-Section Rate	22	15.2%	
V-BAC Rate	28	80%	
Nosocomial Inf Rate	3	1.71%	
Surgical Wound Inf Rate	2	3.8%	
Mortality Rate	1	0.57%	

PERFORMANCE REVIEW:

Category	# Reviewed	# Appropriate/%	Comments:
Surgical/Inv/Non-Invasive Procedures	6	5/83%	
Medication Use	10	8/80%	
Blood Use	2	2/100%	
Utilization Management	18	18/100%	
Other Peer Review	N/A		

DATA QUALITY

			Comments:
Data Quality Monitoring			
Delinquency (>21 days)	3	12.5%	
Suspensions	1	4.2%	

RISK/SAFETY MANAGEMENT

			Comments:
Incidents reported by other professionals/ administration	0	0%	
Litigation	1	0.57%	

MEETING ATTENDANCE

			Comments:
Medical Staff Meetings	4	100%	
Committee Meetings	10	80%	

Figure 10.5.   *(Continued)*

FOR COMPLETION BY SERVICE CHAIRMAN OR CREDENTIALS COMMITTEE CHAIRMAN

CATEGORY	YES	NO	Comments:
Has the applicant been considered for or subject to disciplinary action since last reappointment?		√	
Have the applicant's privileges or staff appointment been suspended, revoked, or diminished in any way, either voluntary or involuntary, since last reappointment?	√		
Are there any currently pending challenges to any licensure or registration or the voluntary relinquishment of such?		√	
Are there any physical or behavioral conditions or limitations?		√	
Has the applicant exhibited satisfactory professional performance?	√		

APPROVALS: **APPROVED?**

REVIEWER	SIGNATURE	YES	NO	DATE
Service Chair				
Credentials Chair				

Figure 10.6. Physician Index Summary for Dr. Doe

Patient Age	LOS	Discharge Status	Final Dx	Diagnosis Text	Final Proc	Procedure Text
52	3	Home	6262	EXCESSIVE/FREQUENT MENSTRUATION	684	TOTAL ABDOMINAL HYSTERECTOMY
			4254	PRIMARY CARDIOMYOPATHIES	6562	REMOVAL OF REMAINING OVARY AND TUBE
			4019	ESSENTIAL HYPERTENSION, UNSPECIFIED BENIGN		
			25000	DIABETES MELLITUS WITHOUT COMPLICATION,		
			2181	INTRAMURAL LEIOMYOMA OF UTERUS		
29	4	Home	65341	FETOPELVIC DISPROPORTION, DELIVERED	741	LOW CERVICAL CESAREAN SECTION
			66111	SECONDARY UTERINE INERTIA, DELIVERED	731	SURGICAL INDUCTION OF LABOR
			65841	INFECTION OF AMNIOTIC CAVITY, DELIVERED	7309	ARTIFICIAL RUPTURE OF MEMBRANES
			64501	PROLONGED PREGNANCY, DELIVERED		
			V270	MOTHER WITH SINGLE LIVEBORN		
27	2	Home	65421	PREVIOUS CESAREAN DELIVERY, DELIVERED	736	EPISIOTOMY (with subsequent repair)
			V270	MOTHER WITH SINGLE LIVEBORN	7359	MANUALLY ASSISTED DELIVERY
					7309	ARTIFICIAL RUPTURE OF MEMBRANES
79	4	Home	6185	PROLAPSE OF VAGINAL VAULT AFTER HYSTERECTOMY	7077	VAGINAL SUSPENSION & FIXATION
			9975	URINARY COMPLICATION, NOT ELSEWHERE CLASSIFIED	5459	OTHER LYSIS OF PERITONEAL ADHESIONS
			5990	URINARY TRACT INFECTION, SITE NOT SPECIFIED		
			9973	RESPIRATORY COMPLICATION, NOT ELSEWHERE		
			5180	PULMONARY COLLAPSE (ATELECTASIS)		
			78831	URGE INCONTINENCE		
			E8788	OTHER SURGICAL OPERATION, WITH ABNORMAL		
			4019	ESSENTIAL HYPERTENSION, UNSPECIFIED BENIGN		
			5680	PERITONEAL ADHESIONS (POSTOPERATIVE)(POS		
25	4	Home	65221	BREECH PRESENTATION WITHOUT VERSION, DELIVERED	741	LOW CERVICAL CESAREAN SECTION
			64661	INFECTIONS OF GENITOURINARY TRACT IN PRE		
			6169	UNSPECIFIED INFLAMMATORY DISEASE OF CERVIX		
			66311	CORD AROUND NECK, WITH COMPRESSION, COMP		
			V270	MOTHER WITH SINGLE LIVEBORN		
39	1	Home	66331	UNSPECIFIED CORD ENTANGLEMENT, WITHOUT C	7359	MANUALLY ASSISTED DELIVERY
			64201	BENIGN ESSENTIAL HYPERTENSION COMPLICATI		
			V270	MOTHER WITH SINGLE LIVEBORN		
			4019	ESSENTIAL HYPERTENSION, UNSPECIFIED BENIGN		

Figure 10.6. (Continued)

Patient Age	LOS	Discharge Status	Final Dx	Diagnosis Text	Final Proc	Procedure Text
34	2	Home	64881	ABNORMAL GLUCOSE TOLERANCE IN MOTHER COM	7359	MANUALLY ASSISTED DELIVERY
			V270	MOTHER WITH SINGLE LIVEBORN	7569	REPAIR OF CURRENT OBSTETRIC LACERATION
			66401	FIRST-DEGREE PERINEAL LACERATION, DELIVERED	7309	ARTIFICIAL RUPTURE OF MEMBRANES
20	1	Home	650	NORMAL DELIVERY	7359	MANUALLY ASSISTED DELIVERY
			V270	MOTHER WITH SINGLE LIVEBORN	736	EPISIOTOMY (with subsequent repair)
36	3	Home	6398	COMPLICATION FOLLOWING ABORTION/ECTOPIC/	684	TOTAL ABDOMINAL HYSTERECTOMY
			6259	UNSPECIFIED SYMPTOM ASSOCIATED WITH FEMA		
			311	DEPRESSIVE DISORDER, NOT ELSEWHERE CLASS		
			30503	ALCOHOL ABUSE IN REMISSION		
			30593	MIXED/UNSPECIFIED DRUG ABUSE IN REMISSION		
			6262	EXCESSIVE/FREQUENT MENSTRUATION		
			2182	SUBSEROUS LEIOMYOMA OF UTERUS		
			2181	INTRAMURAL LEIOMYOMA OF UTERUS		
			78701	NAUSEA WITH VOMITING		
48	3	Home	2181	INTRAMURAL LEIOMYOMA OF UTERUS	684	TOTAL ABDOMINAL HYSTERECTOMY
			57410	CALCULUS OF GALLBLADDER WITH CHOLECYSTITIS	6561	REMOVAL OF BOTH OVARIES AND TUBES AT SAM
			6170	ENDOMETRIOSIS OF UTERUS	595	RETROPUBIC URETHRAL SUSPENSION
			2189	LEIOMYOMA OF UTERUS, UNSPECIFIED	7052	REPAIR OF RECTOCELE
			6256	STRESS INCONTINENCE, FEMALE	7092	OPERATION ON CUL-DE-SAC
			6180	PROLAPSE OF VAGINAL WALLS WITHOUT MENTION	5123	LAPAROSCOPIC CHOLECYSTECTOMY
					8753	INTRAOPERATIVE CHOLANGIOGRAM
42	2	Home	65421	PREVIOUS CESAREAN DELIVERY, DELIVERED	734	MEDICAL INDUCTION OF LABOR
			V270	MOTHER WITH SINGLE LIVEBORN	7301	INDUCTION OF LABOR BY ARTIFICIAL RUPTURE
			66331	UNSPECIFIED CORD ENTANGLEMENT, WITHOUT	7359	MANUALLY ASSISTED DELIVERY
			64881	ABNORMAL GLUCOSE TOLERANCE IN MOTHER COM	7351	MANUAL ROTATION OF FETAL HEAD
			65291	UNSPECIFIED MALPOSITION/PRESENTATION OF		
22	2	Home	66421	THIRD-DEGREE PERINEAL LACERATION, DELIVERED	7562	REPAIR OF CURRENT OBSTETRIC LACERATION O
			65681	FETAL & PLACENTAL PROBLEM, AFFECTING MAN	7359	MANUALLY ASSISTED DELIVERY
			V270	MOTHER WITH SINGLE LIVEBORN		

(Continued on next page)

Figure 10.6. *(Continued)*

Patient Age	LOS	Discharge Status	Final Dx	Diagnosis Text	Final Proc	Procedure Text
37	14	Home	65971	ABNORMALITY IN FETAL HEART RATE/RHYTHM,	741	LOW CERVICAL CESAREAN SECTION
			67131	ANTEPARTUM DEEP PHLEBOTHROMBOSIS COMPLIC	6632	BILATERAL LIGATION AND DIVISION OF FALLO
			64821	ANEMIA IN MOTHER COMPLICATING PREGNANCY,		
			65821	DELAYED DELIVERY AFTER SPONTANEOUS/UNSPEC		
			65221	BREECH PRESENTATION WITHOUT VERSION, DEL		
			64421	EARLY ONSET OF DELIVERY, DELIVERED		
			65961	ELDERLY MULTIGRAVIDA, DELIVERED		
			64891	CURRENT CONDITION IN MOTHER COMPLICATING		
			2898	DISEASE OF BLOOD/BLOOD-FORMING ORGANS		
			7821	RASH AND NONSPECIFIC SKIN ERUPTION		
			2859	ANEMIA, UNSPECIFIED		
			V270	MOTHER WITH SINGLE LIVEBORN		
			V252	STERILIZATION		
28	1	Home	66331	UNSPECIFIED CORD ENTANGLEMENT, WITHOUT	736	EPISIOTOMY (with subsequent repair)
			65921	MATERNAL PYREXIA DURING LABOR, UNSPECIFIED	734	MEDICAL INDUCTION OF LABOR
			V270	MOTHER WITH SINGLE LIVEBORN	7301	INDUCTION OF LABOR BY ARTIFICIAL RUPTURE
22	2	Home	66331	UNSPECIFIED CORD ENTANGLEMENT, WITHOUT	7309	ARTIFICIAL RUPTURE OF MEMBRANES
			65921	MATERNAL PYREXIA DURING LABOR, UNSPECIFIED	7359	MANUALLY ASSISTED DELIVERY
			V270	MOTHER WITH SINGLE LIVEBORN	7569	REPAIR OF CURRENT OBSTETRIC LACERATION
42	2	Home	66411	SECOND-DEGREE PERINEAL LACERATION, DELIVERED	731	SURGICAL INDUCTION OF LABOR
			65961	ELDERLY MULTIGRAVIDA, DELIVERED	7359	MANUALLY ASSISTED DELIVERY
			V270	MOTHER WITH SINGLE LIVEBORN	7569	REPAIR OF CURRENT OBSTETRIC LACERATION
			66551	INJURY TO PELVIC ORGANS, DELIVERED		
67	3	Home	6271	POSTMENOPAUSAL BLEEDING	684	TOTAL ABDOMINAL HYSTERECTOMY
			4465	GIANT CELL ARTERITIS	6561	REMOVAL OF BOTH OVARIES AND TUBES AT SAM
			2765	VOLUME DEPLETION DISORDER (DEHYDRATION)	5459	OTHER LYSIS OF PERITONEAL ADHESIONS
			2181	INTRAMURAL LEIOMYOMA OF UTERUS		

Figure 10.6. (Continued)

Patient Age	LOS	Discharge Status	Final Dx	Diagnosis Text	Final Proc	Procedure Text
			6210	POLYP OF CORPUS UTERI		
			5680	PERITONEAL ADHESIONS (POSTOPERATIVE)(POS		
			V1251	PERSONAL HISTORY OF VENOUS THROMBOSIS AN		
			49390	ASTHMA, UNSPECIFIED TYPE, WITHOUT STATUS	684	TOTAL ABDOMINAL HYSTERECTOMY
51	3	Home	6270	PREMENOPAUSAL MENORRHAGIA	6561	REMOVAL OF BOTH OVARIES AND TUBES AT SAM
			2800	IRON DEFICIENCY ANEMIA SECONDARY TO BLOOD LOSS		
			2181	INTRAMURAL LEIOMYOMA OF UTERUS		
			6208	NONINFLAMMATORY DISORDER OF OVARY/FALLOP		
			6200	FOLLICULAR CYST OF OVARY		
			6259	UNSPECIFIED SYMPTOM ASSOCIATED WITH FEMALE		
33	1	Home	66702	RETAINED PLACENTA WITHOUT HEMORRHAGE, DEL	7309	ARTIFICIAL RUPTURE OF MEMBRANES
			V270	MOTHER WITH SINGLE LIVEBORN	7351	MANUAL ROTATION OF FETAL HEAD
			65281	MALPOSITION/MALPRESENTATION OF FETUS, DELIVERED	7359	MANUALLY ASSISTED DELIVERY
			64501	PROLONGED PREGNANCY, DELIVERED	736	EPISIOTOMY (with subsequent repair)
					754	MANUAL REMOVAL OF RETAINED PLACENTA
22	2	Home	66331	UNSPECIFIED CORD ENTANGLEMENT, WITHOUT	7359	MANUALLY ASSISTED DELIVERY
			V270	MOTHER WITH SINGLE LIVEBORN	7309	ARTIFICIAL RUPTURE OF MEMBRANES
					736	EPISIOTOMY (with subsequent repair)
25	2	Home	65281	MALPOSITION/MALPRESENTATION OF FETUS, DEL.	7351	MANUAL ROTATION OF FETAL HEAD
			V270	MOTHER WITH SINGLE LIVEBORN	736	EPISIOTOMY (with subsequent repair)
					7359	MANUALLY ASSISTED DELIVERY
					734	MEDICAL INDUCTION OF LABOR
					7309	ARTIFICIAL RUPTURE OF MEMBRANES
31	2	Home	66411	SECOND-DEGREE PERINEAL LACERATION, DELIV	7359	MANUALLY ASSISTED DELIVERY
			V270	MOTHER WITH SINGLE LIVEBORN	7569	REPAIR OF CURRENT OBSTETRIC LACERATION
					7301	INDUCTION OF LABOR BY ARTIFICIAL RUPTURE
40	3	Home	6172	ENDOMETRIOSIS OF FALLOPIAN TUBE	684	TOTAL ABDOMINAL HYSTERECTOMY
			2189	LEIOMYOMA OF UTERUS, UNSPECIFIED	6561	REMOVAL OF BOTH OVARIES AND TUBES AT SAM
			25000	DIABETES MELLITUS WITHOUT COMPLICATION,		
			6146	PELVIC PERITONEAL ADHESIONS, FEMALE (POS		

(Continued on next page)

Figure 10.6. (Continued)

Patient Age	LOS	Discharge Status	Final Dx	Diagnosis Text	Final Proc	Procedure Text
32	3	Home	65221	BREECH PRESENTATION WITHOUT VERSION, DEL	741	LOW CERVICAL CESAREAN SECTION
			66881	COMPLICATION OF ANESTHESIA/SEDATION IN L	0395	SPINAL BLOOD PATCH
			3490	REACTION TO SPINAL/LUMBAR PUNCTURE		
			64811	THYROID DYSFUNCTION IN MOTHER COMPLICATI		
			2449	UNSPECIFIED ACQUIRED HYPOTHYROIDISM		
			V270	MOTHER WITH SINGLE LIVEBORN		
81	4	Home	6185	PROLAPSE OF VAGINAL VAULT AFTER HYSTERECTOMY	7050	REPAIR OF CYSTOCELE AND RECTOCELE
			5180	PULMONARY COLLAPSE (ATELECTASIS)	595	RETROPUBIC URETHRAL SUSPENSION
			6256	STRESS INCONTINENCE, FEMALE		
			4019	ESSENTIAL HYPERTENSION, UNSPECIFIED BENIGN		
			2449	UNSPECIFIED ACQUIRED HYPOTHYROIDISM		
			71690	ARTHROPATHY, UNSPECIFIED, UNSPECIFIED SI		
			9110	TRUNK, ABRASION/FRICTION BURN, WITHOUT		
			78701	NAUSEA WITH VOMITING		
			5640	CONSTIPATION		
28	2	Home	65231	TRANSVERSE/OBLIQUE PRESENTATION OF FETUS	7309	ARTIFICIAL RUPTURE OF MEMBRANES
			66622	DELAYED & SECONDARY POSTPARTUM HEMORRHAGE	7351	MANUAL ROTATION OF FETAL HEAD
			66481	TRAUMA TO PERINEUM & VULVA, DELIVERED	7569	REPAIR OF CURRENT OBSTETRIC LACERATION
54	3	Home	V270	MOTHER WITH SINGLE LIVEBORN	7271	VACUUM EXTRACTION WITH EPISIOTOMY
			1820	MALIGNANT NEOPLASM OF CORPUS UTERI, EXCE	684	TOTAL ABDOMINAL HYSTERECTOMY
			4240	MITRAL VALVE DISORDER	7052	REPAIR OF RECTOCELE
			6182	UTEROVAGINAL PROLAPSE, INCOMPLETE	595	RETROPUBIC URETHRAL SUSPENSION
			6256	STRESS INCONTINENCE, FEMALE	6561	REMOVAL OF BOTH OVARIES AND TUBES AT SAM
			6271	POSTMENOPAUSAL BLEEDING		
			6171	ENDOMETRIOSIS OF OVARY		
			6170	ENDOMETRIOSIS OF UTERUS		
			27800	OBESITY, UNSPECIFIED		
			9095	LATE EFFECT OF ADVERSE EFFECT OF DRUG, M		
			E9470	DIETETICS CAUSING ADVERSE EFFECTS IN THE		
			E8490	INJURY OR POISONING OCCURRING AT/IN THE		

Figure 10.6. *(Continued)*

Patient Age	LOS	Discharge Status	Final Dx	Diagnosis Text	Final Proc	Procedure Text
19	1	Home	64421	EARLY ONSET OF DELIVERY, DELIVERED	7309	ARTIFICIAL RUPTURE OF MEMBRANES
			V270	MOTHER WITH SINGLE LIVEBORN	7359	MANUALLY ASSISTED DELIVERY
			65841	INFECTION OF AMNIOTIC CAVITY, DELIVERED	736	EPISIOTOMY (with subsequent repair)
37	3	Home	65221	BREECH PRESENTATION WITHOUT VERSION, DEL	741	LOW CERVICAL CESAREAN SECTION
			V270	MOTHER WITH SINGLE LIVEBORN		
			65801	OLIGOHYDRAMNIOS, DELIVERED		
24	2	Home	66421	THIRD-DEGREE PERINEAL LACERATION, DELIVE	—	—
			66331	UNSPECIFIED CORD ENTANGLEMENT, WITHOUT C		
			V270	MOTHER WITH SINGLE LIVEBORN		
21	2	Home	650	NORMAL DELIVERY	736	EPISIOTOMY (with subsequent repair)
			V270	MOTHER WITH SINGLE LIVEBORN	7359	MANUALLY ASSISTED DELIVERY
					7309	ARTIFICIAL RUPTURE OF MEMBRANES
					734	MEDICAL INDUCTION OF LABOR
39	2	Home	65941	GRAND MULTIPARITY, DELIVERED	—	—
			65961	ELDERLY MULTIGRAVIDA, DELIVERED		
			66401	FIRST-DEGREE PERINEAL LACERATION, DELIVERED		
			V270	MOTHER WITH SINGLE LIVEBORN		
			V252	STERILIZATION		
33	1	Home	650	NORMAL DELIVERY	736	EPISIOTOMY (with subsequent repair)
			V270	MOTHER WITH SINGLE LIVEBORN	7359	MANUALLY ASSISTED DELIVERY
					7309	ARTIFICIAL RUPTURE OF MEMBRANES
					734	MEDICAL INDUCTION OF LABOR
22	1	Home	66331	UNSPECIFIED CORD ENTANGLEMENT, WITHOUT C	7359	MANUALLY ASSISTED DELIVERY
			V270	MOTHER WITH SINGLE LIVEBORN	7309	ARTIFICIAL RUPTURE OF MEMBRANES
			64891	CURRENT CONDITION IN MOTHER COMPLICATING	736	EPISIOTOMY (with subsequent repair)
			V0251	CARRIER OR SUSPECTED CARRIER OF GROUP B		
20	1	Home	65811	PREMATURE RUPTURE OF MEMBRANES, DELIVERED	736	EPISIOTOMY (with subsequent repair)
			65971	ABNORMALITY IN FETAL HEART RATE/RHYTHM,	7359	MANUALLY ASSISTED DELIVERY
			64421	EARLY ONSET OF DELIVERY, DELIVERED		
			66311	CORD AROUND NECK, WITH COMPRESSION, COMP		
			64891	CURRENT CONDITION IN MOTHER COMPLICATING		
			V270	MOTHER WITH SINGLE LIVEBORN		
			V0251	CARRIER OR SUSPECTED CARRIER OF GROUP B		

(Continued on next page)

Figure 10.6. *(Continued)*

Patient Age	LOS	Discharge Status	Final Dx	Diagnosis Text	Final Proc	Procedure Text
34	3	Home	65221	BREECH PRESENTATION WITHOUT VERSION, DEL	741	LOW CERVICAL CESAREAN SECTION
			65811	PREMATURE RUPTURE OF MEMBRANES, DELIVERE	6632	BILATERAL LIGATION AND DIVISION OF FALLO
			64841	MENTAL DISORDER IN MOTHER COMPLICATING P		
			3051	TOBACCO USE DISORDER		
			V270	MOTHER WITH SINGLE LIVEBORN		
			V252	STERILIZATION		
22	1	Home	65281	MALPOSITION/MALPRESENTATION OF FETUS, DE	7351	MANUAL ROTATION OF FETAL HEAD
			65971	ABNORMALITY IN FETAL HEART RATE/RHYTHM,	7569	REPAIR OF CURRENT OBSTETRIC LACERATION
			66331	UNSPECIFIED CORD ENTANGLEMENT, WITHOUT C	7309	ARTIFICIAL RUPTURE OF MEMBRANES
			66401	FIRST-DEGREE PERINEAL LACERATION, DELIVERED	757	MANUAL EXPLORATION OF UTERINE CAVITY, PO
			V270	MOTHER WITH SINGLE LIVEBORN		
41	2	Home	64881	ABNORMAL GLUCOSE TOLERANCE IN MOTHER COM	7309	ARTIFICIAL RUPTURE OF MEMBRANES
			V270	MOTHER WITH SINGLE LIVEBORN	7351	MANUAL ROTATION OF FETAL HEAD
			64421	EARLY ONSET OF DELIVERY, DELIVERED	721	LOW FORCEPS OPERATION WITH EPISIOTOMY
			65701	POLYHYDRAMNIOS, DELIVERED		
			65951	ELDERLY PRIMIGRAVIDA, DELIVERED		
			65981	INDICATION FOR CARE/INTERVENTION RELATED		
			78703	VOMITING ALONE		
			66111	SECONDARY UTERINE INERTIA, DELIVERED		
			65671	PLACENTAL CONDITION, AFFECTING MANAGEMENT		
59	3	Home	6182	UTEROVAGINAL PROLAPSE, INCOMPLETE	6859	VAGINAL HYSTERECTOMY
			2182	SUBSEROUS LEIOMYOMA OF UTERUS	7050	REPAIR OF CYSTOCELE AND RECTOCELE
			6210	POLYP OF CORPUS UTERI	5718	SUPRAPUBIC CYSTOSTOMY
			2409	GOITER, UNSPECIFIED		
33	1	Home	66031	DEEP TRANSVERSE ARREST & PERSISTENT OCCI	7309	ARTIFICIAL RUPTURE OF MEMBRANES
			66401	FIRST-DEGREE PERINEAL LACERATION, DELIVE	7569	REPAIR OF CURRENT OBSTETRIC LACERATION
			V270	MOTHER WITH SINGLE LIVEBORN	7351	MANUAL ROTATION OF FETAL HEAD

Figure 10.6. *(Continued)*

Patient Age	LOS	Discharge Status	Final Dx	Diagnosis Text	Final Proc	Procedure Text
30	2	Home	65281	MALPOSITION/MALPRESENTATION OF FETUS, DE	721	LOW FORCEPS OPERATION WITH EPISIOTOMY
			65921	MATERNAL PYREXIA DURING LABOR, UNSPECIFIED	7359	MANUALLY ASSISTED DELIVERY
			65421	PREVIOUS CESAREAN DELIVERY, DELIVERED	757	MANUAL EXPLORATION OF UTERINE CAVITY, PO
67	3	Home	V270	MOTHER WITH SINGLE LIVEBORN	7092	OPERATION ON CUL-DE-SAC
			6180	PROLAPSE OF VAGINAL WALLS WITHOUT MENTION	7050	REPAIR OF CYSTOCELE AND RECTOCELE
			6256	STRESS INCONTINENCE, FEMALE	595	RETROPUBIC URETHRAL SUSPENSION
81	3	Home	6186	VAGINAL ENTEROCELE, CONGENITAL OR ACQUIRED	684	TOTAL ABDOMINAL HYSTERECTOMY
			6181	UTERINE PROLAPSE WITHOUT MENTION OF VAGI	6561	REMOVAL OF BOTH OVARIES AND TUBES AT SAM
			6227	MUCOUS POLYP OF CERVIX	7092	OPERATION ON CUL-DE-SAC
			6210	POLYP OF CORPUS UTERI		
			2181	INTRAMURAL LEIOMYOMA OF UTERUS		
			25000	DIABETES MELLITUS WITHOUT COMPLICATION,		
			4019	ESSENTIAL HYPERTENSION, UNSPECIFIED BENIGN		
			2724	UNSPECIFIED HYPERLIPIDEMIA		
26	1	Home	650	NORMAL DELIVERY	7359	MANUALLY ASSISTED DELIVERY
			V270	MOTHER WITH SINGLE LIVEBORN	734	MEDICAL INDUCTION OF LABOR
					736	EPISIOTOMY (with subsequent repair)
18	1	Home	66411	SECOND-DEGREE PERINEAL LACERATION, DELIVERED	7569	REPAIR OF CURRENT OBSTETRIC LACERATION
			64841	MENTAL DISORDER IN MOTHER COMPLICATING P	7359	MANUALLY ASSISTED DELIVERY
			3051	TOBACCO USE DISORDER	7309	ARTIFICIAL RUPTURE OF MEMBRANES
			V270	MOTHER WITH SINGLE LIVEBORN		
72	3	Home	1820	MALIGNANT NEOPLASM OF CORPUS UTERI, EXCE	684	TOTAL ABDOMINAL HYSTERECTOMY
			2449	UNSPECIFIED ACQUIRED HYPOTHYROIDISM	6561	REMOVAL OF BOTH OVARIES AND TUBES AT SAM
			6202	OVARIAN CYST	403	REGIONAL LYMPH NODE EXCISION
			7912	HEMOGLOBINURIA		
38	3	Home	6185	PROLAPSE OF VAGINAL VAULT AFTER HYSTEREC	7077	VAGINAL SUSPENSION & FIXATION
50	3	Home	6170	ENDOMETRIOSIS OF UTERUS	684	TOTAL ABDOMINAL HYSTERECTOMY
			2800	IRON DEFICIENCY ANEMIA SECONDARY TO BLOOD	6561	REMOVAL OF BOTH OVARIES AND TUBES AT SAM

(Continued on next page)

Figure 10.6. *(Continued)*

Patient Age	LOS	Discharge Status	Final Dx	Diagnosis Text	Final Proc	Procedure Text
			6172	ENDOMETRIOSIS OF FALLOPIAN TUBE	595	RETROPUBIC URETHRAL SUSPENSION
			6171	ENDOMETRIOSIS OF OVARY		
			6256	STRESS INCONTINENCE, FEMALE		
			6262	EXCESSIVE/FREQUENT MENSTRUATION		
			2181	INTRAMURAL LEIOMYOMA OF UTERUS		
			6160	CERVICITIS & ENDOCERVICITIS		
			6173	ENDOMETRIOSIS OF PELVIC PERITONEUM		
			6259	UNSPECIFIED SYMPTOM ASSOCIATED WITH FEMALE		
			25000	DIABETES MELLITUS WITHOUT COMPLICATION,		
			5533	DIAPHRAGMATIC HERNIA		
28	1	Home	65801	OLIGOHYDRAMNIOS, DELIVERED	721	LOW FORCEPS OPERATION WITH EPISIOTOMY
			65921	MATERNAL PYREXIA DURING LABOR, UNSPECIFI	7351	MANUAL ROTATION OF FETAL HEAD
			65281	MALPOSITION/MALPRESENTATION OF FETUS, DE	7569	REPAIR OF CURRENT OBSTETRIC LACERATION
			66951	FORCEPS/VACUUM EXTRACTOR DELIVERY WITHOUT	754	MANUAL REMOVAL OF RETAINED PLACENTA
			66411	SECOND-DEGREE PERINEAL LACERATION, DELIV	734	MEDICAL INDUCTION OF LABOR
			66331	UNSPECIFIED CORD ENTANGLEMENT, WITHOUT		
			V270	MOTHER WITH SINGLE LIVEBORN		
24	2	Home	65651	POOR FETAL GROWTH, AFFECTING MANAGEMENT	734	MEDICAL INDUCTION OF LABOR
			65921	MATERNAL PYREXIA DURING LABOR, UNSPECIFIED	7301	INDUCTION OF LABOR BY ARTIFICIAL RUPTURE
			V272	MOTHER WITH TWINS, BOTH LIVEBORN	7351	MANUAL ROTATION OF FETAL HEAD
			65281	MALPOSITION/MALPRESENTATION OF FETUS, DEL	736	EPISIOTOMY (with subsequent repair)
			V043	NEED FOR PROPHYLACTIC VACCINATION AND IN	757	MANUAL EXPLORATION OF UTERINE CAVITY, PO
					7359	MANUALLY ASSISTED DELIVERY
39	2	Home	66331	UNSPECIFIED CORD ENTANGLEMENT, WITHOUT C	736	EPISIOTOMY (with subsequent repair)
			V270	MOTHER WITH SINGLE LIVEBORN	734	MEDICAL INDUCTION OF LABOR
					7301	INDUCTION OF LABOR BY ARTIFICIAL RUPTURE
30	1	Home	66331	UNSPECIFIED CORD ENTANGLEMENT, WITHOUT C	7301	INDUCTION OF LABOR BY ARTIFICIAL RUPTURE
			V270	MOTHER WITH SINGLE LIVEBORN	734	MEDICAL INDUCTION OF LABOR
					7351	MANUAL ROTATION OF FETAL HEAD
					736	EPISIOTOMY (with subsequent repair)
					7359	MANUALLY ASSISTED DELIVERY

Figure 10.7. Blank Physician Profile for Case Study

COMMUNITY HOSPITAL OF THE WEST
PHYSICIAN PERFORMANCE REVIEW SUMMARY FOR REAPPOINTMENT

PHYSICIAN		Profile Timeframe:
SERVICE		From:
CATEGORY		To:

UTILIZATION:				
Admissions		Procedures		
Patient Days		V-BAC's		
Deliveries		Blood Given		
C-Sections				

OUTCOMES:			
Category	#	%	Comments:
C-Section Rate			
V-BAC Rate			
Nosocomial Inf Rate			
Surgical Wound Inf Rate			
Mortality Rate			

PERFORMANCE REVIEW:			
Category	# Reviewed	# Appropriate/%	Comments:
Surgical/Inv/Non-Invasive Procedures			
Medication Use			
Blood Use			
Utilization Management			
Other Peer Review			

DATA QUALITY			
Data Quality Monitoring			Comments:
Delinquency (>21 days)			
Suspensions			

RISK/SAFETY MANAGEMENT			
Incidents reported by other professionals/ administration			Comments:
Litigation			

MEETING ATTENDANCE			
Medical Staff Meetings			Comments:
Committee Meetings			

(Continued on next page)

Figure 10.7.   *(Continued)*

FOR COMPLETION BY SERVICE CHAIRMAN OR CREDENTIALS COMMITTEE CHAIRMAN

CATEGORY	YES	NO	Comments:
Has the applicant been considered for or subject to disciplinary action since last reappointment?			
Have the applicant's privileges or staff appointment been suspended, revoked, or diminished in any way, either voluntary or involuntary, since last reappointment?			
Are there any currently pending challenges to any licensure or registration or the voluntary relinquishment of such?			
Are there any physical or behavioral conditions or limitations?			
Has the applicant exhibited satisfactory professional performance?			

APPROVALS: **APPROVED?**

REVIEWER	SIGNATURE	YES	NO	DATE
Service Chair				
Credentials Chair				

Case Study Questions

1. How did Dr. Doe perform in comparison to the rest of the service?

2. Should Dr. Doe be reappointed to the medical staff? Why or why not?

Project Application

Students should identify any human resources issues that may have a bearing on their project. They should determine what types of issues these are and how they can obtain the data needed to evaluate them. Then they should develop recommendations for staffing.

Summary

The effective management of human resources is critically important in healthcare organizations. Quality of care depends on the skill and dedication of caregivers. Healthcare services are complex and require specialized knowledge and experience. The licenses and other credentials of the clinical professionals who provide services in healthcare organizations must be maintained and verified. The competence of licensed caregivers must be reevaluated on an annual or biannual schedule to ensure their continued ability to provide healthcare services. Healthcare organizations must also be able to demonstrate that they have contributed to the ongoing development of employees and medical staff.

References and Suggested Readings

Berenson, R. 1995. Profiling and performance measures: what are the legal issues? *Medical Care* 33(1, Suppl):JS53–59.

Delorese, Ambrose. 1995. *Leadership: The Journey Inward.* Dubuque, Iowa: Kendall-Hunt Publishing.

Field, R. I. 1995. Sharing clinical data for provider profiling: protection of privacy versus the public's need to know. *Behavioral Healthcare Tomorrow* 4(3):71–73.

Hendryx, M. S., et al. 1995. Using comparative clinical and economic outcome information to profile physician performance. *Health Services Management Research* 8(4):213–20.

Joint Commission on Accreditation of Healthcare Organizations. 1995. *Accountability and Quality in Health Care.* Oakbrook Terrace, Ill.: JCAHO.

Joint Commission on Accreditation of Healthcare Organizations. 2000. *Joint Commission Survey Process Guide.* Oakbrook Terrace, Ill.: JCAHO.

Orsund-Gassiot, Cindy, and Sharon Lindsey. 1990. *Handbook of Medical Staff Management.* Rockville, Md.: Aspen Publishers.

Schachter, W. 1995. The role of provider credentialing in quality-of-care improvement and clinic risk reduction. *Behavioral Healthcare Tomorrow* 4(4):71–73.

Chapter 11
Analyzing Performance Improvement Data

Learning Objectives

- To be able to describe the various data types

- To recognize the correct graphic presentation for a specific data type

- To be able to design graphic displays for a given set of data

- To be able to analyze the data for changes in performance shown in graphic form

Background and Significance

After the performance improvement team has administered its survey or collected data by abstracting information from other sources, the team is ready to analyze the data. Other sources of data include medical records, registration information, and so forth. Abstracted data and survey results can provide invaluable information about a process and thereby point the team in a specific direction for improving the process under consideration. Data comparisons provide additional information about why and how well the process works as it should—or does not—to meet the customers' expectations. Three types of comparisons can provide more information about the process:

- The results from measurements collected over a period of time can be compared. Measurements that go up and down over time may indicate a very different situation than measurements that show a continuous increase or decrease over the same time period.

- Literature searches into the current scientific literature can provide excellent guidelines or standards against which the team can compare its process. If, for instance, the national standard for the average number of adverse drug reactions were X, then comparing the organization's number to the national average would give the team information about the effectiveness of the organization's medication program.

- Comparison of the organization's performance to the performance of other organizations that provide the same types of services is known as **benchmarking.** The other organizations need not be in the same region of the country, but they should be comparable in terms of size and other characteristics. The use of benchmarks can be very helpful, especially when comparisons can be made to an organization that is doing an outstanding job with a process similar to the process on which the PI team is focusing.

Several tools can be used by PI teams for data analysis and presentation. The tools are discussed later in this chapter.

Data Analysis Terminology

Before decisions can be made on how to display performance data, a determination of what type of data has been collected must be made. The four data categories are nominal, ordinal, discrete, and continuous.

Nominal data, also called categorical data, include values assigned to specific named categories. For example, gender can be subdivided into two groups named "male" and "female" or two categories labeled "1" and "2." Nominal data are usually displayed in bar graphs and pie charts. (See figures 11.2 and 11.5, respectively.)

Ordinal data, also called ranked data, express the comparative evaluation of various characteristics or entities and relative assignment of each to a class according to a set of criteria. Many surveys use a Likert scale to quantify or rank statements. A Likert scale usually ranges from 1 to 5, where the respondent may state the degree to which he disagrees or agrees with the statement (for example, 1 = strongly disagree, 2 = disagree, 3 = neutral, 4 = agree, and 5 = strongly agree). This type of scale allows one to determine how respondents feel about issues. Ordinal or ranked data, like nominal data, are best displayed in bar graphs and pie charts (figures 11.2 and 11.5, respectively).

Discrete data are numerical values that represent whole numbers, for example, the number of children in a family or the number of unbillable patient accounts. Discrete data can be displayed in bar graphs (figure 11.2).

Finally, **continuous data** assume an infinite number of possible values in measurements that have decimal values as possibilities. Examples of continuous data include weight, blood pressure, temperature, and so on. Continuous data are displayed in histograms or run charts. (See figures 11.3 and 11.6, respectively.)

Two other data analysis terms often used in data analysis are **absolute frequency** and **relative frequency.** Absolute frequency refers to the number of times that a score or value occurs in the data set. For example, in the data set shown in table 11.1, the frequency of the score or value 25 is 3. Relative frequency is the percentage of the time that the characteristic appears. In the example, the percentage of observations on which the respiration rate was 25 was 3:7, or 42.9 percent, its relative frequency.

Data Collection and Display Tools

The data collection and display tools most commonly used in PI activities include check sheets, bar graphs, histograms, Pareto charts, pie charts, run charts, and control charts.

Check Sheets

A **check sheet** is used when one needs to gather data based on sample observations in order to detect patterns. When preparing to collect data, a team should consider the three *W* questions:

- What data will be collected?

- Where will the data be collected?

- When will the data be collected?

Once the team has the answers to the three *W* questions, it can develop a check sheet to collect the data. (See figure 11.1.) Check sheets make it possible to collect a lot of data

Table 11.1.	Sample Data Set
Date and Time	**Respiration Rate Recorded**
Jan. 5, 8:00 a.m.	22/min
Jan. 5, 12:00 noon	25/min
Jan. 5, 4:00 p.m.	25/min
Jan. 5, 8:00 p.m.	22/min
Jan. 5, 12:00 midnight	21/min
Jan. 6, 4:00 a.m.	23/min
Jan. 6, 8:00 a.m.	25/min

Figure 11.1.	Example of a Check Sheet			
Problem	**Day**			
	1	**2**	**3**	**TOTAL**
A	II	III	II	7
B	I	I	I	3
C	IIII	II	IIII	10
TOTAL	7	6	7	20

systematically. It is important to make sure that the data are unbiased, accurate, properly recorded, and representative of typical conditions for the process.

A check sheet is a simple, easy-to-understand form used to answer the question, "How often are certain events happening?" It starts the process of translating opinions into facts. Constructing a check sheet involves the following steps:

1. The PI team comes to an agreement on exactly what event it wants to observe. Everyone must be looking for the same thing.

2. The team decides on the time period during which the data will be collected. The time period can range from a matter of hours to a matter of weeks.

3. Next, the team designs a form that is clear and easy to use. The team should make sure that every column is clearly labeled and that there is enough space on the form to enter the data.

4. The team collects the data consistently and honestly. Enough time should be allowed for this data-gathering task.

Check sheets can also be used to tally responses on surveys. For example, if a survey included a question that asked for the days of the week on which patients had surgery, the results could be tabulated by using a check sheet that included each day of the week. The check sheet would make counting the responses easy.

Once the data have been collected, the PI team should sort the data and identify any significant findings. Charts and graphs of the data, because they are pictures, make it easier to identify trends and significant relationships. Graphs can be used to compare data sets from different years or over time to visually illustrate a trend in the data or a change in performance. For example, in a bar graph, a change in the height of a bar would indicate an increase or decrease in the data represented by the bar. The PI team would then have to determine whether this increase or decrease was a significant change in the performance of the related process.

When constructing charts, graphs, and tables, the team must provide explanatory labels and titles. Data display should be simple and accurate. Team members must remember to report all of the data even when the data appear to have positive or negative implications for the organization. Sometimes, what appears to be a negative trend may actually turn out to be a positive trend after the team fully analyzes the data. Therefore, all of the data should be reported.

Bar Graphs

Bar graphs are used to display discrete categories, for example, the gender of respondents or the type of health insurance respondents have. Such categories are shown on the horizontal, or X, axis of the graph. The vertical, or Y, axis shows the number or frequency of responses. The vertical scale must always begin with 0. Most spreadsheet software programs can be used to "draw" a bar graph from a given data set. See the example of a bar graph in figure 11.2.

Figure 11.2.   Example of a Bar Graph

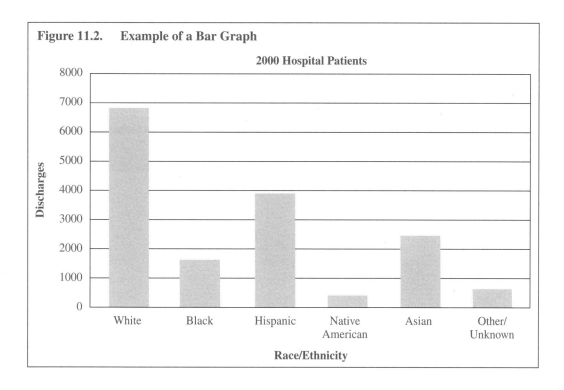

2000 Hospital Patients

Histogram

A **histogram** is a bar graph that displays data proportionally, something like a linear pie chart. Histograms are used to identify problems or changes in a system or process. They are based on raw data and absolute frequencies, which determine how the graphs will be structured. Unlike a **Pareto chart** (described next), the data remain in the order of the scale against which they were obtained. The horizontal axis measures intervals of continuous data such as time or money. The scale is grouped into intervals appropriate to the nature of the data. For example, time might be grouped into intervals of six hours, and money into groups of $5000. The vertical axis shows the absolute frequency of occurrence in each of the interval categories. Because of its visual impact, a histogram is more effective for displaying data than a check sheet, particularly when the frequencies are large. A histogram can be used in place of a pie chart for continuous data, which should not be displayed in pie charts.

Histograms have the following characteristics:

- They display large amounts of continuous data that are difficult to interpret in lists or other nongraphic forms.

- They show the relative frequency of occurrence of the various data categories, but only indirectly via the height of the bars relative to each other.

- They quickly show the distribution of the absolute frequencies of the data in the grouped intervals.

The first step in creating a histogram is to gather the data. The data can be collected on check sheets or gathered from department logs or other resources. A histogram should be used in situations in which numerical observations can be collected. Cost in dollars for a surgical procedure is one example. Once the data have been gathered, the team can begin to group data into a series of intervals or categories. A check sheet can be used to count how many times a data point appears in each interval grouping. For the example of the cost of a surgical procedure, the cost of the procedure to each patient might be grouped into the following intervals: $0 to $2,499, $2,500 to $4,999, $5,000 to $7,499, and $7,500 to $9,999.

To create the actual histogram, one should set up the horizontal axis with the interval groupings and the vertical axis with the absolute frequencies, always beginning at 0 for both. Each bar should be drawn upward as it relates to the tabulated frequencies from the check sheet.

To analyze a histogram, one should look for things that seem suspicious or strange. The team should review the various interpretations and write down their observations.

An example of a histogram is provided in figure 11.3. The example shows data related to the length of time patient accounts are in suspense, that is, after the patient has been discharged but the bill has not been mailed.

Pareto Charts

A **Pareto chart** is a kind of bar graph that uses data to determine priorities in problem solving. Using a Pareto chart can help the team to focus on problems and their causes and to demonstrate which are most responsible for the problem. Following these steps will result in a Pareto chart:

1. Use a check sheet to collect the required data.

2. Arrange the data in order, from the category with the greatest frequency to the category with the least frequency.

3. Calculate the totals for each category.

4. Compute the cumulative percentage.

5. Draw horizontal and vertical axes on graph paper.

6. Scale the vertical axis for absolute frequency (0 to the total calculated above).

7. Working from left to right, construct a bar for each category, with height indicating the frequency. Start with the largest category and add categories in descending order.

8. Draw a vertical scale on the right side of the graph, and add a percentage scale (0 to 100 percent).

9. Plot the cumulative percentage line as shown in figure 11.4.

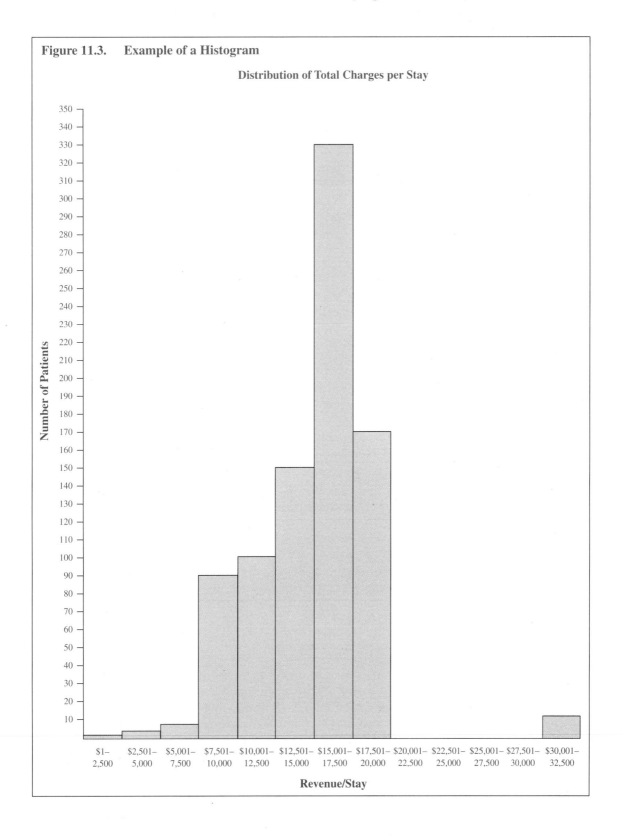

Figure 11.3.   Example of a Histogram

Distribution of Total Charges per Stay

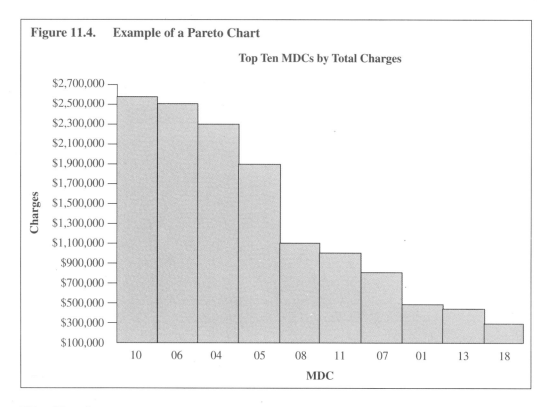

Figure 11.4.   Example of a Pareto Chart

Top Ten MDCs by Total Charges

Pie Charts

Pie charts are used to show the relationship of each part to the whole; that is, how each part contributes to the total product or process. The 360 degrees of the circle, or pie, represent the total or 100 percent. The pie is divided into "slices" proportionate to each component's percentage of the whole. To create a pie chart, one should first determine the percentages for each data element of the total population and then draw the slice accordingly. Creating pie charts by hand requires the use of a protractor. For example, if a slice were to represent 45 percent of the whole, one would multiply the 360 degrees of the circle by .45 to find that 45 percent of the pie equals 162 degrees. Then, using the protractor, one could mark off 162 degrees on the pie and draw lines to the center to configure the slice. Spreadsheet programs can automatically create pie charts from a given data set. See figure 11.5 for an example of a pie chart.

Run Charts

A **run chart** is a simple, plotted chart of data that shows the progress of a process over time. By analyzing the chart, the PI team can identify trends, shifts, or changes in a process over time. The chart tracks the time frame (days, weeks, months, minutes, or hours) on the horizontal axis and the measurement (the number of occurrences or the actual measure of a parameter) on the vertical axis. The data are gathered from sources specific to the process that has been evaluated. Each set of data (measurement/number of occurrences and time frame/days or months, and so on) must be related.

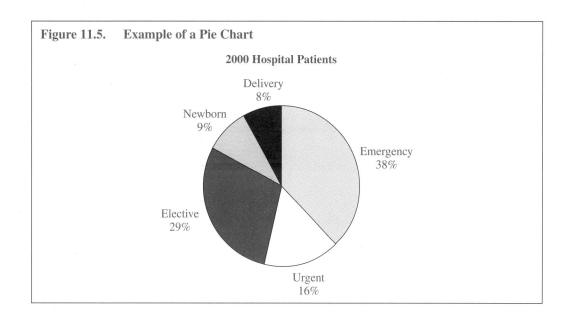

Figure 11.5.   Example of a Pie Chart

2000 Hospital Patients

A run chart can be created by going through the following steps:

1. Select a time frame.

2. Identify the data that are to be tracked.

3. Use a check sheet to collect frequency data or a tally sheet to collect measurement data.

4. Draw the chart and place the measurement or frequency on the vertical axis and the time frame on the horizontal axis.

5. Label the chart with specific details.

6. Plot the data in the sequence they appear.

7. Connect the points to form a relationship line.

8. Take the average of the data points collected.

9. Finally, draw a line parallel with the horizontal axis to represent the average.

To analyze the chart, the team should look for peaks and valleys that indicate that there may be a problem with the process.

Periodically redoing the run charts for a process helps the team to monitor changes over time. A run chart is a good way to display trends in the data. For example, a run chart could be displayed on a large plastic graph that could be updated month by month. When the team evaluates the results, they should look for seasonal peaks and valleys. For example, summer vacation times may show a change in a chart plotting staff productivity. Figure 11.6 provides an example of a run chart.

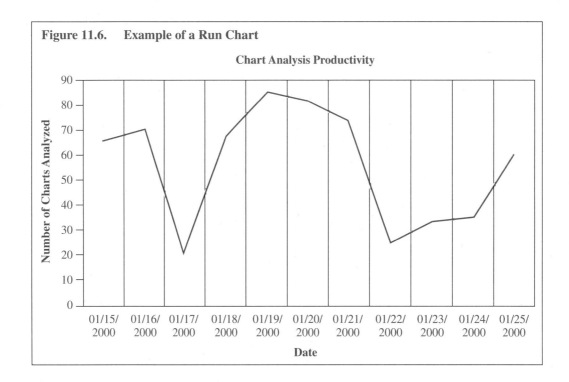

Figure 11.6.   Example of a Run Chart

Control Charts

Control charts can be used to measure key processes over time. Using a control chart focuses attention on any variation in the process and helps the team to determine whether that variation is normal or a result of special circumstances.

The following list shows the steps in developing a control chart:

1. Determine which data are to be measured.

2. Collect about twenty different measures of the data type.

3. Calculate the **mean** and **standard deviation** for the data. Various spreadsheet software programs can be used to make this calculation. The mean, or average, becomes the center line for the control chart.

4. Calculate an upper control limit and a lower control limit. The upper control limit is two standard deviations above the mean, and the lower control limit is two standard deviations below the mean.

The resulting control chart becomes the standard against which the team can compare all future data for the process. For example, figure 11.7 displays the incidence of nosocomial infections for a facility. The mean is calculated at 0.01 and the standard deviation is calculated at 0.012. The upper control limit (UCL) is two standard deviations above the mean, or 0.034. Some organizations, however, use a standard for nosocomial infection rate

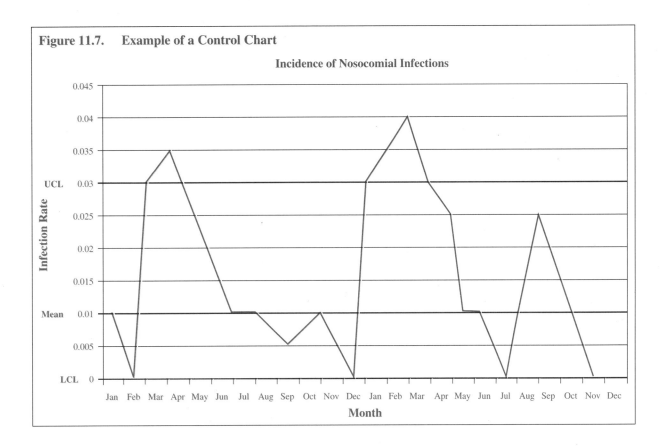

Figure 11.7.   Example of a Control Chart

of 0.03, and so the UCL for these data is 0.03. The lower control limit (LCL) is two standard deviations below the mean, or -0.014. Because the calculated LCL is a negative number, 0 becomes the lower control limit.

Advanced Statistical Analysis

More advanced forms of statistical analysis are sometimes used in performance improvement activities. Examples include ANOVA, linear regression, and correlation. Information on these methods is available in the suggested readings for this chapter.

Real-Life Example

Table 11.2 shows a portion of a patient profile for one hospital in the years 1995 and 2000. When the 1995 data are compared to the 2000 data in a bar graph (figure 11.8), it can be concluded that the hospital has experienced an increase in the number of Asian patients in its customer base. The hospital must look at how this increase affects its processes. For example, what changes might need to be made in the dietary area? What staffing changes might need to be made to accommodate patients who might not speak English?

Table 11.2.	Data Set for Bar Graph		
Profile of Hospital Patients			
1995		**2000**	
Race/Ethnicity	**Discharges**	**Race/Ethnicity**	**Discharges**
White	6,254	White	6,874
Black	1,859	Black	1,763
Hispanic	4,251	Hispanic	3,954
Native American	254	Native American	301
Asian	1,352	Asian	2,514
Other/Unknown	750	Other/Unknown	594

Table 11.3 shows another set of data from the hospital's patient profile. Comparison of the two pie charts created from the data (figure 11.9) shows that the number of emergency admissions has increased 14 percent over five years and that the number of urgent admissions has decreased by about 12 percent over five years. This information indicates that either the admissions are being categorized incorrectly or the incidence of trauma is increasing. The facility may need to look at its emergency department capacity and procedures.

Case Study

From the data provided in table 11.4, students should select three sets of data and create an appropriate graph to represent the data. They should keep in mind that the type of data in the table and choose the best graphic display tool for those data.

Project Application

Using the data collected from their QI projects, students should select data to be displayed and then determine the best graphic presentation. They should use a spreadsheet software program to design graphs for their student projects.

Summary

Using data analysis tools is an important skill for PI teams to learn. Making improvement decisions on the basis of actual experience is much better than making decisions on the basis of intuition, or gut feelings. Graphic depictions of process outputs are also easier to track over time when the team can clearly see the magnitude of changes. The most commonly used graphic tools include bar graphs, pie charts, Pareto charts, histograms, run charts, and control charts.

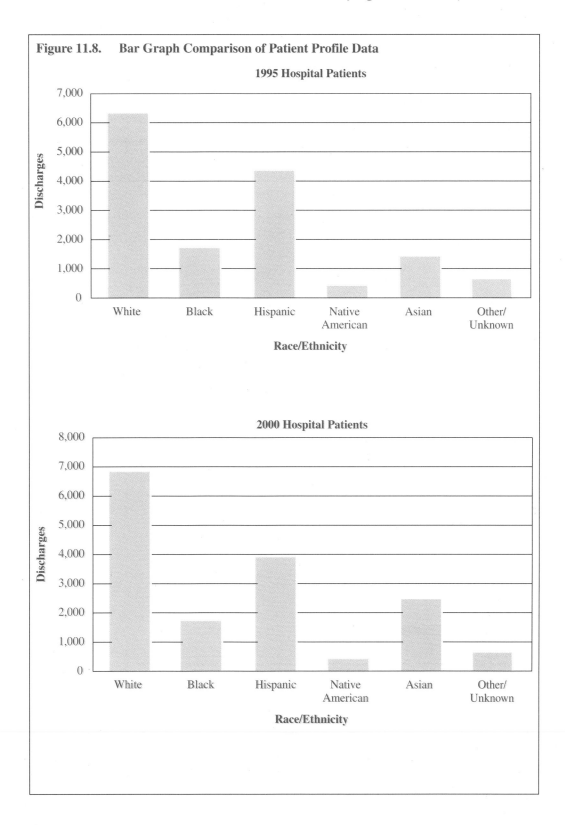

Figure 11.8.   Bar Graph Comparison of Patient Profile Data

Table 11.3.	Data Set for Pie Chart		
Profile of Hospital Patients			
1995		**2000**	
Admission Type	**Discharges**	**Admission Type**	**Discharges**
Emergency	2,163	Emergency	5,987
Urgent	4,325	Urgent	2,478
Elective	5,784	Elective	4,458
Newborn	1,659	Newborn	1,342
Delivery	1,478	Delivery	1,270

Figure 11.9.   Pie Chart Comparison of Patient Profile Data

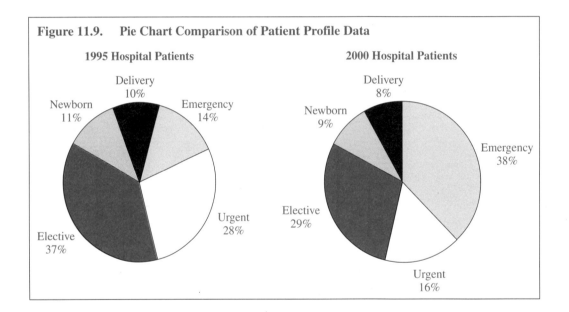

References and Suggested Readings

Fields, Willa L., and Dale Glaser. 1997. Using statistical process control tools in the quality process. *Improving Quality: A Guide to Effective Programs,* Claire Meisenheimer, editor. Gaithersburg, Md.: Aspen Publishers.

Lighter, Donald, and Douglas C. Fair. 2000. *Principles and Methods of Quality Management in Health Care.* Gaithersburg, Md.: Aspen Publishers.

Osborn, Carol. 2000. *Statistical Applications for Health Information Management.* Gaithersburg, Md.: Aspen Publishers.

Rudman, William. 1997. *Performance Improvement in Health Information Services.* Philadelphia: W. B. Saunders.

Table 11.4. Data Set for Case Study

HSA 11 — HFPA 933 — LAKEWOOD REGIONAL MED CTR – SOUTH ST
PROFILE OF HOSPITAL PATIENTS, CALIFORNIA ID# 106190240 SEE VOLUME III FOR LTC REPORTS

AGE	MALE	FEMALE	TOTAL	AVER STAY	ADJUSTED TOTAL CHARGES # TOTAL $	$/DAY	$/STAY
<29 DAYS	546	502	1,048	1.6	781,716	476	746
29-364 DY	6	5	11	1.9	29,432	1,402	2,676
1- 4 YRS	14	10	24	1.9	74,596	1,622	3,108
5-14 YRS	28	33	61	2.3	280,570	1,990	4,600
15-18 YRS	24	121	145	2.1	641,857	2,077	4,427
19-44 YRS	616	1,672	2,288	3.0	17,251,826	2,528	7,540
45-64 YRS	835	798	1,633	4.9	24,390,763	3,064	14,936
65-69 YRS	291	397	688	5.8	12,545,685	3,159	18,235
70-74 YRS	381	437	818	6.2	15,700,837	3,078	19,194
75-84 YRS	417	700	1,117	6.6	21,994,942	2,998	19,691
85+ YRS	128	278	406	6.4	6,490,931	2,499	15,988
TOTAL	3,286	4,953	8,239	4.4	100,183,155	2,787	12,160

EXPECTED SOURCE OF PAYMENT

SOURCE OF PAYMENT	DISCHARGES	%	AVER STAY	TOTAL $	$/DAY	$/STAY
MEDICARE	2,862	34.7	6.5	52,618,588	2,836	18,385
MEDI-CAL	1,836	22.3	3.2	12,966,166	2,194	7,062
INSURANCE CO	812	9.9	3.0	6,189,201	2,512	7,622
HMO/PHP	2,020	24.5	3.3	21,706,087	3,269	10,746
BLUE X/SHIELD	31	0.4	3.2	291,884	2,919	9,416
SELF PAY	423	5.1	2.9	3,139,734	2,551	7,423
MED INDIGENT	0	0.0	0.0	0	0	0
OTHER GOVMT	3	0.0	3.3	32,663	3,266	10,888
WORKERS COMP	251	3.0	4.1	3,236,576	3,124	12,895
OTHER	0	0.0	0.0	0	0	0
NONGOVMT	0	0.0	0.0	0	0	0
NO CHARGE	0	0.0	0.0	0	0	0
TITLE V	1	0.0	1.0	2,256	2,256	2,256
UNKNOWN	0	0.0	0.0	0	0	0
TOTAL	8,239	100.0	4.4	100,183,155	2,787	12,160

RACE/ETHNICITY

RACE/ETHNICITY	DISCHARGES	%	AVER STAY
WHITE	5,235	63.5	4.8
BLACK	772	9.4	4.3
HISPANIC	1,597	19.4	3.1
NATIVE AMER	98	1.2	3.8
ASIAN	482	5.9	3.8
OTHER & UNKNOWN	55	0.7	3.3

ADMISSION SOURCE

ADMISSION SOURCE	DISCHARGES	%	AVER STAY
ROUTINE	3,585	43.5	4.2
EMERGENCY ROOM	3,299	40.0	5.2
HOME HEALTH SVC	117	1.4	3.0
SHRT TERM ACUTE HOS	167	2.0	4.5
SNF/ICF	38	0.5	8.4
OTHER FACILITY	1	0.0	4.7
NEWBORN	1,032	12.5	1.6
OTHER & UNKNOWN	0	0.0	0

DISPOSITION

DISPOSITION	DISCHARGES	%	AVER STAY
ROUTINE	6,710	81.4	3.6
SHRT TERM ACUTE HOS	318	3.9	3.6
OTHER FACILITY	187	2.3	7.8
HOME HLTH SRVC	277	3.4	9.1
SNF/ICF	417	5.1	10.2
DIED	245	3.0	8.2
LEFT AGNST MED ADV	85	1.0	2.9
OTHER & UNKNOWN	0	0.0	.0

ADMISSION TYPE

ADMISSION TYPE	DISCHARGES	%	AVER STAY
EMERGENCY	606	7.4	7.2
URGENT	4,704	57.1	5.2
ELECTIVE	868	10.5	4.3
NEWBORN	1,032	12.5	1.6
DELIVERY	1,022	12.4	1.7
OTHER & UNKNOWN	7	0.1	1.7

UTILIZATION & CHARGES FOR MOTHERS & BABIES

	DISCHRGS	DAYS	ALOS	ADJUSTED TOTAL CHARGES # TOTAL	$/DAY	$/STAY
NORMAL NEWBRN (1)	910	1,379	1.5	623,095	452	685
DELVRY—VAGINL (2)	853	1,275	1.5	2,594,805	2,035	3,042
DELVRY—C.SECT. (3)	168	490	2.9	1,073,141	2,190	6,388

DEFINITIONS: (1) DRG 391; (2) DRGS 372 THRU 375; (3) DRGS 370 & 371.

MAJOR DIAGNOSTIC CATEGORY

MAJOR DIAGNOSTIC CATEGORY	DISCHARGES	%	AVER STAY	ADJUSTED TOTAL CHARGES # TOTAL $	$/DAY	$/STAY	PERCENTILES OF $/STAY # 10TH	50TH	90TH
01 NERVOUS SYSTEM	433	5.3	5.4	6,037,289	2,587	13,943	3,462	8,682	27,240
02 EYE	11	0.1	3.1	91,369	2,687	8,306			
03 EAR, NOSE, ETC	63	0.8	3.5	494,246	2,247	7,845	1,413	5,497	13,293
04 RESPIR SYSTEM	783	9.5	6.7	14,830,414	2,807	18,941	4,905	13,088	40,052
05 CIRCU SYSTEM	1,728	21.0	5.1	33,469,870	3,788	19,369	4,218	10,712	48,831
06 DIGESTIV SYSTM	598	7.3	5.0	8,158,578	2,723	13,643	3,160	7,335	22,872
07 HEPATO SYSTEM ETC	209	2.5	4.7	3,208,921	3,268	15,354	3,976	8,740	27,930
08 MUSCULOSKEL SYSTEM	656	8.0	5.5	9,884,375	2,760	15,068	4,153	11,050	26,487
09 SKIN, BREAST, ETC	174	2.1	5.3	2,008,206	2,195	11,541	3,096	7,001	19,284
10 ENDOCRIN, NUTRI, ETC	469	5.7	4.8	4,547,948	2,017	9,697	2,533	5,973	17,435
11 KIDNEY/URINARY	257	3.1	4.8	2,713,015	2,222	10,556	2,999	8,177	18,577
12 MALE REPRODUCTV	148	1.8	4.1	1,664,124	2,742	11,244	5,793	9,014	19,010
13 FEMALE REPRODUCTV	132	1.6	3.6	1,311,264	2,738	9,934	5,587	8,815	14,482
14 PREGNCY/CHILDBIRTH	1,104	13.4	1.8	4,058,449	2,092	3,676	2,214	3,101	8,245
15 NEWBORN/NEONATE	1,047	12.7	1.6	781,465	476	746	438	567	1,177
16 BLOOD, ETC.	35	0.4	4.6	362,063	2,249	10,345	3,632	6,887	26,568
17 MYELOPROLIF, ETC	54	0.7	5.6	731,165	2,413	13,540	2,517	8,806	29,828
18 INFEC & PARASIT	142	1.7	8.5	3,225,324	2,668	22,714	4,442	13,583	52,218
19 MENTAL DISORDERS	23	0.3	3.3	162,376	2,165	7,060	2,886	5,201	15,823
20 ALC/DRUG USE ETC	43	0.5	4.0	398,022	2,341	9,256	1,990	3,381	22,500
21 INJURY/POISON/DRUG	104	1.3	4.1	1,389,320	3,223	13,359	2,733	5,074	17,604
22 BURNS	3	0.0	13.0	68,008	1,744	22,669			
23 OTHER FACTORS	14	0.2	4.7	127,105	1,926	9,079			
24 MULTI SIG TRAUMA	1	0.0	5.0	14,540	2,908	14,540			
25 HIV INFECTIONS	8	0.1	20.3	445,699	2,751	55,712			
UNGROUPABLE	0	0.0	.0	0	0	0			
TOTAL	8,239	100.0	4.4	100,183,155	2,787	12,160	886	6,684	25,358

EXCLUDES DISCHARGES WHERE TOTAL CHARGES WERE REPORTED AS UNKNOWN

Chapter 12
Communicating Team Activities and Recommendations

Learning Objectives

- To be able to apply team communication tools such as minutes, quarterly reports, and storyboards

- To recognize the key elements in a storyboard and critique a storyboard layout

Background and Significance

The effective communication of information about the activities of performance improvement teams is vital to the performance improvement process in healthcare organizations. Each PI team's activities should be reported to the organization's leadership or quality council, which will in turn report significant process improvements to the governing board. (See the discussion on communicating with governing boards in chapter 13.)

Documentation of PI activities is also required by various regulatory and accreditation agencies. Such organizations require that process improvement activities take place within every healthcare organization, and they look for evidence of compliance during the survey process.

Healthcare organizations also use PI team communications in employee and program evaluations. In addition, effective communication promotes interaction among PI teams and helps the entire organization to keep up with progress on PI projects.

Some common methods of communicating team activities include minutes from team meetings, quarterly reports to the organization's quality council, and summary presentations of PI team activities and results in a storytelling format. Other forms of communicating performance improvement activities include minutes of the healthcare organization's quality council meetings, standard reports to the medical staff and the governing board, and presentations to representatives of regulatory and accreditation agencies. This chapter focuses on three basic communication tools used in performance improvement activities: minutes, reports, and storyboards.

Minutes

The team must keep track of its progress and activities. Documentation of the activities that take place in team meetings usually takes the form of **minutes.**

At the beginning of each PI project, the team should select the method it will use to set agendas for its meetings and allocate meeting time for action items and discussions. (See the discussion of agendas in chapter 3.) The responsibility for distributing the agendas for upcoming meetings and the minutes from past meetings should be discussed and assigned. The role of recorder can be made a rotating position, or the role can be assigned to one person for the whole project. In addition, the team should decide how the minutes of meetings and other documentation will be stored.

Many different formats can be used to record the minutes of group meetings. One method that is particularly helpful for performance improvement documentation is the CRAF method. In this method, the C stands for the *conclusions* of group discussion, the R stands for the *recommendations* made by the team, the A stands for the *actions* that the team or individual members decide to take, and the F stands for *follow-up.* (See figure 12.1 for an example.) By using this format, the recorder can avoid getting distracted from the discussion. The format allows the recorder to focus only on necessary documentation.

The conclusions section of the minutes should document the end result of the discussion and any decisions made by the team about future actions. The recorder should be sure to clarify the team's final conclusion at the end of a discussion when there is any possibility of ambiguity.

The recommendations section of the minutes should capture the team's plan for putting its decision into effect. The team's approach to solving the problem at hand should be listed as a recommendation.

The recorder then documents the actions the team or its individual members plan to take on specific process steps. Here, the minutes document who was assigned to accomplish what activities during the next period of work. Activities between meetings might include gathering data, talking with persons collateral to the process being examined, or doing a literature search.

The follow-up section of the minutes documents the team's assessment of how well the actions were accomplished and whether the group is ready to make decisions and recommendations for future activities. Documenting the team's progress ensures that the PI process is being followed appropriately and that sufficient analysis of previous actions has been undertaken.

Reports

In addition to documenting its meeting activities, the team must report on a regular basis to the organization's quality council. The frequency of reporting is usually determined at the time the quality council sets its charter. At a minimum, each PI team should submit a quarterly report of its progress to the organization's quality council. The quarterly report is developed on the basis of the documented team's meeting minutes. The quarterly report should include information about the team's composition, opportunity statement, mission, vision, performance measures, summary of data collection to date, conclusion, and recommendations. (See sample reporting form in figure 12.2.)

Figure 12.1.   Sample Minutes from a PI Meeting

Committee Name: HIM Laboratory

Approval:

Attendance/Name and Title: HIM 3320 Class

Date: January 15

Beginning/Ending Time: 10:05 a.m.–11:20 a.m.

Recorder: John Smith

Leader: Sue Jones

Facilitator: Kathy Anderson

Conclusions	Recommendations	Actions	Follow-up
Reviewed and finalized customer survey tool.	Additions/changes to customer survey: • Add "WSU" and class name to survey title. • Add A, B, C, . . . to question responses on survey (all questions as applicable). • Add "on average" to question #2 on survey x2. • Change question #5 wording on survey from "do you have knowledge" to "are you aware." • Add to question #6, "If not applicable to you, circle NA." • Change under question #6 "CPU" to "computer." • Add "NA" column for each response in #6. • Add month and year (1/00) to last page of survey—bottom left corner to indicate design date.	Terry to update survey per team recommendations by 1/20. Request HIM department secretary to copy survey once changes have been made.	Consensus reached on survey tool questions and administration of same.

(Continued on next page)

Figure 12.1. *(Continued)*

Conclusions	Recommendations	Actions	Follow-up
Administer survey next week during Stats class and HIM 3010 classes.		Lori and Terry to administer survey to Stats class next week. Michelle to administer survey to HIM 3010 class next week.	
Tabulate results of survey during meeting next week.	Break out in teams, compile data, decide on best QI tool(s) to use in presenting data and which software applications to use.		
Individual teamwork completed on outputs, i.e., identifying customer requirements, possible measure(s) for each requirement and flowcharting the process.	Break out in teams, assign leader, facilitator, and recorder per each team. Document and report all meeting decisions/actions.	Teamwork completed on following outputs: • Transcription • Chart analysis • Lab/resource accessibility	Assignment complete. Team roles practiced
Additional assignments given in preparation for next week's meeting: • Read handout "Developing an Information Management Plan." • Be prepared to discuss JCAHO IM Standards, which ones relate to HIM Laboratory.			
Evaluate meeting. Trouble with amount of time allotted per each agenda item. Adjourn.			

Figure 12.2.   Example of a Quarterly Report

Committee Name: HIM Laboratory
Leader: Sue Jones
Facilitator: Kathy Anderson
Date: January 15

Opportunity Statement	Student complaints have been received about the quality of resources and technology available in the HIM Laboratory.
Mission	Evaluate the HIM lab in regard to accessibility, resources, library access, Internet access, quality of equipment, and adequacy of equipment for HIM students.
Vision	The HIM lab provides access to a variety of application software resources, library knowledge bases, and the Internet. A convenient, comfortable work environment exists.
Performance Measure	Survey student satisfaction with HIM Laboratory.
Sample	All HIM and HIT students
Summary of Progress to Date	Survey will be administered to the students during the next week. Data will be tabulated and recommendations will be made. PI team should wrap up its activities by the end of February.
Conclusions	Not applicable at this time
Recommendations	In progress

Reported To: _____   Date: _____

Signature: _____   Date: _____

Storyboards

In addition to documenting the PI team's progress in the form of meeting minutes and quarterly progress reports, the team should be prepared to tell the story of process improvement activities to other people within the organization who are affected by the proposed changes. Storytelling has always been a powerful method of teaching and learning. **Storyboards** and similar electronic presentations help teams explain their work to people who may not be familiar with the performance improvement process. The purpose of storyboarding is to summarize the entire performance improvement project in a single graphic presentation. The team uses words, pictures, and graphs to tell the story of the project in a fashion that permits listeners to grasp the thinking of the team and to understand its specific applications of PI tools. The storyboard also communicates the team's growing knowledge of customers' needs and its understanding of the statistical data it has gathered.

Who started performance improvement storytelling? In the early 1990s, Kaoru Ishikawa called attention to the importance of telling quality stories in a structured manner to support learning and organizationwide performance improvement (Ishikawa, 1991). Since the technique was introduced, elaborate rules that outline how storytelling should be done have been developed. Leaders in continuous quality improvement and total quality management continue to emphasize its importance.

Who benefits from performance improvement storytelling? Actually, very few people do not benefit from learning in a clear, concise manner how a performance improvement effort proceeded. Examples of how individuals can benefit from the storytelling process include the following:

- By organizing a succinct presentation that documents the accomplishments of a team working together over an extended period of time, the presenter learns to focus his or her presentation skills and gains practice in sharing the pride that comes from working on PI projects.

- By helping the presenter to sharpen the presentation of their work, team members often crystallize their thinking about the process of improvement. In addition, the team learns to keep track of its work in a succinct and focused way, thus facilitating communication while reducing the accumulation of paper. By attending the presentation of the PI story, team members receive the public recognition that they are due and learn how they might contribute more in the future.

- By listening to an organized application of systematic methods for performance improvement to widely varying processes throughout the organization, department heads learn how they might think in new ways about their work and the improvement of the systems that they manage. Questioning each other helps create clearer awareness of how much people can learn from their associates.

- By reviewing the application of the process to particular teams, the professional staff can begin to see more clearly the impact of their role in the overall care of their patients. They can also learn how they might actively participate in performance improvement work themselves.

- By studying the application of the performance improvement to processes and the effect of process improvements on outcomes, the board can learn a great deal about the organization. It can also better meet its responsibility to ensure that the organization provides quality patient care.

- By gaining a clear understanding of the performance improvement process, the administrative team can prepare itself to lead and teach the process of management and improvement throughout the organization. In addition, it can recognize the contributions of the staff and encourage everyone to do just a little bit more. It can also provide regular opportunities to celebrate gains made in the continuing journey of performance improvement.

- By viewing the methods PI teams use, other employees have an inexpensive learning opportunity with practical application for their own participation on teams. Storytelling also provides an outstanding forum for new employees to be introduced to what performance improvement is all about.

- By observing a performance improvement storytelling session, guests, suppliers, and others can learn about performance improvement without imposing a significant additional burden on the presenters.

- By regularly reviewing the methods by which processes are improved, the whole organization learns the habit of making improvements in everything it does. The dominant culture of the organization becomes one of continuous improvement in every facet of the facility's life.

There are several keys to successful storytelling:

- Organize the individual stories well.

- Tell the stories in a structured and timely manner.

- Perform the process frequently enough so that it does not become a burden for presentation and can become part of the regular way of life in the organization.

- Link storytelling to the mission and vision of the PI project.

- Provide genuine opportunities to celebrate the improvement efforts of many people working together for better service.

- Regularly improve performance improvement storytelling techniques through feedback from participants and customers of the process.

- Have fun!

To create effective storyboards:

- Map the board in advance with labels for each section.

- Prepare clean boards for group presentation and display.

- Keep detailed information in a team record binder for reference.

- Plan the presentation to fit the size of the storyboard (36 × 48 inches is standard) and the general size of the panels.

- Use large fonts (24 point or greater) so that people can read the boards from a distance.

The basic storyboard format is illustrated in figure 12.3.

Figure 12.3. Sample Storyboard Layout		
Storyboard Title		
• Opportunity statement (mission/vision) • Team members • Customers • Relevant dimension of performance	• Key team activities in process steps • Flowcharts • Cause-and-effect (fishbone) diagram • Benchmarks	• Data gathered and analyzed (baseline and during PI activities) • Gantt chart • Future plans and goals

External Communications

Once a performance improvement project is complete, the organization may decide to communicate the outcome to its communities of interest: patients, medical staff, employers in the region, and others. Organizations that have improved their services often want to showcase their performance as a marketing technique.

Several approaches can be used to communicate information on performance improvements. For example, many healthcare organizations have developed sites on the Internet. Large healthcare corporations such as Intermountain Health Care and Columbia routinely present performance data on their Web sites to show customers and other stakeholders how well they are doing with respect to important performance measures.

Many healthcare organizations also publish information about efforts to improve the quality of the care they provide in their annual reports. Annual reports are an excellent vehicle for communicating performance information and for emphasizing an organization's mission in its community and continuing efforts to provide the community with the best healthcare possible.

In some segments of the healthcare industry (long-term care, for example), report cards provide consumers and other stakeholders with information on the performance of individual facilities. Report cards usually present data on an organization's performance with respect to a preestablished set of criteria relevant to the organization's service segment. For example, the Department of Health in Utah annually publishes report cards for every licensed long-term care facility in the state. The report cards show how each facility performed with respect to meeting the state's established licensing criteria.

Real-Life Example

The storyboard in figure 12.4 shows a student project. The PI project looked at the campus student health center. The group of students was concerned about customer satisfaction in terms of hours of operation, quality of care, and confidentiality. The student PI team developed mission and vision statements and identified the center's customers and the customers' requirements. Then the group conducted a survey of students, faculty, and staff to assess customer satisfaction with the center.

Case Study

Using the criteria listed below, students should critique the storyboard shown in figure 12.4.

Case Study Questions

1. Is the storyboard pleasing to look at, colorful, and easy to read?

2. Is the storyboard set up logically; are each of the process improvement steps taken into account?

3. Are the steps in the process easy to read and understand?

4. Are all of the elements of a good mission statement present? p. 19 - 21

5. Are all of the elements of a good vision statement present?

Figure 12.4.   Example of a Student Team's Storyboard Presentation

WSU STUDENT HEALTH CENTER
AND PHARMACY:
GOOD OR BAD?

MISSION STATEMENT:
Weber State University's
student health center
and pharmacy are
dedicated to providing
high-quality healthcare
to students, faculty, and staff.

BENCHMARK COMPARISON:
Hours of operation

Hours per Day

7
6
5
4
3
2
1
0

Weber State   University   Utah State
University   of Utah   University

SURVEY

How would you rate your overall
experience at GMS Hospital?
Excellent   Fair   Not Applicable

Were you courteously treated?
Excellent   Fair   Not Applicable

How was the food?
Excellent   Fair   Not Applicable

Was staff friendly, considerate?
Excellent   Fair   Not Applicable

VISION STATEMENT:
To provide high-quality
care in a patient-
focused environment.

BENCHMARK COMPARISON:
Drop-in versus scheduled appointments
Weber has drop-in appointments.
The University of Utah and
Utah State University schedule
appointments.

SURVEY OUTCOME:

All areas rated 3.5 or better on a 5-point
scale except for "Hours of operation
adequate" and "Length of time
waiting to be seen"

ACTION PLAN:
Determine whether there are
any problems with the services
provided by Weber State University's
student health center and pharmacy
by conducting a survey.

CUSTOMERS:
Students, faculty, and staff

TEAM MEMBERS:
Davis Christensen
James Clark
Mary Hancock
Anne Wheeler

RECOMMENDATIONS:
Student health center hours
should be extended.
The drop-in system should be
replaced with scheduling
by appointment.

CUSTOMERS' REQUIREMENTS:
Patient focused
Respect and compassion for individuals
Responsible use of resources
Responsive and user-friendly

6. Are the external and internal customers of the process identified?

7. Does the storyboard identify the requirements of the customers? If so, how well? If not, why?

8. Does the storyboard display the team's findings in the improvement process?

9. Are the team's recommendations based on the data they collected? Are the recommendations sound? Are there other recommendations that the team did not identify?

Project Application

Students should develop a storyboard or electronic presentation for their projects. The presentation or storyboard should include each of the steps in the improvement process as well as the students' findings and recommendations. Electronic presentations should include no more information than a storyboard would include.

Summary

Communication among the various constituencies involved in healthcare performance improvement activities is of paramount importance. Team members must keep the organization's leadership and/or quality council informed of their progress. The team must also track its activities carefully so that it stays focused on the issues for which it was constituted. The use of meeting minutes facilitates this communication and tracking. When the team has completed its work, communication of its activities to the organization as a whole informs everyone of changes in work processes and allows the people not involved in the project to see how the team arrived at its conclusions. Storyboards or electronic presentations are effective vehicles for this internal communication. Sometimes the organization may want to communicate performance improvement information to external stakeholders. Annual reports, information on Web sites, and report cards are tools that facilitate external communication.

Reference

Ishikawa, Kaoru. 1991. *Guide to Quality Control*. New York City: Asian Productivity Association.

Part III
Management of Performance Improvement Programs

Chapter 13
Organizing for Performance Improvement

Learning Objectives

- To understand the role of the organization's leaders in performance improvement activities

- To recognize the various configurations of leadership commonly assigned responsibility for performance improvement activities

- To be able to explain the types of education that may need to be undertaken to optimize the performance of an organization's board of directors

- To understand the best ways to organize performance improvement data for effective review by a board of directors

Background and Significance

Performance improvement is not an activity that happens effortlessly. Sometimes, however, healthcare organizations assume that improvements will occur naturally, seemingly without effort or commitment, because people will automatically do the "right" thing on their own. But the term *continuous* is often attached to improvement efforts (as in *continuous quality improvement*) for a reason. This term should remind healthcare workers that performance improvement activities require organizational and individual commitment and need to be carried out regularly if the organization is to benefit from them.

Given that performance improvement requires commitment and a continuous approach, who, then, makes it happen? Commitment is not a quality that every individual working in an organization exhibits spontaneously. Many people come from traditional management environments, where managers might have directed first-line personnel on exactly what to do and when to do it. The guiding principle of quality improvement in the Deming–Juran–Crosby–Donabedian model, however, is that all members of an organization must contribute to the PI program if it is to be successful. (See the discussion of the quality movement in the introduction to this textbook.)

Leading Performance Improvement Activities

Healthcare organizations must put formal structures in place to help the members of the organization develop the capacity for meaningful performance improvement. Members of the organization on all levels must recognize the commitment of the organization to quality improvement and understand the expectation that all must participate in order to accomplish improvements. At the same time, members of the organization must be accorded a certain amount of flexibility in their approaches to process improvement so that they are able to use PI techniques to accomplish improvements as rapidly and effectively as possible.

Over the years of development in process improvement methodology, it has become clear that the same methodology need not always be followed. (For example, review the discussion in chapter 3 about the necessity of developing a PI team in order to improve a process.) In addition, it may not always be feasible for permanent members of the organization to undertake improvement of every process. In some cases, the permanent members of the organization may not have the best knowledge base and expertise to improve the process in the most effective way. Often, in this situation, consultants are hired who have worked through the issues in other organizations and have the knowledge base and expertise to help the organization construct the best solutions. What the permanent members of the organization must be willing to accept responsibility for, however, is prioritizing the issues that the organization needs to improve. Those involved in daily operations can recognize, if given the opportunity, those aspects of the organization that have the greatest impact on patient care. They know whether those impacts are positive or negative.

Obviously, someone within the healthcare organization must help to make these kinds of decisions and ensure that the performance improvement process continues moving forward. Ultimately, most organizations have discovered that the "someone" is the *leadership* of the organization. The leadership of a healthcare organization comprises its board of directors (sometimes called trustees) and senior administrative officers, including the chief executive officer and administrators responsible for patient care services, finance, operations, and other major departments and service areas. Executive officers of the medical staff are also included in the leadership.

Today, it is commonly recognized across the industry that unless the leadership is committed to maintaining and empowering PI activities in the organization, real performance improvement that reaps real benefits for the organization cannot take place. Their valuing of performance improvement is a crucial and integral contribution to an organization's health.

A summary of the expectations of the leadership in healthcare organizations can be found in the leadership chapter of any set of JCAHO standards for accreditation. Review of one of these chapters is highly recommended to the student of healthcare performance improvement.

What in general does *leadership* mean in a healthcare organization? Recall from the study of management theory that boards of directors are responsible for setting the overall mission of the organization. Ultimately, boards of directors are held accountable by the public for the quality of the products and services provided by an organization. Through strategic planning, they validate the mission, vision, goals, and values for the organization as a whole and approve the direction of the organization as a business entity.

The leadership, including the organization's administrative officers, carefully considers the community the organization serves, the technologies available to it, the expectations of customers, and the expertise of personnel and medical staff when crafting the mission, vision, goals, and values. In response, the employees of the organization make the mission, vision, goals, and values "real" as a product or a service. Operational personnel determine through their actions the quality of the product or service.

Customers of the product or service (which, remember, might include patients, physicians, and employers) judge the quality and return their opinions about the products and services to the employed personnel and ultimately to the leadership through the performance improvement activities discussed in part II of this text. It is then the responsibility of the leadership to review the outcomes of the organization's mission and processes and approve modifications that enhance the quality of the organization's products and services. Modifications are communicated to the organization via the organization's annual **strategic plan** and its administrators and managers, and the cycle begins again. This cycle follows the performance improvement model discussed in chapter 1; the PI team in this context, however, is the leadership itself.

Leadership, however, is not an organizational body that meets and directs the actions of the organization every minute of every day. The administrators and managers of the organization are charged with day-to-day operations. How, then, are the leadership's plans executed? A variety of approaches have been undertaken by different healthcare organizations.

Ideally, every individual in the organization understands the principles of performance improvement and can contribute to PI activities when the need for improvement is recognized. In some organizations, most performance improvement activities derive from initiatives of first-line employees, those responsible for providing products and services to healthcare consumers. Some refer to this as a "bottom-up improvement initiative." Figure 13.1 shows a list of prioritized PI opportunities developed by the employees and managers of the Community Hospital of the West in 1998.

In other organizations, however, commitment to the performance improvement philosophy and activities is not as widespread. In such organizations, leaders actively promote performance improvement philosophies and encourage healthcare workers at all levels to participate in improvement efforts. The leaders are usually department managers or administrators.

In some organizations, an interdisciplinary quality improvement council is developed. The council is made up of interested and experienced individuals who lead PI efforts. In other organizations, a quality management department is developed to coordinate, oversee, and document performance improvement activities. Some organizations retain the services of consultants to lead performance improvement activities.

Finally, some approaches place the responsibility for performance improvement activities in the hands of top management. This is usually the most conservative and traditional management approach to improving products and services. Because improvements come by mandate from higher levels of management, this is often referred to as a "top-down improvement initiative."

Whatever approach an organization follows, the community the organization serves as well as its consumers and customers expect that the organization will provide the highest-quality products and services possible. Accreditation organizations such as the Joint Commission on Accreditation of Healthcare Organizations commonly want to see evidence of performance improvement activities and the ways in which those activities have benefited the organization's customers and consumers. Ultimately, that expectation is what the organization's performance will be judged against.

Figure 13.1.   Example of a Strategic Planning Document Showing Potential Performance Improvement Opportunities

Community Hospital of the West
Important Functions and Opportunities
1998 Strategic Planning

Functions and Opportunities	Priority
Patient care	
• Define restraint protocol	22
• Provide physical therapy services on weekends	1
• Change menu service	4
• Improve patient transport process	10
Patient education	
• Develop community awareness program	12
• Expand patient and family education	48
• Improve discharge instruction and documentation procedures	25
• Improve education for surgical patients	16
• Expand blood donor program	9
Patient rights	
• Include discussion of patient rights as part of admissions process	23
• Educate staff, families, and patients about the function of the ethics committee	21
• Respect patient's right to privacy and treatment with dignity	22
Patient assessment	
• Define assessment process	34
• Code status on admission	55
• Do more complete assessment on preop patients	11
Infection control	
• Enforce universal precautions	58
• Develop infection control program for home care	14
• Ensure that patient rooms are clean before assigning new patients to rooms	19
• Improve traffic control in patient care areas	18
Continuum of care	
• Address regional psychiatric services support	12
• Target high-risk patients for preventive care	17
• Respond to changing regulations on authorized procedures	15
• Define proper follow-up call from hospital to patient	10
• Define proper protocol for standing orders	27
Management of environment of care	
• Develop master plan for remodeling patient care areas	22
• Refine role of housekeeping	26
• Look at complaints about waiting areas	22
• Develop a system for providing hazardous spill carts	2
• Address afterhours/weekend security issues	25
• Remodel the operating room transitional area	3
• Upgrade operating room furniture and equipment	8

Figure 13.1. *(Continued)*	
Functions and Opportunities	**Priority**
Organizational improvements	
• Develop plan to reduce medication errors	21
• Explore concurrent data collection and reporting processes	13
• Implement supply chain management	4
• Improve radiology and operating room scheduling process	18
• Support process improvement activities through development of teamwork	16
Leadership	
• Develop a physician–hospital organization to work with managed care	13
• Conduct a community needs assessment	7
• Build feedback from employee and physician satisfaction surveys into the strategic planning process	7
• Develop a vision and goals for each department/service	5
• Downsize the number of committees	9
• Clarify leadership's role in all important organizationwide functions	8
• Introduce staff to board of trustees and define board's expectations of staff	2
• Define protocol for charity care	1
• Define hospital's system for acknowledging patients' deaths	2
• Clarify role of administrator on call	1
• Update and maintain all departmental policies and procedures	8
Management of human resources	
• Provide identity badges for all physicians	4
• Improve communications with key customers (patients, employees, physicians)	14
• Improve mandatory staff education process	20
• Develop and implement competencies/skills checklists for every department	18
• Improve system for designating PRN staff—who to call, how many, etc.	1
• Update physician directory	1
• Utilize intranet training	3
• Develop policy on lab testing for employees and physicians	2
• Develop staff cross-training program	10
• Decrease staff turnover	1
Management of information	
• Standardize organization of policies and procedures among departments	18
• Raise awareness of confidentiality issues	41
• Inventory the information the organization collects and determine what is necessary for quality control and leadership/governance needs	9
• Provide Internet access in the library	6
• Provide training and policy development on HCFA coding rules	6

Managing the Board of Directors' PI Activities

Members of healthcare boards of directors are appointed from the community at large. It is unlikely that the directors will have specific knowledge of healthcare operations or organizations when they are first appointed. Even after serving for several years, most directors will not have expertise in clinical processes or decision making. Therefore, it is important that the individuals leading performance improvement activities in healthcare organizations know how to optimally manage the board of directors' performance improvement oversight responsibility.

The board's oversight responsibility, after all, is a difficult task and in many ways a daunting one. Most directors feel awkward judging the work of physicians and other clinical staff. Coordinated systems of review are imperative to assist them in making decisions about the organization's quality of care and in taking appropriate action when action is necessary.

According to the American Hospital Association, four key elements affect the board's ability to carry out its performance improvement responsibilities:

- The board's "understanding of the quality assessment and improvement system" followed in the organization

- "Adequate reporting to the board by the staff on specific performance measures"

- The board's "oversight and approval of the process to ensure the continued competence of physicians and other clinical and technical staff"

- The board's "active questioning of the information" supplied on the quality of the care provided in the organization through performance monitoring and improvement activities (Umbdenstock, 1992)

Developing the board's ability to perform its responsibilities thus becomes of paramount importance. Carol Dye (1991, pp. 68–69) believes that education of the board should center on the following questions:

- "What type of coordinated program does this facility have in place to integrate the review activities of all services for the purpose of both enhancing the quality of patient care and identifying current and potential problems?"

- "How are the clinical and nonclinical activities of the institution monitored, and how are these two components integrated to ensure that the [PI] program is comprehensive?"

- "How is the [institution] organized to carry out the [PI] program? How are the services and departments organized for this function, and how are their activities coordinated?"

- "To whom do the various committees concerned with aspects of [PI] report, and how often?"

- "What are the institution's regular quality [monitoring] . . . activities and how often are they undertaken?"

- "What kinds of information [are] reported to the board, how often, and in what form? Because boards undertake much of their activities through committee structure, how [is the board] organized to receive and review information?"

She goes on to say that "the board's ability to oversee [PI] functions depends on its access to timely and meaningful data. When boards are given relevant information in a form they can understand, they are in a better position to respond appropriately; that is, to review, question, and set policy in an effective manner. Providing data that are concise, appropriately displayed, and organized in a comparative format will maximize the use of the board's time and assist its members in accomplishing [its oversight] activities in an efficient and effective manner." Because many board directors come from the business community, they "have become adept at reviewing financial data presented in forms such as current ratios, liquidity ratios, cash flow to total debt ratios, and so forth. Thus, for the most part, [members] will be comfortable reviewing quality-of-care information presented in similar statistical formats. Other [members] may benefit from having the data put into formats such as bar graphs, pie charts, and so forth that translate the statistical information into a visual image of the institution's progress. . . . When sharing data with a board of directors, it is important to remember that few [board members] are health care professionals. Thus, they may be unfamiliar with the data when first exposed to them. Careful attention should be paid to educating the trustees about certain concepts that govern data, such as validity, statistical confidence intervals, sample mean, and standard deviation."

Dye also suggests that the answers to several additional questions provide useful information for board members reviewing data on the quality of patient care:

- "How were the data collected and by whom?"

- "How often are data collected?"

- "How large is the sample?"

- "How do these data compare to data from previous assessments?"

- "What do the data suggest about the quality of care? Can specific patterns be identified? Are there individual sentinel events that require action?"

- "Are there other reviews that need to be undertaken in order to provide a more complete and/or accurate picture of the [organization's] quality of care?"

- "What should [the organization] strive for as a final goal in a particular area? What would be an appropriate objective for improvement?"

- "How does [the organization] compare to other similar organizations?"

According to Dye (1991, pp. 68–69), the board of directors should be provided information that answers the following questions when PI data identify adverse trends or occurrences:

- "If a problem or a potential problem emerges, what actions will be taken to correct or eliminate the problem and prevent or reduce its recurrence?"

- "Is there an area (department, procedure) that requires focused review?"

- "What departments and which professionals will be notified of the findings, and what role will they have in the followup?"

- "Will a report be provided to the board or an appropriate committee of the board and at what point in time?"

- "Have the problem, the review, and the plan of correction been documented?"

Ordinarily, boards of directors meet at least monthly; the subcommittees of the board may meet more frequently. From the preceding comments (Dye, 1991), it should be obvious that performance monitoring and improvement activities should be a regular subject of inquiry and decision making at all board meetings.

Other Resources for Performance Improvement Programs

In addition to the leadership and the board of directors, two other important organizational resources should be considered by healthcare organizations in their planning of a performance improvement program: standing committees of the medical staff and formal quality management structures.

Standing Committees of the Medical Staff

Standing committees of the medical staff have made significant contributions to the improvement of quality in healthcare for many decades. Standing committees are usually characteristic of large healthcare organizations. Small organizations usually have small medical staffs that are not able to support a standing committee dedicated solely to the quality of patient care.

Commonly, standing committees are organized to review specific aspects of patient care services, such as the use of blood products, morbidity and mortality, intensive care, perinatal and high-risk obstetrics care, surgical care, oncologic care, and others. Standing committees are usually chaired by a physician who specializes in an area related to the purview of the standing committee. The membership is usually drawn from the medical staff, nursing units, and administrative areas related to that specialty.

Routine review of care is usually undertaken by standing committees according to a preestablished protocol stipulating the means by which cases are selected for review each month. Special review of particular cases is also undertaken when negative outcomes have been identified through administrative channels or through referral from other organizational care review processes. The intent of the review is to identify case-specific patterns of care that could have achieved better outcomes had the care processes involved been better designed or implemented. Review also seeks to identify the need for education among the clinicians or others involved in the particular area of care.

For example, one common area of care review today centers on use of cesarean section for delivery of newborns. Contemporary obstetrical practice has clearly defined situations in which cesarean section delivery is appropriate because of the risk involved to infant and mother. When cesarean section is utilized in questionable circumstances, it is the responsibility of the obstetrical staff to determine the appropriateness and make recommendations to the clinicians involved regarding better practice decisions.

Findings of standing committee reviews are reported to the executive committee of the medical staff as well as to clinicians' professional files for reflection in recredentialing processes. (See the discussion of credentialing in chapter 10.) Findings are also considered by nursing and operations administrators when issues uncover opportunities for improvement of nursing or other functions supporting patient care. With reference to the quality improvement program, it is important that the reviews and findings of standing committees of the medical staff be documented and reflected as program outcomes, because standing committee reviews and findings are clear evidence of the involvement of the medical staff in patient care improvement activities.

Quality Resources Management Department

Consideration of a formal quality management structure usually revolves around the question of whether an organization should develop a quality resources management department. Answering this question is in turn dependent on a number of factors.

First and foremost, it is important to recognize whether the organization is considering development of a quality resources management department to deflect and perhaps hide its unwillingness to commit to a more authentic performance improvement culture. Some organizations develop departments to keep from having to develop organizationwide skill in performance improvement processes and to keep from having to deal with issues inherent in a more empowered, nonmanagement staff.

The former of these two issues is daunting to many organizations because educating an entire organization in the application of performance improvement techniques is a time-consuming and expensive proposition. Creating a quality *department* thus allows the organization to package its quality efforts in a less expensive box. Only a small number of people have to be trained in quality management activities, and they supposedly go out into the organization and improve performance. The problem with this approach, however, is that it effectively lets everyone in the organization off the hook with respect to taking on responsibility for improvement of patient care products and services. Everyone in the organization can point to the quality department and say to themselves that performance improvement is that department's responsibility. Such a mind-set is antithetical to the philosophical foundation of quality improvement in healthcare. Performance improvement must be everyone's responsibility.

The empowerment issue can provoke anxiety among managers as staff becomes more expressive of opinions and ideas for improving work processes and functioning. In order for performance improvement to be everyone's responsibility, managers in an organization have to be willing to let go of some authority for making decisions. They must be willing to listen to line staff who have suggestions for improving departmental processes and to support group decisions on how to make those processes perform better. Again, housing quality improvement activities in a department may be used so that managers will not be forced to let go of some of their power. When a separate department is responsible for quality, managers can look to performance improvement as an external entity that they can either take or leave, cooperate with or resist. When a department is responsible for performance improvement, managers will not need to change.

When, however, neither of these two unhealthy reasons for wanting a quality resources management department is present in an organization, there are important reasons why an organization may want to develop such a department, despite the costs involved. First, performance improvement activities are data- and information-intensive activities. (See the discussion of information management in chapter 15.) Quality resources management departments can assist an organization in managing the information related to performance improvement activities. They can become the centralized managers of repositories of information from performance improvement activities so that individual team leaders do not have to perform that function. They can become the experts in the organization on facilitation of team activities and use of the QI toolbox techniques. They can take the lead in the education of the organization's staff on the use of whatever performance improvement model the organization has decided to use. Finally, they can take the lead on the development of cross-functional and organizationwide reporting of performance improvement activities to quality councils and boards of directors. When used effectively and with a healthy performance improvement culture already in place across the organization, quality resources management departments can be an important supporting structure to a healthcare organization's quality improvement initiatives.

Case Study

The following case study was developed by Marie Kotter, Ph.D., professor, College of Health Professions, Weber State University, Ogden, Utah.

When a large regional medical center became part of an integrated delivery system that had a central board of directors, the medical center's board began to struggle with its role. Its new organizational environment included several outpatient clinics, multispecialty physician practices, and an insurance entity. Many of the current board members had served the organization since the medical center was built, and board activities had always been performed in a certain way. Board meetings were rigidly controlled by the administration. No questions were asked, and the members routinely voted approval on committee reports. The reports covered very important topics such as the organization's current financial status and future financial plans, physician credentialing, care quality monitoring reports, new policies, and plans for a new hospital.

A new female board member with a healthcare background was appointed after extensive screening and a personal interview with the executive committee. She was not part of the local business power structure, and the administration was concerned that her appointment might not be a wise move. During her first board meeting, two very interesting reports were given. One report detailed some reengineering projects that were going on. One of these was redesigning nursing staffing patterns and decreasing the number of RNs and replacing them with LPNs and CNAs. The current quality report documented a very high quality of care and positive patient satisfaction surveys. Data excerpted from this report can be seen in the left column of figure 13.2. Given that this was her first board meeting, the new board member remained silent and did not ask questions.

Four months later, the new nursing staffing pattern had been implemented and had been used in the interim. Data excerpted from the quality indicators report presented to the board at that time can be seen in the right column of figure 13.2. The new female board member was very concerned and decided to ask the nurse administrator presenting the quality report whether the values, which were decreasing, were for the nursing units with the new nursing staffing patterns. The administrator reported that there was a direct correlation. This answer initiated discussion among other board members who were accustomed to using quality indicators in their businesses. This was the first substantive discussion at the board level that the new board member had seen. One board member wanted to know whether any data had been gathered from patient focus groups. Another board member asked whether the average length of stay data had increased, and someone else asked about a cost–benefit analysis of the new staffing patterns. Following the usual

Figure 13.2.   Data for the Case Study

Quality Indicators—January 1, 1997		Quality Indicators—April 1, 1997	
14. Medication errors	3.20%	14. Medication errors	10.42%
25. Patient falls	4.21%	25. Patient falls	8.56%
32. Cesarean sections	14.72%	32. Cesarean sections	17.87%
35. VBAC rate	18.27%	35. VBAC rate	15.72%
40. Nosocomial infections	1.78%	40. Nosocomial infections	4.85%
46. X-ray discrepancies	0.15%	46. X-ray discrepancies	0.21%

Patient Satisfaction Survey—January 1, 1997		Patient Satisfaction Survey—April 1, 1997	
1. Service overall	40.52%	1. Service overall	20.74%
2. Clinical overall	86.72%	2. Clinical overall	70.82%
3. Overall quality of service	45.40%	3. Overall quality of service	22.34%
4. Food	30.56%	4. Food	32.54%
5. Overall cleanliness	85.89%	5. Overall cleanliness	83.26%

process, the chair called for approval of the report and presentation of the next item on the agenda.

Case Study Questions

1. What changes or patterns do you see in the data? What remedies might be suggested for any problems?

2. Is there further opportunity to influence how the current board is structured and functioning? Why or why not?

3. If so, what strategies would you recommend?

4. If the board were redesigned, what quality data should be reported and utilized?

Summary

Several important aspects of performance improvement programs should be reflected in organizational structure. First and foremost, it is important for a healthcare organization to determine the roles of its leadership group and governing board in the performance improvement program. A significant amount of board development is needed with respect to understanding healthcare processes and issues and analyzing PI data and information. Some organizations use their standing medical staff committees as important adjuncts to team-based performance improvement activities. Some develop formal quality resource management departments in support of PI activities.

References

Arrington, B., K. Gautam, and W. M. McCabe. 1995. Continually improving governance. *Hospital and Health Services Administration* 40(1):95–110.

Dye, Carol. 1991. Quality assurance data management: the trustees' role. *Quantitative Methods in Quality Management.* Chicago: American Hospital Publishing.

Umbdenstock, Richard J. 1992. *So You're on the Hospital Board!* Chicago: American Hospital Publishing.

Chapter 14
Surviving the Accreditation, Certification, or Licensure Survey Process

Learning Objectives

- To differentiate between compulsory reviews and voluntary reviews

- To understand the performance improvement perspectives of accreditation, certification, and licensure organizations

- To understand the various approaches of accreditation, certification, and licensure agencies to the site visit and survey

- To identify approaches that lead to success in the survey process

Background and Significance

It should be obvious by this point in the text that complex accreditation, certification, and licensure requirements have a significant impact on healthcare organizations. Few healthcare professionals can work in the industry for long without taking part in an accreditation, certification, or licensure process. This chapter provides a basic introduction to the concepts and processes involved.

Accreditation is the act of granting approval to a healthcare organization. The approval is based on whether the organization has met a set of voluntary standards that were developed by the accreditation agency. The Joint Commission on Accreditation of Healthcare Organizations (JCAHO) is an example of an accreditation agency. Healthcare organizations value accreditation because accreditation confirms the quality of the services they provide. For example, hospitals accredited by the JCAHO have a competitive advantage over nonaccredited hospitals in their geographical area.

Licensure is the act of granting a healthcare organization or an individual healthcare practitioner permission to provide services of a defined scope in a limited geographical area. State governments issue licenses on the basis of regulations specific to healthcare practices. For example, states issue licenses to individual hospitals, physicians, and nurses. It is illegal for unlicensed organizations and professionals to provide healthcare services in all fifty states.

Certification is the act of granting approval for a healthcare organization to provide services to a specific group of beneficiaries. Healthcare organizations must meet the federal *Conditions of Participation* to receive funding through the Medicare and Medicaid programs. The Medicare and Medicaid programs are administered by the Health Care Financing Administration (HCFA), which is an agency of the U.S. Department of Health and Human Services.

Healthcare Accreditation, Certification, and Licensure Standards

In healthcare today, many different agencies develop and monitor standards on the quality of healthcare services. These agencies accomplish their missions through a comprehensive review process. Some of the review processes are compulsory, and others are voluntary. **Compulsory reviews** are performed to fulfill legal or licensure requirements. **Voluntary reviews** are conducted at the request of the healthcare facility seeking accreditation from the reviewing agency.

Every accreditation, certification, and licensure agency develops written standards or regulations that serve as the basis of the review process. To prepare for a review, the healthcare organization must obtain a current set of standards or regulations from the accreditation, licensure, or certification agency. The materials may be provided in the form of manuals (for example, the JCAHO's *Comprehensive Accreditation Manual for Hospitals*) or state and federal regulations (for example, the Medicare *Conditions of Participation*). It is imperative that the healthcare facility monitor any changes and updates to the various standards and regulations and keep current sets of them on hand at all times to maintain their **compliance** status. **Compliance** is the process of meeting a prescribed set of standards or regulations in order to maintain active accreditation, licensure, or certification status.

Joint Commission on Accreditation of Healthcare Organizations

The JCAHO has been the organization responsible for accrediting healthcare organizations since the middle 1950s. According to the organization (JCAHO, 2000):

> The mission of the Joint Commission on Accreditation of Healthcare Organizations is to continuously improve the safety and quality of care provided to the public through the provision of health care accreditation and related services that support performance improvement in health care organizations.
>
> The Joint Commission evaluates and accredits more than 19,500 health care organizations in the United States, including hospitals, health care networks, managed care organizations, and health care organizations that provide home care, long term care, behavioral health care, laboratory, and ambulatory care services. The Joint Commission is an independent, not-for-profit organization, and the world's leading health care standards-setting and accrediting body.

The primary focus of the JCAHO at this time is to determine whether organizations seeking accreditation are continually monitoring and improving the quality of care they provide. The JCAHO requires that this continual improvement process be in place throughout the entire organization, from the board of directors down, as well as across all department lines. The JCAHO's Web address is http://www.jcaho.org.

Commission on Accreditation of Rehabilitation Facilities

In 1966, the Commission on Accreditation of Rehabilitation Facilities (CARF) was established. CARF is a private, not-for-profit organization committed to developing and maintaining practical, customer-focused standards to help organizations measure and improve the quality, value, and outcomes of behavioral health and medical rehabilitation programs. CARF accreditation means that the organization has made a commitment to continually enhancing the quality of its services and programs and that its focus is on customer satisfaction. More information about CARF can be found on the Internet at http://www.carf.org.

American Osteopathic Association

The accreditation of healthcare organizations became a focus of the American Osteopathic Association (AOA) in 1945. Initially, the primary initiative of the AOA was to ensure that osteopathic students received their training through rotating internships and residencies in facilities that provided a high quality of patient care. The AOA has since developed accreditation standards for hospitals, ambulatory care facilities, ambulatory surgery centers, behavioral health facilities, substance abuse treatment facilities, and physical rehabilitation facilities. The American Osteopathic Association's Internet site is http://www.am-osteo-assn.org.

National Committee for Quality Assurance

The National Committee for Quality Assurance (NCQA) began accrediting managed care organizations in 1991. Since then, the NCQA's activities have broadened to include accreditation of managed behavioral health organizations and credentials verification for physician organizations. As a private, not-for-profit organization, the NCQA is dedicated to improving the quality of healthcare by assessing and reporting on the quality of the nation's managed care plans. Its efforts are focused on the development of performance measurements in key areas such as member satisfaction, quality of care, access, and service. NCQA uses the Health Plan Employer Data and Information Set (HEDIS) to accomplish these assessments of managed healthcare plans. The performance measures in HEDIS are related to significant public health issues and are a basis for purchasers and consumers to compare the performance of healthcare plans. HEDIS data along with NCQA accreditation provide organizations a method for selecting healthcare plans based on demonstrated value rather than simply on cost. The NCQA's Internet address is http://www.ncqa.org.

Conditions of Participation

Every healthcare organization that provides services to Medicare and Medicaid beneficiaries must demonstrate its compliance with HCFA's *Conditions of Participation*. The compliance process is known as certification, and it is usually carried out by state departments of health. The *Conditions of Participation* for healthcare facilities cover issues related to medical necessity, level of care, and quality of care. HCFA also contracts with nongovernmental agencies across the country to monitor the care provided by independent healthcare practitioners. The agencies are called **peer review organizations** (PROs). PROs retrospectively review patient records to ensure that the care provided by practitioners meets the federal standards for medical necessity, level of care, and quality of care.

State Licensure

Every healthcare facility must have a license to operate within the state in which it is located. The license grants the facility the legal authority to provide healthcare services within its scope of services. To maintain its licensed status, the organization must adhere to the state regulations that govern issues related to staffing, physical facilities, services provided, documentation requirements, and quality of care. The regulations are usually monitored and evaluated on an annual basis by the licensing agencies of state departments of health.

Development of Policies and Procedures to Meet Multiple Standards

At a minimum, healthcare organizations must consider state licensure regulations when they develop policies and procedures that relate to the documentation and quality of the healthcare services they provide. When a facility provides care to Medicare and Medicaid patients (and most do), it must also determine which of the *Conditions of Participation* apply. When a facility is accredited by the JCAHO, CARF, AOA, and/or some other accreditation organization, those standards must also be taken into consideration.

To ensure compliance, the healthcare organization must review all of the standards and regulations that affect facilities in its geographical location. The most stringent standard or regulation on each aspect of care should be identified, and organizational policies and procedures should be based on that standard or regulation.

For example, when the healthcare facility is setting policy on charting by exception, the state licensure regulations must be reviewed for their requirements. Then the *Conditions of Participation* regulations must be reviewed for their requirements. And, finally, all relevant accreditation standards must be reviewed for their requirements. The strictest standard among all of these standards should be written into the policy and procedure for chart documentation by exception.

Surviving the Survey Process

Ongoing foresight and planning are the keys to successfully completing accreditation and licensure reviews. The leaders of the healthcare organization must stay focused on the organization's accreditation, certification, and licensure status to ensure that these issues are not overlooked in the flurry of day-to-day operations. Preparation for accreditation and/or licensure processes cannot be accomplished a few weeks before the organization is due for review. A solid accreditation and licensure infrastructure must be built and maintained so that the organization is ready for an inspection at any time.

Some accreditation processes are scheduled processes. Although the JCAHO states in its manuals that surveyors may drop in to perform review activities at any time, it conducts unscheduled reviews at only 5 to 10 percent of its accredited organizations each year. State agencies representing state licensing or federal Medicare/Medicaid certification programs may drop in at any time. In California, for instance, long-term care facilities must be ready for representatives of state licensing agencies to walk in at any time.

HCFA accepts accreditation by the JCAHO and CARF as what it calls **deemed status.** Deemed status means that HCFA assumes that an organization meets the *Conditions of*

Participation when the organization is currently accredited by the JCAHO or CARF. HCFA's regional offices, however, frequently review psychiatric facilities accredited by CARF for compliance with the *Conditions of Participation.*

Going through a review process with any of these agencies is largely an issue of packaging. Surveyors from the JCAHO, for example, want to be assured that the facility's leadership and staff can successfully execute organizational policies and procedures. They want to be assured that the leadership and staff are continuously monitoring and improving performance in the organization and that those improvements are tied to the strategic plan of the organization. Therefore, these aspects are the ones that surveyors will want to validate as operative in the organization when they arrive for a review.

Although state licensure surveys may be more focused on a facility's ability to meet department of health regulations, the emphasis is still on whether patients receive high-quality care. It is important to remember that the goal of reviewers is to help healthcare organizations reflect upon their own performance. Members of the organization are often too close to everyday activities and events to recognize important trends or consequences of the organization's inaction.

The actual review processes of accrediting and licensing agencies are not standardized. Processes also may change from year to year as philosophies change within the agencies. In general, voluntary accreditation processes such as those of the JCAHO and CARF are more flexible and tailored to the type of organization that is being reviewed. Governmental processes tend to be more bureaucratic. The point is for the organization's leaders to be aware of, and prepared for, the type of review activities that will be undertaken by the applicable accrediting or licensing agency.

The remainder of this chapter will provide an overview of the more prominent accreditation and licensure processes.

Accreditation of Acute Care and Other Facilities: Joint Commission on Accreditation of Healthcare Organizations

The JCAHO's accreditation survey for acute care hospitals is usually scheduled in advance. Organizations interested in becoming accredited by the JCAHO must file an application that provides information on the type of organization it is, the services it provides, certain statistical characteristics, and the names of its executive officers. Most hospitals undergo a **site visit** every three years.

The JCAHO **survey team** usually has three members, although additional members may be added for special purposes unique to the organization to be surveyed. In most cases, the team is made up of one surveyor who is a physician, one surveyor who is an administrator, and one surveyor who is a registered nurse. JCAHO surveyors have many years of experience practicing in the acute care segment of the healthcare industry. Every surveyor undergoes considerable training in JCAHO accreditation processes prior to being assigned to a survey team.

The JCAHO process commonly follows a generic schedule, which is presented here. However, the surveyors may tailor the actual review activities to the characteristics and services of the organization under review. It is important to remember that JCAHO processes are not static from year to year, and the Joint Commission institutes annual improvements in its own survey processes. Any healthcare professional involved in preparations for a JCAHO accreditation survey must be aware of the current requirements, constraints, and expectations of surveyors. Again, it is not the intent of the authors of this text to provide all-encompassing preparation guidelines for JCAHO surveys but rather an overview of common survey activities.

The survey process lasts for about three days, although the length of the process depends on the size and complexity of the organization. In a large and highly complex organization (for example, a university medical center), accreditation survey activities may last for five days. Commonly, opening activities and document review take up the entire first day of the site survey.

The site visit begins with an **opening conference** and performance improvement overview involving the surveyors and the leaders of the organization. At the opening conference, the surveyors outline the schedule of activities and list any individuals whom they would like to interview.

At this time, the organization's leaders are expected to provide an overview of the organization's mission and vision, strategic goals and objectives, current experiences and outcomes, and performance monitoring and improvement activities. If the organization is experiencing significant challenges in any areas, it is expected that those areas of challenge will be identified for the surveyors. Information about the organization's recent achievements is very important as well. The surveyors want an accurate picture of the status of the organization.

As mentioned earlier, much of the accreditation process is a matter of packaging. The surveyors are interested in seeing how the members of the organization, both leaders and staff members, provide healthcare services and products, how they measure the quality of those services and products, and how they identify and develop opportunities for improvement. Therefore, the opening conference is an important opportunity for the organization to set the tone for the remainder of the site visit.

When the organization projects an objective and verifiable image of itself as an organization committed to providing high-quality patient care, surveyors are more likely to carry a positive impression of the organization throughout the remainder of their review activities. Similarly, when an organization projects a disorganized, subjective, and unverifiable image and is unable to show clearly defined organizational responsibility for care processes and quality, surveyors may approach the remainder of survey activities with skeptical attitudes and negative impressions of the organization's overall compliance with accreditation standards.

The second major component of the survey agenda is **document review.** In practice, document review may be the most important part of the survey process. Surveyors conduct an in-depth study of the organization's policies and procedures, administrative records, human resources records, performance improvement documentation, and other similar documents as well as a review of closed patient records. Closed records are the records of discharged patients and are assumed by the surveyors to be complete with respect to all necessary and appropriate documentation.

Again, the expectation is that the organization will be able to produce documents that reflect established policies and procedures that employees recognize and can execute appropriately. Sample documents should be up-to-date and carefully organized so that a surveyor can easily identify what is going on in a particular area of the organization. **Closed record review** should evidence completeness, organization, effective communication, and appropriate care planning and assessment by the organization's personnel. Records should also show that the products and services ordered by physicians are provided efficiently. In addition, records should reflect the clinical pertinence of diagnostics and therapeutics to patient symptoms, presentation, and continuing assessment.

After document review, the surveyors visit patient care settings and conduct interviews with the organization's leaders and program and department staff. Commonly, the interviews and visits to patient care areas take about a day and a half on average to complete. During interviews with the organization's leaders, the surveyors gain insight into the organization's recent successes and current challenges. They develop a background in the philosophy of management followed in the organization and the means by which the organization effects needed change.

The number of interviews conducted depends on the size and complexity of the organization. Smaller organizations may experience interviews with only administrative staff and top medical staff officers. Larger and more complex organizations will likely field requests for interviews with additional nonadministrative staff. The chairpersons of important committees such as the patient services committee and the infection control committee may be interviewed. Directors of vital departments such as quality management and human resources are also likely to be interviewed in large organizations.

As the surveyors tour patient care settings, their mission is to verify the status of the organization as conveyed in the document review. Commonly, the surveyors divide up the visits to various areas of the organization according to their professional expertise. Administrator surveyors review the physical plant and financial services offices, for example. Nurse and physician surveyors visit nursing and other patient care areas, and they may review the records of current patients on the nursing units. Surveyors interview staff members in various areas to see whether they understand the organization's mission and vision and to determine how the staff members see themselves as contributors to that mission and vision.

Surveyors may also request access to areas of the organization that may seem unusual, such as the areas between the floors of buildings that house utility lines, water pipes, vacuum lines, and heating ducts to see whether those areas conform to standard construction codes. Surveyors often want to hear reports from staff members about the means by which the staff monitors departmental performance and how they have improved departmental performance in the recent past.

Trigger issues may be reviewed in depth with staff encountered during visits to care settings. The trigger issues on which JCAHO surveyors have focused in recent surveys include patient rights, the use of restraints in patient care, and general safety in the care environment. Whatever the current trigger issues are, the organization's leaders must be aware of them and have taken proactive steps to ensure that all employees have appropriate and well-developed conceptions of how the issues affect their provision of patient care and other services.

Following completion of the interviews and visits to patient care areas, the survey team sequesters itself to consider its findings. It develops a preliminary report of the onsite survey at this time and identifies any deficiencies that it feels are evident in the organization. Following development of the preliminary report of the survey, the surveyors and members of the organization's leadership team reconvene for an **exit conference.**

During the exit conference, JCAHO surveyors summarize their findings and explain any deficiencies that have been identified during the site visit. Leaders have a short opportunity to discuss the surveyors' perspectives or provide additional information related to any deficiencies the surveyors intend to cite in their final reports. Finally, the surveyors report the probable accreditation decision of the commission on the basis of the survey findings.

The JCAHO uses seven categories to report its decisions on accreditation. Each decision category and typical conditions that lead to it are described in the following list (JCAHO, 2000):

- *Accreditation with commendation:* Accreditation with commendation is the highest decision category. To meet the requirements for this category, the healthcare organization must have a summary grid score of 90 or higher for all applicable services *and* require no follow-up monitoring.

- *Accreditation without type I recommendations:* This category means that the organization has complied with all of the JCAHO's performance standards.

- *Accreditation with type I recommendations:* This category is assigned when an organization did not demonstrate sufficient compliance in one or more specific performance areas. The organization must meet the JCAHO's type I recommendations within a specified time period in order to maintain its accreditation.

- *Provisional accreditation:* This accreditation decision category is assigned when the organization has demonstrated compliance with selected standards during an initial survey. A second survey conducted about six months later allows the organization enough time to demonstrate satisfactory performance and receive one of the other accreditation decisions.

- *Conditional accreditation:* An organization that receives this accreditation decision did not meet the JCAHO's standards on an initial survey and was given the opportunity to correct its performance *or* it experienced one or more adverse clinical events that reflected potential systems issues. Organizations that receive conditional accreditation must develop a plan for correcting the problem and demonstrate sufficient improvement in a follow-up survey conducted within six months.

- *Preliminary nonaccreditation:* This decision category is assigned to organizations that were in significant noncompliance with the JCAHO's standards *or* to organizations that had their accreditation preliminarily withdrawn for other reasons *before* the final accreditation decision was made.

- *Not accredited:* This accreditation decision results when accreditation is denied because of significant noncompliance with standards, because accreditation was withdrawn for other reasons, or because the organization withdrew from the accreditation process.

All other JCAHO-sponsored accreditation processes follow the same basic agenda as outlined for acute care. Site visits begin with an opening conference, then proceed to document review, care unit visits (even if that means going to a client's home as in home health accreditation), and exit conference.

Certification and Licensure of Long-Term Care Facilities: State Departments of Health

Long-term care facilities are subject to government-directed certification and licensure programs. Licensure regulations are published by each state, and long-term care facilities are expected to comply with the regulations continuously. In addition to state regulations, the federal government developed its own set of regulations in 1974 as an attempt to improve the care provided in long-term care facilities that receive federal Medicare and Medicaid funds.

State departments of health usually conduct unscheduled reviews of long-term care facilities. All long-term care facilities must have a license to provide services in the states in which they operate, and licenses usually must be renewed annually. Facility administrators understand that the state department of health will return for the next annual review within fifteen months of the previous on-site review.

In addition, for those long-term care facilities that receive Medicare/Medicaid funding, certification of compliance with the *Conditions of Participation* must be achieved as well. State departments of health also conduct Medicare/Medicaid certification reviews, which may or may not be performed concurrent with licensure review. Scheduling of certification reviews depends on the organizational structure of the department of health in any given state. When there have been complaints from residents, families, or employees against a long-term care facility, department of health surveyors may drop in to perform a special investigation at any time.

Department of health survey teams commonly consist of two surveyors who come from a nursing background. The surveyors are usually permanent employees of the department. When the review is not being conducted in response to a complaint, the survey process encompasses all aspects of facility operations. The surveyors determine at the time of site visit which of those operations will be investigated.

The state review process is not standardized among states. The survey process in the state of California is presented here as an example.

In California, the annual site visit begins with the posting of a notification of survey on the doors to the facility and at every nursing station. The notification of survey requests that anyone—resident, staff member, or visitor—who has issues or perspectives that they wish to communicate to the surveyors make themselves known. An opening conference is held with the facility's administrators and the director of nurses to explain the purpose of the survey, that is, whether it is an annual review or an investigation in response to a complaint, and the sequence of the survey activities is outlined during the opening conference.

Long-term care site surveyors always look for evidence of three trigger issues in long-term care: excessive percentages of patients suffering from dehydration, decubitus ulcers in low-risk residents, and fecal impaction. Current federal regulations mandate the primary importance of these issues in the long-term care setting. Whether the facility has excessive percentages is determined on the basis of the Facility Quality Indicator Profile. The profile is compiled on the basis of information provided to state departments of health via the long-term care Minimum Data Set (MDS). An MDS must be maintained for every resident of a long-term care facility. (See the earlier discussion of this subject in chapter 8.) Focused review of the health records of residents with these conditions is carried out when excessive numbers are identified.

Following the delineation of the survey objectives, the surveyors begin examination of facility operations. Members of the facility's residents' council are interviewed to determine whether any issues have been raised by residents in the facility since the last site review. Ancillary departments such as nutrition services are visited, and operations are reviewed for continuing adherence to public health standards. Nursing units are visited, and resident records are reviewed as deemed necessary by the surveyors. Records are reviewed for compliance with state regulations regarding such issues as annual care plan review by physicians, authentication of physicians' orders, proper administration of medication by nurses, and appropriate charting of care by nursing assistants.

When their review activities are complete, the surveyors meet again with the facility's administrators and director of nurses to summarize their findings. Any deficiencies that require citations are also discussed at this time.

Accreditation of Psychiatric and Rehabilitative Care Facilities: Commission on Accreditation of Rehabilitation Facilities

CARF's accreditation reviews are usually scheduled in advance. Organizations interested in CARF accreditation must file an application that outlines the type of organization, the services that it provides, some statistical and textual description of its characteristics, and names of individuals comprising its leadership. Most CARF-accredited organizations undergo a site visit every three years.

The CARF survey team commonly includes three members, although additional members may be added for special purposes unique to the applying organization. Usually, the team is made up of professionals from other CARF-accredited organizations. Their areas of expertise are similar to those in which the organization undergoing accreditation specializes. For example, when the organization under review is an inpatient psychiatric institution, the surveyors have psychiatric inpatient experience and have practiced as administrators or clinicians in that setting. Surveyors undergo considerable training in CARF accreditation processes before they are assigned to a survey team.

In contrast to the JCAHO process, the CARF accreditation process is much more flexible and is highly tailored to the patient care services and communities of interest of the organization. However, a quasi generic review schedule is followed. Within each segment of the schedule, however, the activities pursued depend on the characteristics of the organization applying for accreditation.

The CARF accreditation site visit begins with an opening conference. CARF requires that the opening conference be accessible to all the communities of interest in the organization. Interested participants may include payers, staff members, referring agencies, members of the community, current and former patients, and others. It is the expectation of the surveyors that these constituencies will be allowed to voice concerns and issues during the opening conference. As in the JCAHO agenda, the survey team then outlines the activities that it wants to pursue over the ensuing two or three days of the site survey.

The second part of the CARF accreditation site visit is also similar to that of the JCAHO: document review. Again, the document review examines policies and procedures, administrative rules and regulations, administrative records, human resources records, and the case records of patients.

The third part of the survey involves interviews with program staff and patients. The surveyors seek to validate the information gathered from the document review and to determine whether staff or patients have any important issues regarding patient care services.

Finally, the CARF process ends with an exit interview with the organization's leaders. Surveyors identify any deficiencies that have been uncovered and present an overall summary of their findings.

Certification: Compliance with the Medicare/Medicaid *Conditions of Participation*

Some healthcare organizations in the United States undergo no accreditation process. A few others have undergone accreditation with an accrediting agency but have been identified by federal Medicare officials as requiring specific review for compliance with the Medicare/Medicaid *Conditions of Participation.*

Surveys to determine a facility's compliance with the *Conditions of Participation* are carried out by state healthcare certification and/or licensure agencies. As with the state certification/licensure processes discussed earlier, state department of health reviews are usually unscheduled. The survey team drops in to the healthcare facility as necessary either on an annual basis or in response to complaints from patients or employees. In addition to the surveyors commonly used by the department of health in a given state, regional Medicare agencies may provide one or two Medicare officials from the regional office.

After the opening conference during which the Medicare officials make it known that the review will be for the purpose of determining compliance with the *Conditions of Participation,* the Medicare officials generally leave and do not participate in the on-site survey activities. Judgments about compliance with the conditions are left to the state certification surveyors because they generally make those judgments anyway.

Real-Life Example

Table 14.1 provides an example of how applicable standards can be reviewed as a basis for developing an organization's policies and procedures to meet multiple standards. The hospital for which this analysis was developed treats patients at many different levels of care (inpatient hospitalization, partial hospitalization, outpatient group home environment, and so on). It wanted to develop a policy for charting by exception that would meet all applicable regulations and standards. Each regulatory and accrediting agency's standards were reviewed, and the standards were organized in a tabular format. This format allowed for easy viewing of all standards to determine which standard set the strictest requirements. None of the standards consulted prohibited the use of charting by exception methodologies.

Case Study 1

Community Hospital of the West is evaluating its medical staff rules and regulations in the area of physician documentation, specifically dictated reports. CHW does have an accredited rehabilitation unit, and so CARF regulations apply. Students should review the state licensure rules, the Medicare *Conditions of Participation,* the JCAHO standards, and the

Table 14.1.	Regulations Pertaining to Charting by Exception	
Regulatory Body	**Regulation**	**Comments**
Medicare *Conditions of Participation*	"All records must document the following as appropriate. . . . All practitioners' orders, nursing notes, reports of treatment, medication records, radiology and laboratory reports, and vital signs and other information necessary to monitor the patient's condition."	Regulations do not require specific documentation for progress notes and other information. The documentation must, however, be sufficient to follow the care process.
	Special medical record requirements for psychiatric hospitals: "The special medical record requirement applicable to psychiatric hospitals was designed so that 'active psychiatric treatment' could be identified. The clinical records, therefore, should provide evidence of individualized treatment or a diagnostic plan that could reasonably be expected to improve the patient's condition."	These standards are more specific to your treatment setting, but still do not appear to prohibit charting by exception.
	"The treatment received by the patient must be documented in such a way to assure that all active therapeutic efforts are included." Surveyors are to verify that all treatment profiled is recorded by the team member(s) providing services." The treatment provided should be clearly documented as well as the patient's response to the treatment.	The standard does not prohibit charting by exception. It does define what charting must be able to accomplish; that is, it must describe the treatment (what was done) and how the patient reacted. This can be done in charting by exception if carefully defined and consistently formatted.
	Surveyors are instructed to verify that progress notes indicate how the patient is responding to the treatment being carried out. Specifically, the progress notes recorded by the professional staff responsible for the patient's treatment must give a chronology.	See comments above.
CARF	"The records of the persons served should communicate appropriate information in a form that is clear, complete, and current. The record of each person served should include: . . . Reports of initial and ongoing assessments, . . . signed and dated reports from each care giver."	The standard does not prohibit charting by exception. It does define what charting must be able to accomplish; that is, charting must communicate appropriate information in a form that is clear, complete, and current. This can be done in charting by exception if carefully defined and monitored.

Table 14.1.	*(Continued)*	
Regulatory Body	**Regulation**	**Comments**
JCAHO	"(IM.7.2) The clinical record contains enough information to identify the individual, support the diagnosis, justify the treatment, document the course and results, and facilitate continuity of care among health care providers."	
	"(IM.7.2.14) . . . Progress notes made by the clinical staff and other authorized individuals and used as the basis for treatment and habilitation plan development and review. . . . (IM.7.2.15) All reassessments, when necessary. . . . (IM.7.2.16) Clinical observations. . . ."	
State regulations	"Information contained in the medical record shall be complete and sufficiently detailed relative to the patient's history, examination, laboratory and other diagnostic tests, diagnosis and treatment to facilitate continuity of care."	
	Medical records service or department: "Progress notes: Shall give a chronological picture of patient's progress and shall delineate the course and results of treatment. Patient's condition shall determine frequency."	
	Special requirements for inpatient psychiatric services	Standards address assessments, written individualized treatment plans, and written aftercare plans when appropriate. They do not address progress notes and other documentation specifically.

SUMMARY: None of the regulations reviewed above have specifically defined time frames for documentation of care or how progress notes need to be completed. Charting by exception, if well planned and implemented, can be used while maintaining compliance.

CARF standards for these documentation requirements. Then they should prepare a comparative report of the standards and make a recommendation as to what the new policy should be.

Case Study 2

Henry McConnell (not his real name) has been an administrator surveyor with the Joint Commission on Accreditation of Healthcare Organizations for five years. He currently serves on a survey team reviewing a large Midwestern tertiary care facility. The survey had been going well, and he and the nurse member of the team were making visits to the patient care areas of the facility. The chief operating officer (COO) and director of nursing (DON) were accompanying the two surveyors to various nursing units. At one point in the visit, they decided to visit the inpatient psychiatric unit.

This particular inpatient psychiatric unit cared for persons with psychotic and other severe emotional disturbances. Many of the patients on the unit frequently suffered hallucinations. Many had had prehospital episodes of violence toward others. The unit was what is known in psychiatric medicine as a locked facility, meaning that special keys were necessary to go in to or out of the unit.

As Mr. McConnell and his fellow nurse surveyor approached the unit with the COO and DON, the COO was commenting on the level of acute psychiatric patients that the institution commonly housed on the unit. As they approached the double doors to the unit, she pointed out that they were made of metal with wired glass windows and that the doors were locked from both sides so that patients would need to have keys to get out of the unit. She made a bit of a production about getting out her set of keys to the unit so that they could enter, making sure that the two surveyors saw that the doorknobs would not open the doors and that one could only enter with a key. After they all went through the door, she turned around to show them that the door had closed securely behind them, that the knobs would not open the door, and so on.

Then, they turned to go onto the unit to do the review. The COO and DON walked carefully out in front of the surveyors toward the nursing station, the surveyors following a little way behind. Suddenly, Mr. McConnell stopped and could not believe his eyes. There on the wall about five feet inside the doorway and up near the ceiling and resting on a pair of metal hooks was a three-foot-long, red-handled fireman's axe.

Case Study Questions

1. How did the axe get there?

2. What common characteristic of healthcare organizations discussed in the background and significance section of this chapter is exhibited in this case?

3. How could these kinds of situations be avoided?

Summary

Accreditation, licensure, and certification activities are a significant component of contemporary quality management programs in healthcare organizations. A variety of accreditation and licensing agencies exist, including the Joint Commission on Accreditation of

Healthcare Organizations, the Commission on Accreditation of Rehabilitation Facilities, and state departments of health. All of these agencies publish standards that organizations must meet in order to be awarded or maintain accreditation or licensure. Preparation for accreditation surveys should be an ongoing and continuous activity, because surveyors may drop in for a focused review at any time in some settings. Continuous preparation also means that the organization will not need to work frantically during the months preceding a scheduled survey. Finally, continuous preparation demonstrates the organization's commitment to quality.

References

Brennan, T. A. 1998. The role of regulation in quality improvement. *Milbank Quarterly* 76(4):709–31.

Jencks, S. F. 1994. The government's role in hospital accountability for quality of care. *Joint Commission Journal of Quality Improvement* 20(7):364–69.

Joint Commission on Accreditation of Healthcare Organizations. 2000. *Comprehensive Accreditation Manual for Hospitals.* Oakbrook, Ill.: JCAHO.

Kelly, M. A. 1993. Thorough preparation key to successful surveys. *Health Facility Management* 6(2):38–44.

Chapter 15
Implementing Effective Information Management Tools for Performance Improvement

Learning Objectives

- To understand the reasons that contemporary information technologies are so important to the improvement of quality in healthcare

- To understand the information management tools commonly used in the performance improvement process

- To understand current developments in healthcare information technologies that will enhance performance improvement activities in the future

- To understand how information resources management professionals can help performance improvement teams pursue their improvement activities

Background and Significance

Performance improvement in healthcare is an information-intensive activity. Because performance improvement models are based on the continuous monitoring and assessment of performance measures, the effective management of the data and information collected is crucial to the success of the performance improvement program. To develop effective data and information management systems, one must have a clear picture of the ramifications of data and information management for performance improvement activities.

Healthcare organizations collect all kinds of data in routine, day-to-day patient care, operations, and administrative activities. According to Elliott (1999, p. 210) and Johns (1997, p. 53):

> The basic unit of recording in health care is an *event*. An event is the observation of an occurrence, subjective characteristic, or objective measurement relevant to an individual's health status that can be described by numeric values, words, character strings, images, or sounds. The observation may be made by a health care worker, health care professional, diagnostic/therapeutic instrument, or a patient/client and family/associates. Commonly, events are further described by type, date and time, observer, and individual observed. It is the web of these recorded events regarding patient after patient that forms the basic data of the health care information system.

Data, however, are facts, simple facts. They are singular units of *knowledge* that never provide a reliable and valid knowledge-picture of an entity—in this case patients and their various health aspects—in its entirety. They rarely provide a competent knowledge-picture of even one aspect of an entity. In addition, data must often be couched in the context of their observation before their real meaning is understood. This understanding of the meaning of data in context transforms the data into information. Johns notes that this transformation comes by means of formatting, filtering, and manipulation: changing the configuration in context, selecting pertinent aspects or recombining aspects of the data to more clearly delineate its meaning. Johns also notes that after the data-to-information transformation the result is "useful to a particular task"; that is, it helps individuals to make decisions. What then, is knowledge? In information sciences, knowledge is commonly held to consist of the collection of information about an entity the abstract concepts of which have been validated by the consensus of multiple interpreters. Here, Johns refers to "a combination of rules, relationships, ideas, and experiences" that, again, facilitate decision-making.

Management of information resources for performance improvement purposes must facilitate the transformation of data to information to knowledge. Collections of data in healthcare organizations may be patient specific, pertaining to the care services provided to each patient; aggregated, summarizing the experiences of many patients regarding a set of aspects of their care; or comparative, using aggregated data to describe the experiences of unique types of patients with one or more aspects of their care. But as the preceding quotation emphasizes, data must be placed in context and they must be formatted, filtered, and manipulated to transform them into information and knowledge that can be used in performance improvement programs.

Transformation of Data to Knowledge

How do the formatting, filtering, and manipulation occur? Fortunately, today's information management technologies enhance that transformation when they are deployed appropriately for that purpose by a healthcare organization. Careful consideration must be given to the support that information technologies can provide.

First, the QI toolbox techniques discussed in part II of this text can help. The QI toolbox techniques provide excellent tools that make it possible for performance improvement teams to see what the data are really showing. Looking at a mass of numbers and picking out the salient points and trends is usually difficult. The QI toolbox techniques make it easier to organize data, work through them to uncover meaningful information, and present them in a way that other people can understand. Many of the QI toolbox techniques are facilitated by the use of computer-based graphics and presentation applications.

Aggregating and performing basic statistical analysis can be facilitated with computer-based spreadsheet applications. Performance improvement teams can download data from computer-based healthcare information systems and perform ratio and correlation analysis or other statistical analyses on the data or compare the outcomes of different groups.

Standardized reporting formats can be developed to track important measures that the organization has selected for periodic review. Figure 15.1 is an example of a performance improvement report that a hospital uses to track its important measures on a quarterly basis. Using spreadsheet applications, what-if scenarios can also be developed to examine possible outcomes of changes in healthcare processes. Presentation development and word-processing applications make it easy for performance improvement teams to communicate effectively to others in the organization and to document progress on a project as it occurs.

Figure 15.1. Example of a Routine Performance Improvement Report for a Community Hospital

General Statistics

Statistics	Jan–March 1999	April–June 1999	July–Sept 1999	Oct–Dec 1999	1999 Average	1998 Average
Admissions	625	711	802	775	728.25	747.25
Discharges	789	690	766	759	751.00	789.25
Patient days	1657	1671	1623	1611	1640.50	1910.00
Lost work hours	0*	33*	22*	17*	18*	17*
Observation patients	146	125	137	144	138.00	153.25
Inpatient mortality rate	1.32%	1.35%	1.03%	0.81%	1.13%	1.11%
Deliveries	234	221	232	245	233.00	268.25
Emergency department visits	5523	5683	5890	5789	5721.25	6232.50
Inpatient/outpatient operative encounters	687	664	665	676	673.00	728.75
Outpatient operative encounters	546	524	530	568	542.00	585.25

Patient Care

Measure	JCAHO Standard	Benchmark	Jan–March 1999	April–June 1999	July–Sept 1999	Oct–Dec 1999	1999 Average	1998 Average
		Operative, Other Invasive, and Noninvasive Procedures That Place Patients at Risk						
Discrepancies: preop/postop/pathological (op report indicates specimen removed)	PI.3.2.1	100% (I)	37%	47%	86%	85%	69%	40%
Procedure appropriateness: criteria met	PI.3.1.1	100% (I)	100%	100%	100%	100%	100%	100%
Patient preparation for procedure: adequate	PI.3.1.1	100% (I)	86%	79%	87%	89%	85%	83%
Procedure performance and patient monitoring: intraoperative incidents	PI.3.1.1	0% (I)	0.13%	0.0%	0.38%	0.29%	0.40%	0.21%
Procedure performance and patient monitoring: unplanned returns to OR (M)	PI.3.1.1	0% (M)	0.13%	0.13%	0.38%	1.1%	0.43%	0.27%

(Continued on next page)

Figure 15.1. (Continued)								
Measure	JCAHO Standard	Benchmark	Jan–March 1999	April–June 1999	July–Sept 1999	Oct–Dec 1999	1999 Average	1998 Average
Postprocedure care: complications of postprocedure care	PI.3.1.1	0% (I)	0.26%	0.40%	0.25%	0.43%	0.33%	0.03%
Postprocedure patient education completed	PI.3.2.1	100% (I)	51%	67%	75%	74%	67%	67%
Medication Use								
Prescribing or ordering: orders changed as result of MD clarification	TX.3.5.2	NI	NI	89%	95.4%	93.8%	65.7%	89%
Preparing and dispensing; dispensing errors	TX.3.4, TX.3.5	0% (I)	0%	≤1%	0%	0%	≤1%	≤1%
Preparing and dispensing: medication delivery time–preop antibiotics within 2 hours of surgery (hips, knees, appendectomies, hysterectomies)	TX.3.5	≤2 hours (N)	89%	93%	93%	91%	91%	87%
Administering: DUE–appropriateness of dosage	TX.3.3, TX.3.5, TX.3.6	90% (I)	73%	67%	73.8%	81.0%	73.1%	89.0%
Monitoring the effects on patients: adverse reactions	TX.3.9	0.1% (I)	0.04%	0.09%	1.0%	0.22%	0.12%	0.36%
Monitoring the effects on patients: drug–drug interactions	TX.3.9	NI	23	2	4	1	7.5	16.0
Monitoring the effect on patients: drug–food interactions	TX.4.5	NI	7	23	44	62	26.5	20.0
Adverse effects during anesthesia	PI.4.5.2	NI	NI	NI	NI	NI	NI	NI

Figure 15.1. *(Continued)*

Measure	JCAHO Standard	Benchmark	Jan–March 1999	April–June 1999	July–Sept 1999	Oct–Dec 1999	1999 Average	1998 Average
				Use of Restraints				
Documented evidence of less restrictive measures used	TX.7.1.3.2.3	NI	3	3	11	6	6	NI
				Use of Blood and Blood Components				
Ordering: blood usage appropriate	TX.5.15	100% (I)	100%	100%	100%	100%	100%	100%
Distributing, handling, and dispensing	TX.5.15	NI	NI	NI	NI	NI	NI	NI
Administering: blood slips completed and on chart	TX.5.15	100% (I)	88.2%	81%	82.6%	86.4%	84.9%	85.7%
Administration: crossmatch: transfusion ratio	TX.5.15	≤2:1 (I)	1.8:1	1.6:1	2.2:1	1.8:1	1.8:1	2.0:1
Monitoring blood and blood component effects on patients: potential transfusion reactions	TX.5.14, TX.5.2, TX.5.4	NI	0.0%	0.0%	0.0%	0.0%	0.0%	0.0%
Monitoring blood and blood component effects on patients: confirmed transfusion reactions	TX.5.4	0% (I)	0.0%	0.0%	0.0%	0.0%	0.0%	0.0%
				Continuum of Care				
Utilization management: patients admitted as inpatients not meeting appropriateness criteria on initial review	CC.2	100% (I)	NI	NI	NI	NI	NI	NI
Utilization management: continuing stay criteria met	CC.4	100% (I)	NI	NI	NI	NI	NI	NI
Utilization management: patients remaining inpatients after discharge criteria met	CC.2.1	100% (I)	NI	NI	NI	NI	NI	NI

(Continued on next page)

Figure 15.1. *(Continued)*

Measure	JCAHO Standard	Benchmark	Jan–March 1999	April–June 1999	July–Sept 1999	Oct–Dec 1999	1999 Average	1998 Average
Autopsy results: number performed/number met criteria	PI.3.1	100% (I)	NI	NI	NI	NI	NI	NI
Critical occurrences	PI.4.3	—	0	1	0	0	0.80	0
C-section rate (O)	PI.3.1	12% (M); 17% (N)	15.3%	12.8%	11.8%	12.4%	13.1%	12.1%
VBAC rate (O)	PI.3.1	50% (M); 36% (N)	37.5%	38%	38%	34%	37%	50%
Primary C-section rate (O)	PI.3.1	6.5% (O)	9.7%	7.8%	5.7%	6.1%	7.3%	7.9%
Percentage of total C-section (O)	PI.3.1	50% (O)	56.9%	55.8%	42.5%	43.6%	34.7%	59.2%
Repeat C-section rate (O)	PI.3.1	65% (O)	62.5%	62.1%	62.2%	65.9%	63.3%	50.0%
X-ray discrepancies resulting in change of care (O)	PI.3.1	1.0% (O)	0.7%	0.42%	0.36%	0.4%	0.5%	NI
Unplanned return to emergency department within 72 hours (M)	PI.3.1	0.6% (O)	0.53%	0.5%	0.7%	0.7%	0.6%	0.6%
Patients in emergency department more than 6 hours (M)	PI.3.1	12% (I)	14.7%	10%	13.1%	8.8%	11.6%	12.0%
Unplanned return to special care unit (M)	PI.3.1	0.0% (I)	1.9%	2.3%	1.8%	2.5%	2.1%	NI
Unplanned admits from outpatient surgery (M)	PI.3.1	2.0% (I)	2.3%	1.9%	2.4%	6.9%	3.6%	1.8%
Cancelled surgeries (M)	PI.4.3	1.4% (I)	1.0%	1.0%	1.9%	1.6%	1.4%	1.3%
Cancelled endoscopies (M)	PI.3.1	1.1% (I)	1.2%	1.9%	1%	1.4%	1.4%	1.1%

Figure 15.1. *(Continued)*

Quality Control Activities

Measure	JCAHO Standard	Benchmark	Jan–March 1999	April–June 1999	July–Sept 1999	Oct–Dec 1999	1999 Average	1998 Average
Clinical lab: number of QC functions completed/number required	PI.3.3.3	100% (I)	0.0%	1.54%	0.78%	2.0%	1.1%	1.2%
Diagnostic radiology: number of QC functions completed/number required	PI.3.3.3	100% (I)	NI	NI	NI	NI	NI	NI
Dietary: number of QC functions completed/number required	PI.3.3.3	100% (I)	NI	NI	NI	NI	NI	NI
Equipment used to administer medication: number of QC functions completed/number required	PI.3.3.3	100% (I)	NI	NI	NI	NI	NI	NI
Pharmacy equipment used to prepare medication: number of QC functions completed/number required	PI.3.3.3	100% (I)	NI	NI	NI	NI	NI	NI
Equipment malfunctions	EC.1.9	0% (I)	NI	1	0	6	7	3

(Continued on next page)

Measure	JCAHO Standard	Benchmark	Jan–March 1999	April–June 1999	July–Sept 1999	Oct–Dec 1999	1999 Average	1998 Average
Patient Rights								
Overall patient satisfaction	PI.3.1	68% (I)	67.2%	63.8%	68.3%	73.8%	68.3%	63.0%
Advance directives: patients asked whether they have an advance directive	RI.1.2.4	100% (I)	67.7%	68.6%	66.7%	82.6%	70%	NI
Advance directives: patients provided information about advance directives	RI.1.2.5	100% (I)	100%	100%	100%	100%	100%	NI
Human Resources								
Employee satisfaction: overall annual employee satisfaction rate	HR.4.3	NI	NI	NI	NI	NI	NI	NI
Annual turnover rate	HR.4.3	NI	8.6%	9.7%	5.6%	8.6%	32.5%	41.0%
Complete new hire orientation	HR.4.0	100% (I)	100%	100%	100%	100%	NI	100%
Management of Information								
Data quality monitoring: documentation appropriateness	IM.3.2.1	90% (I)	95.3%	97.1%	95.4%	97.8%	96.4%	NI
Medical record delinquency: overall	IM.3.2.1	50% (J)	8.7%	8.4%	8.8%	11.1%	9.1%	11.1%
Medical record delinquency: history and physicals	IM.3.2.1	≤2% (I)	1.0%	0.3%	0.3%	0.12%	0.6%	0.6%

Figure 15.1. (Continued)

Figure 15.1. *(Continued)*

Measure	JCAHO Standard	Benchmark	Jan–March 1999	April–June 1999	July–Sept 1999	Oct–Dec 1999	1999 Average	1998 Average
Medical record delinquency: operative reports	IM.3.2.1	≤2% (I)	3.0%	4.1%	3.6%	4.8%	3.9%	2.9%
Verbal orders countersigned	IM.7.7	100% (I)	68.0%	NI	81.3%	95.6%	81.3%	NI
Medical records dated (all entries)	IM.7.8	90% (I)	48%	NI	53%	NI	50%	NI
Surveillance, Prevention, and Control of Infection								
Nosocomial surgical site infection rate	IC.2	2.5% (I)	0.8%	1.2%	0.6%	2.2%	1.2%	1.2%
Postop nosocomial pneumonia rate	IC.2	1.0% (I)	0.0%	0.3%	0.3%	0.6%	0.3%	0.13%
New Programs								
Measures of new program effectiveness	PI.3	NI	NI	NI	NI	NI	NI	NI

Benchmarking Key: N = national; J = JCAHO; S = state; L = local; I = internal; C = corporate; O = ORYX; M = Maryland Quality Indicator Project; NI = no information

*Number of incidents per 200,000 hours worked

Internet access and various indexing search engines provide information to performance improvement teams on the resources contained in the journal and professional literatures in healthcare. Access to the Internet facilitates the comparison of an organization's performance with that of other similar institutions and identification of possible solutions to a problem that other organizations have used.

Ideally, the healthcare information resources supporting performance improvement activities are based in an environment that has enhanced communications and information management technologies already implemented. Most healthcare performance measures are used to assess everyday healthcare service activities, and so the easiest and most effective places to find data about those measures is in the already-deployed information systems that support those service activities. For example, if a performance improvement team wanted to assess the effectiveness of blood transfusion services, probably the best place to find data about those services would be in the blood bank component of clinical laboratory systems. If a performance improvement team wanted to assess the effectiveness of wound care, probably the best place to find data about that service would be in the nursing component of clinical information systems. However, healthcare organizations have found over the past few years that stand-alone information systems are more difficult to use for performance improvement activities, because the examination and improvement of a process often involves the analysis of data and information from a variety of organizational information resources. Thus, the objective has become to provide integrated configuration and access to information resources from a variety of systems across the organization. Important developments that can assist an organization in this objective are discussed in the following sections of this chapter.

Data Repositories

Late in the 1990s, some healthcare organizations began to develop data repositories to facilitate performance improvement activities and long-range strategic planning. Into these data repositories, organizations that have deployed this technology are copying every instantiation of every datum collected in the course of providing healthcare services to customers. In addition, they are collecting the secondary data acquired in the course of using the technologies to support care such as that collected to provide audit trails and to support other administrative aspects of running information systems. What user actually entered data, from what access terminal, and on what date and time of entry are key examples of this type of administrative data. As these repositories become more common in healthcare information systems implementations, they will provide healthcare professionals involved in performance improvement activities with timely data and information that can be used continuously to monitor the quality of many different aspects of the care they provide.

Many healthcare organizations, however, have not yet implemented such cutting-edge information technology resources. In their absence, organizations must design information collection and transmission systems that can effectively support performance improvement initiatives. Many routine reports produced in healthcare organizations should be made available across departments and across performance improvement teams. The medical records of specific patients contain immense stores of data about all aspects of patient care. These paper-based records are repositories as well. But they cannot be accessed as easily as a computer-based repository. Systems must be developed to make these data available in spite of the organization's not having computer-based patient records.

Intranet-Based Communication Technologies

Everyone in the organization who is concerned with quality issues must be kept apprised of the current status of performance improvement activities. A performance improvement team working on one issue in one work unit of the organization may discover important information that could be used by another PI team working on a different issue in a different work unit of the organization. Forcing the second team to recapture information or reanalyze collected data wastes time and money.

Deploying intranet-based communication technologies can help keep everyone in the organization apprised of the current status of performance improvement projects. Intranets are wide-area or local-area network-based resources that allow members of a healthcare organization access to information resources from a variety of contexts within the organization. Only valid users from within the organization should have access to intranet-based materials. Commonly, the presentation of materials uses the standard presentation of the Internet and its Web browsers, but other presentations may be supported by the intranet.

Using the Web site configuration, however, can facilitate communication about performance improvement activities. Each PI project can be accorded a Web on the intranet, where performance improvement team members can post project documentation or presentations as the various milestones of the project are achieved. Team members can also present data that have been collected for their project so that other teams can use the data for their projects. At any time, the organization's members can look up the status of PI projects within the organization and review what improvement projects have been accomplished in the past.

Standardization and Support of Information Management Tools

Another important aspect of utilizing information systems in PI activities is standardization. A common response to the need for information management technologies is for the leadership of each PI team to want to use his or her personal favorites. This is understandable, given that each leader may have developed expertise in using particular products. A leader familiar with Microsoft® products would want to use those applications to collect and analyze data for his team. Other leaders may be more familiar with Corel® products. Statistical analysis applications are available from several vendors.

This situation should point to the need for organizations to standardize data collection and analysis technologies across all performance improvement activities. Standardization facilitates the use of data by multiple individuals and multiple teams. Sharing can decrease the time and cost to the organization for performance improvement activities. To accomplish sharing ability, organizations should carefully consider the kind of information technology support that is most appropriate.

Today, of course, most organizations use general office packages that include word-processing and spreadsheet applications. Software should be standardized across all departments. Statistical analysis and graphing applications should also be acquired to facilitate analysis of data sets collected during PI team activities. All staff involved in performance improvement activities should be provided with some access to the Internet with periodical literature and scientific journal literature search capability. The National Library of Medicine now provides nationwide access to its clinical and scientific journal index through its PubMed search engine. Other indexes for a variety of social science, biological science, physical science, and healthcare professions publications are available through the home pages of any university or public library in the country.

User support must be provided for all information technology resources used across the organization. Expert users should be identified and made available to performance improvement teams to optimize the use of the technologies. Training sessions should be held periodically to acquaint staff across the organization with techniques for the analysis of data and the use of statistical and other packages.

Information Warehouses

A recent development related to the issues of standardization and duplication in information resources management in healthcare is the deployment of information warehouses. Information warehouses allow organizations to store reports, presentations, profiles, and graphics interpreted and developed from stores of data for reuse in subsequent organizational activities. For example, a report developed by a performance improvement team on the occurrence of methicillin-resistant *Staphylococcus aureus* infection in a neonatal ICU could subsequently be used by the perinatal morbidity and mortality committee in a monthly review of infant morbidity. A marketing report developed on the need for services pertinent to women and children in an organization's locale could be used by a performance improvement team that wants to delineate the important aspects of customer satisfaction with women's and children's services.

Providing access to warehouses using intranets and Web browser user interfaces facilitates information resource distribution. Browser search engines allow users within the organization to search the warehouse for previously compiled and interpreted information on any subject contained in the warehouse. Then, users click on the links that the search engine discovers and review the materials for relevance to current projects. Because the browser allows the user to print, any materials available in the warehouse can be printed and redistributed to PI team members. Materials in electronic formats can be downloaded and reused in appropriate information technologies: word processing, spreadsheets, graphics, presentations, or statistical applications.

Comparative Performance Data

As discussed in part II of this textbook, **benchmarking** can make an important contribution to the improvement of performance in healthcare organizations. Benchmarking is so important that the Joint Commission on Accreditation of Healthcare Organizations (JCAHO) has developed a standard (IM.10) that requires healthcare organizations to contribute data on significant performance measures to national data collections. In turn, the organization has access to data from the collection. The organization then can compare its performance to the performance of similar organizations. The comparison can assure the organization that it is performing up to industry standards or help the organization to identify opportunities for improvement.

Information Resources Management Professionals

Irrespective of the configuration of a healthcare organization's technical infrastructure, the staff involved in performance improvement activities should recognize important resources usually already developed within the organization—health information services managers, information systems managers, and knowledge-base librarians. These information management professionals are usually already working in the facility and possess a wealth of professional expertise that can be of significant assistance to performance improvement activities. Each has unique contributions to make to performance improvement activities, but organizations must be willing to call on these professionals' expertise for assistance.

Information resources management professionals can assist quality improvement programs in a variety of ways. First, they can assist in training performance improvement teams to utilize appropriate sources for data regarding an improvement opportunity. They can assist the team in evaluating the quality of the data harvested from internal data sources and the reliability of data harvested from external sources. They can help to train PI team members to use information management technologies such as spreadsheets and database management systems. When applications are to be acquired to support specific PI activities, they can assist in the development of system requirements and requests for proposal. When new information technology applications must be developed to track PI measures, information resources management professionals should be called upon to oversee development with an appropriate cost–benefit reference within the organization.

JCAHO Information Management Standards

Effective information management for performance improvement entails an understanding of the information management standards of the JCAHO. The information management chapter of the accreditation standards was developed during the mid-1990s to focus healthcare organizations on the importance of information systems issues in the provision of quality patient care. Any healthcare organization that uses accreditation as a component of its performance improvement program must ensure that it meets these standards. Even healthcare organizations that do not use JCAHO accreditation as a component of their performance improvement programs would be wise to consider the standards in developing performance improvement systems and procedures.

The JCAHO information management standards focus on information systems *issues,* not on information *systems.* The systems implemented may be computer based or paper based. The point is that solutions to the issues identified in the information management standards must be developed and consciously implemented in healthcare organizations so that information systems can contribute to quality patient care as they should.

The information management standards speak to ten areas of consideration regarding the contribution of information resources management to quality patient care and the improvement of patient care. Each first-level standard is cited and followed by relevant elaboration of its intent as developed by the JCAHO (1999):

IM.1   The healthcare organization plans and designs information management processes to meet internal and external information needs.

Intent: [Healthcare organizations] vary in size, complexity, governance, structure, decision-making processes, and resources. Information management systems and processes vary accordingly. The [organization] bases its information management processes on a thorough analysis of internal and external information needs. The analysis considers what data and information are needed within and among departments, the medical staff, the administration, and the governing body, as well as information needed to support relationships with outside services, companies, and agencies. Leaders seek input from staff in a variety of areas and services. Appropriate individuals ensure that required data and information are provided efficiently for patient care, research, education, and management at every level.

IM.2   Confidentiality, security, and integrity of data and information are maintained.

Intent: The [healthcare organization] maintains the security and confidentiality of data and information and is especially careful about preserving the confidentiality of sensitive data and information. The balance between data sharing and data confidentiality is addressed. The [healthcare organization] determines the level of security and confidentiality maintained for different categories of information. Access to each category of information is based on need and defined by job title and function.

IM.3   Uniform data definitions and data capture methods are used whenever possible.

Intent: Standardizing terminology, definitions, vocabulary, and nomenclature facilitates comparison of data and information within and among organizations. Abbreviations and symbols are also standardized. Uniformly applied and accepted definitions, codes, classifications, and terminology support data aggregation and analysis and provide criteria for decision analysis. Quality control systems are used to monitor data content and collection activities, and to ensure timely and economical data collection. Standardization is consistent with recognized state and federal standards. The [healthcare organization] minimizes bias in data and regularly assesses the data's reliability, validity, and accuracy. . . . Medical records address the presence, timeliness, legibility, and authentication of . . . data and information as appropriate to the organization's needs.

IM.4   Decision-makers and other appropriate staff members are educated and trained in the principles of information management.

Intent: Education and training enables individuals to understand security and confidentiality of data and information; use measurement instruments, statistical tools, and data analysis methods for transforming data into relevant information; collect unbiased data, gathered with a control for confounding or corrected on the basis of acceptable methodologies; assist in interpreting data; use data and information to help in decision making; educate and support the participation of patients and family in care processes; and use indicators to assess and improve systems and processes over time.

IM.5 Transmission of data and information is timely and accurate.

Intent: Internally and externally generated data and information are accurately transmitted to users. The integrity of data and information is maintained, and there is adequate communication between data users and suppliers. The timing of transmission is appropriate to the data's intended use.

IM.6 Adequate integration and interpretation capabilities are provided.

Intent: The information management process makes it possible to combine information from various sources and generate reports to support decision making. Specifically, the information management process coordinates collection of information; makes information from one system available to another; organizes, analyzes, and clarifies data; and generates and provides access to longitudinal data. In addition, the information management process provides the capability to link [data and information from a variety of sources internal and external to the organization and from the clinical and management literatures].

IM.7 The healthcare organization defines, captures, analyzes, transforms, transmits, and reports patient-specific data and information related to care processes and outcomes.

Intent: Information management processes provide for the use of patient-specific data and information to facilitate patient care, serve as a financial and legal record, aid in clinical research, support decision analysis, and guide professional and organizational performance improvement. . . . Administrative and direct patient care providers produce and use this information for professional and organization improvement. . . .

IM.8 The [healthcare organization] collects and analyzes aggregate data to support patient care and operations.

Intent: The [healthcare organization] aggregates and analyzes clinical and administrative data to support patient care, decision making, management and operations, analysis of trends over time, performance comparisons over time and with other organizations, and performance improvement. . . . Aggregate performance improvement information includes information from risk management, utilization review, infection control, and [hazard and] safety management.

IM.9 The [healthcare organization] provides systems, resources, and services to meet its needs for knowledge-based information in patient care, education, research, and management.

Intent: Knowledge-based information, often referred to as "literature," includes journal literature, reference information, and research data. . . .

Knowledge-based information is authoritative and up to date. It supports clinical and management decision making, performance improvement activities, patient and family education, continuing education of staff, and research. . . . Appropriate knowledge-based information is acquired, assembled, and transmitted to users . . . [is accessible and in appropriate formats].

IM.10 Comparative performance data and information are defined, collected, analyzed, transmitted, reported, and used consistent with national and state guidelines for data set parity and connectivity.

Intent: The [healthcare organization uses and contributes] to collections of performance data from multiple institutions. As part of its information management activities, the [healthcare organization] exchanges clinical and knowledge-based data and information with other health care organizations. These activities help the [organization] develop its future capabilities and goals. The [organization] uses external data and information to identify areas in which its own performance deviates from expected patterns. The [organization] also contributes its own information to external reference databases. To ensure that the data is comparable across institutions, the [organization] follows national and state guidelines on form and content.

An in-depth discussion of the information management standards is not possible in this chapter. Each of the principal standards has multiple subdivisions that discuss and provide examples of the issues evident around the standard. The student of performance improvement in healthcare is cautioned not to forget the existence of these standards and to refer to a JCAHO accreditation manual for more detailed discussion of them.

Case Study

The following excerpt is from a consultant's report on the status of information technologies at Community Hospital of the West:

Infrastructure: As is true with many organizations trying to keep up with the rapid developments in information technology, Community Hospital of the West has a variety of hardware and software that is used in its departments. PCs are widely used across the organization, but there are many departments that have PCs too old to provide an adequate platform for the later versions of software that would most effectively support departmental reporting responsibilities. There is no organization-wide local-area network in place. Software applications and versions are not standardized across the organization, and so members of different departments cannot share data and information in electronic formats. This forces members of the organization to duplicate effort in report generation when reports contain the same or similar data. An office suite application served to users on a local-area network could help to solve this problem.

The absence of a local-area network and an administrative database accessible to department managers means that reports must be prepared in the generating department, output on paper, and then input again in administrative departments to be utilized in administrative applications. An administrative database served by a network to all departments would mean data would be gathered only once and then be available for subsequent users and purposes without redefinition or reprocessing. All of the logs that the organization currently generates, many of which are on an hourly or daily basis, could be more effectively administered and accessed if they were in electronic formats.

Organizational Knowledge of Computing Applications: Although there is broad distribution of hardware and software across the organization, organizational knowledge regarding the use of applications software available to it has not been optimized. Many of the respondents in the interviews stated that they had access to a PC and applications but had not had access to adequate training on the application. Consequently, most reporting is done without the use of software applications (some even on a typewriter) where the use of software could accomplish the process more effectively and efficiently. This situation is intensified because there are so many different versions in existence across the organization. There appears to be no organizational expert with reference to software application use to assist personnel in solving their information *processing* problems. Maintenance of all the different versions of all the different applications must be essentially impossible for Information Systems personnel.

Interfacing and Use of Existing Databases: Several respondents felt that access to existing mainframe databases would improve the performance of their administrative reporting activities. This issue is also one that many organizations face as they try to make database information available and accessible yet maintain data integrity and security. In particular, four of the respondents noted that they felt their productivity reporting could be more effectively accomplished if it were pulled from the payroll database. Some felt that information should be made available from financial and patient care systems and shared directly to an administrative database.

Archival of Administrative Reporting: The organization does not appear to have an archiving policy. Departmental staff decide for themselves how long they should keep reports that they generate or receive. The archival period varies widely from no archival at all to decades. Many departments receive and archive reports for which they have no use, the author of which they do not know, and the purpose of which is unknown. Most administrative reporting is archived on paper. If the organization had an administrative database, archival of many if not all reports could be accomplished electronically, increasing the availability, reliability, and security of administrative information for long-term use. There is no formal distinction made at this time between that information that is valuable in the long term and that for short-term monitoring purposes only.

Case Study Questions

1. What issues does the consultant's report raise that may have an impact on performance improvement activities in this facility?

2. Compare the case study situation to the JCAHO information management standards. What issues does this analysis raise?

Summary

Because performance improvement activities are information intensive, healthcare organizations must pay special attention to the management of information resources to support improvements. Ideally, the organization would make available common business-oriented applications such as spreadsheets and word-processing software as well as statistical analysis and presentation packages. Many organizations make information available across the organization via intranets and archive clinical information system data permanently in data repositories. In this way, clinical data are made available for performance improvement activities. Information resources must also include access to national comparative data collections for organizations accredited by the JCAHO, and organizations must ensure that they meet the other JCAHO information management standards as well. Information resources management personnel such as directors of health information services and information systems and institutional librarians with expertise in healthcare literatures should also work to support performance improvement activities.

References

Dearmin, J., J. Brenner, and R. Migliori. 1995. Reporting on QI efforts for internal and external customers. *Joint Commission Journal of Quality Improvement* 21(6):277–88.

Elliott, Chris. 1999. Introducing the electronic health record user community. In *Electronic Health Records: Changing the Vision,* Gretchen F. Murphy et al., editors, pp. 209–30. New York City: W. B. Saunders.

Johns, Merida. 1997. *Information Management for Health Professions.* Albany, N.Y.: Delmar Publishers.

Joint Commission on Accreditation of Healthcare Organizations. 1999. Information management standards. *Accreditation Manual for Hospitals.* Oakbrook Terrace, Ill.: JCAHO.

Rosen, L. S., et al. 1996. Adapting a statewide patient database for comparative analysis and quality improvement. *Joint Commission Journal of Quality Improvement* 22(7):468–81.

Chapter 16
Developing Effective Performance Improvement Teams

Learning Objectives

- To recognize the single most important aspect of organizational culture that promotes effective performance improvement teams

- To understand the contributions that team charters, team roles, ground rules, listening, and questioning can make to improve the effectiveness of performance improvement teams

Background and Significance

In part I of this textbook, the importance of teams to performance improvement activities in healthcare was discussed. Team approaches to improving quality are helpful, because they tend to uncover and reflect a variety of perspectives and a more complete knowledge base than do improvement approaches dominated by one or two individuals.

Even though the authors accept this premise, it must also be noted that teams do not always function effectively. Therefore, developing effective team functioning often becomes an issue crucial to the success of performance improvement programs in healthcare organizations. Program leaders can take a variety of initiatives to help teams to function more effectively. There appears to be one major issue, however, that predicts more than any other the likelihood of team effectiveness in performance improvement—the organization's expectations.

Some consultants believe that every team needs building, and consequently many use team-building exercises to help teams develop more effectiveness. The exercises are often built along the lines of some of the topics discussed in this chapter, such as helping team members to listen more effectively. The authors of this text, however, believe that the single most important way for an organization to achieve effective teams is to make team problem solving and team performance improvement part of the culture of the organization. From the moment each individual is hired to work within the healthcare organization, it should be overtly communicated by the organization that the individual is expected to participate in team projects and that participation in teams is part of *everyone's* job description. By making team participation part of the organization's culture, no individual employees should then be able to believe that they are exempt or that they do not need to cooperate in team approaches to organizational issues.

That is not to say, however, that occasionally there will not be individuals on a team who are uncooperative or have their own agendas. There may be. Those individuals' contributions can be channeled into positive team production, however, by knowledgeable and experienced facilitation and other techniques that have already been discussed or are discussed further in this chapter.

Team Charters

In many healthcare organizations, the implementation of a performance improvement team is formalized with a team charter. Team charters explain what issues the team was implemented to improve, describe the goals and objectives and a desired end-state (a vision), and list the initial members of the team and their respective departments. Team charters are helpful, because they clearly state why the team was brought together in the first place. They keep the organization focused on the opportunity for improvement and the team focused on its mission. See figure 16.1 for an example of a team charter.

Team Roles

The role of team leader was discussed in chapter 3, where the team approach to performance improvement activities was introduced. Other possible roles in PI teams that may enhance team performance are included here.

First, performance improvement teams may want to identify a team facilitator. The facilitator should be someone who knows the performance improvement process well and has facilitated a performance improvement team in the past. The facilitator may also be required to train the team in the performance improvement process and quality improvement tools. The facilitator is primarily responsible for ensuring that an effective performance improvement process occurs. The responsibilities of the team facilitator include the following:

- Serving as advisor and consultant to the team

- Remaining a neutral, nonvoting member

- Suggesting alternative PI methods and procedures to keep the team on target and moving forward

- Managing group dynamics

- Acting as coach and motivator for the team

- Assisting in consensus building when necessary

- Recognizing team and individual achievements

Figure 16.1.   Example of a Team Charter

PERFORMANCE IMPROVEMENT TEAM CHARTER
(Page 1 of 2)

Team Name	Date Submitted to Performance Improvement Council
Clinical Laboratory Services	*February 15th*

Statement of the Problem, Issue, or Concern to Be Addressed by the PIT

Safety issues or other problems concerning the hospital labs increased 207% over a one-year time frame.

Statement of the Goals, Objective, and Desired End State

Identify specific problem areas with laboratory services, conduct a baseline study to assess each area, analyze results, develop an action plan, implement improvements, and evaluate results.

Proposed Team Members

Name	Title	Department
Roger Jones	*Chief Clinical Officer*	*Administration*
Jill Andrews	*Lab Manager*	*Laboratory*
Ben Carlson, M.D.	*Emergency Physician*	*E.R.*
Sandy Johnson	*Director of Clinical Ser.*	*Administration*
Kathy Smith, R.N.	*Director of Nursing*	*Nursing*
John Rasmussen	*Lab tech*	*Laboratory*
Sue Holt	*Lab tech*	*Laboratory*
Pam Richards	*Coordinator*	*Quality Management*

Project Resources

Planned Start Date	Planned Completion Date	Planned Frequency of Meetings
February 20th	*June 1st*	*weekly*

Administrative/PIC Support Needed (if any)	Estimated Cost of Team's Work
	$1000.00

(Continued on next page)

Figure 16.1. *(Continued)*

PERFORMANCE IMPROVEMENT TEAM CHARTER
(Page 2 of 2)

What Important JCAHO Functions Will the Project Measure or Improve (check all that apply)?

☐ Rights, Responsibilities and Ethics   ☐ Leadership

☐ Continuum   ☑ Management of the Environment of Care

☐ Assessment   ☐ Management of Information

☐ Care   ☑ Management of Human Resources

☑ Education   ☐ Surveillance, Prevention, and Control of Infection

☑ Improving Organizational Performance

What Dimensions of Performance Will the Project Improve (check all that apply)?

☐ Efficacy   ☐ Continuity

☐ Appropriateness   ☑ Safety

☐ Availability   ☑ Efficiency

☑ Timeliness   ☐ Respect and Caring

☐ Effectiveness

Project Benefits
How Will the Project Support the Mission/Values and/or Achieve the Organization's Strategic Goals?

☐ Improved Patient Outcomes   ☐ Time Savings

☑ Cost Savings   ☐ Other _____

☑ Improved Service   _____

How? *reduce safety violations in the laboratory and rework*

_____

_____

_____*Jill Andrews*_____   _____*Feb. 15th*_____
Signature of Applicant   Date

To Be Completed by Performance Improvement Council

Comments

_____

_____

Performance Improvement Council Recommendations _____

_____

_____   _____
Signature   Date

The team recorder/scribe role is vital to the team's success. This individual maintains records of the team's work during the meetings, including any documentation required by the organization. The recorder/scribe performs the following functions:

- Recording information on a flipchart for the group

- Creating appropriate charts and diagrams

- Assisting with notices and supplies for meetings

- Distributing notices and other documentation to team members

- Developing meeting minutes

Finally, teams may assign someone to be a timekeeper. The timekeeper helps the team manage its time. The timekeeper notifies the team during meetings of time remaining on each agenda item in an effort to keep the team moving forward on its PI project.

Ground Rules for Meetings

Establishing ground rules for meetings helps a team maintain a level of discipline. Ground rules include a discussion of attendance, time management, participation, communication, decision making, documentation, room arrangements and cleanup, and so on. Ground rules probably will not be the same for every team, as each team should decide how it wants to proceed. But the ground rules should be well known to everyone on the team, and everyone should have participated in their development. Most teams that use them also allow for their periodic review and revision, particularly when membership in the team changes. New members must be brought up to speed on the ground rules when they begin coming to team meetings. (See figure 16.2.)

The attendance discussion should establish who will schedule meetings, arrange for a meeting room, and notify members. The ground rules should also cover the team's expectations regarding absences, including whether team members can be removed from the team and replaced for absenteeism and whether proxies or substitutes can attend meetings.

Cancellation of meetings should be discussed in the ground rules, as well as how the team defines "on time"; that is, they should decide ahead of time whether starting and ending times will be enforced. Discussion should also include how the time allotted to agenda items will be monitored.

Discussion of team member participation should include the team's expectations regarding advance preparation. The team should plan the means by which equal contribution from all members can be ensured; the means by which activities can be monitored to ensure productive meetings; the means by which assignments and expectations for their completion are made; and the means by which ad hoc members will be invited and prepared for their input.

Communication ground rules are imperative for team effectiveness, particularly regarding how candid members may be and whether information discussed in the team process must remain confidential. The team should also decide what will happen when discussions get off track; how interruptions or side conversations will be handled; what listening skills are expected; how differences of opinion and conflict among members will be expressed and resolved; and how creativity will be encouraged and negative thinking

---

Figure 16.2.   Meeting Ground Rules Worksheet

Ground Rules Worksheet

1. Every individual has a viewpoint that is valuable, every individual can make a unique contribution, and every individual can speak freely.

2. All team members must listen attentively and respectfully without interrupting. Only one person should speak at a time.

3. All team members must be willing to accept responsibility for assignments and complete any assigned tasks between meetings.

4. The organizational positions/levels of team members will not be recognized during team meetings. Every member of the team is an equal participant.

5. Solutions must be created with resources that are currently available. Money and additional staff are not considered issues.

6. _____

7. _____

8. _____

9. _____

10. _____

---

discouraged. The team must also decide whether consensus or majority decisions will be taken on issues requiring voting.

Other questions that may require discussion:

- How will breaks be handled if there are to be any?

- Who is responsible for meeting room setup and cleanup?

- What support services are necessary to this team (that is, does the team need training in information technologies or is a secretary necessary)? If so, who will coordinate them?

- How, when, and why should administration be involved?

- How will department managers be notified of the need for department employees to participate on a team?

- Is overtime or casual staff necessary for this team to complete its assignment?

Problem-Solving Techniques, Listening, and Questioning

Encouraging meetings and other team interactions to be productive can be a major issue in many organizations. This is an outgrowth of the common management styles that most organizations exhibit. For reasons far more complex than can be explored here, people tend to gravitate to one of two management styles. One style is inclusive; its goal is to gather all viewpoints and consider each carefully with respect to its contribution to solving the problem. The other style is exclusive; its goal is to get to a result as quickly as possible. Each style has its positive and negative aspects. People who operate by the inclusive style can get mired in detail and discussion and achieve results only after extensive processing. People who operate by the exclusive style can fail to perceive important details in their rush to get to the objective and implement a solution. A combination of the two styles is more effective than either style alone. Each style can be employed at appropriate points in the development of team process.

The concept of facilitation was developed to help move teams along. The cyclical PI methodology was developed to give teams a structure by which to proceed in problem solving. QI toolbox techniques were developed to give teams an easy way to organize and analyze data.

One other area that is extremely important in the development of good team interaction and functioning is the ability to listen and question. PI team members need to be able to do both, however, and this may take some development on the part of team leaders. Commonly, in human communication in organizations, individuals tend to be active communicators or passive listeners. Active communicators can quickly dominate a team meeting. They usually have grown accustomed to expressing themselves and to being listened to. Sometimes, their listening skills have been eclipsed by their own volubility. They may have to be reoriented to practice listening more often, allowing the quieter individuals on the team an opportunity to express their perspectives. Similarly, the quieter members may have become accustomed to listening to other people and not voicing their own perspectives. They may have to be reoriented to practice contributing more often, sharing their knowledge and expertise with the group so that important details are not ignored.

Often, too, in human communication in organizations, individuals become invested in their own perspectives and ways of seeing and interpreting situations. This can happen among active communicators as well as passive listeners. The active communicators often react by trying to persuade everyone else on the team of the justness of their perspectives. The passive listeners may say nothing but internally retain their commitment to their own perspectives. Neither of these tactics moves the team to resolution of the problem it was convened to solve. Team members may have to be reoriented to listening carefully to others' perspectives and seeking a common understanding of those perspectives through questioning techniques.

The power of the question lies in the fact that it compels an answer. When one asks the right questions, one acquires important answers in terms of information, experience, reactions, perspectives, attitudes, and so on. When one fails to ask questions, one is left with only one's own perspectives, which may or may not reflect the reality of various situations. An individual can never know as much about an opportunity for improvement as can the members of the team collectively. When the team tries to make decisions concerning the opportunity without sufficient information, the likelihood that the new solution solves the problem decreases. Using questioning techniques effectively becomes, therefore, an important tool for PI team members to learn how to use.

In using questioning methods, it is important that team members have a positive attitude on the importance of asking rather than telling and a conviction that people, because of their unique experience, background, and training, can potentially contribute unique information. It is also important to recognize that there is more than one type of questioning.

Different styles of questioning can be used to accomplish different types of information gathering. Note the types of questions shown in figure 16.3 and the purposes for which each can be used.

People Issues

Finally, in discussing the effectiveness of PI teams, one must specifically recognize the effects that individuals have on PI processes. In reality, all of the team development techniques are intended to help teams function *through* the people issues and become effective teams. In a nutshell then, what constitutes an effective team?

- Effective teams establish goals cooperatively with all members participating when they have perspectives on the issues.

- Effective teams communicate in a two-way mode. All members participate, and the occurrence of real, two-way communication is validated in team processes. Members who do not spontaneously communicate their perspectives are encouraged and made responsible for doing so.

- Effective teams value the open and accurate expression of both ideas and feelings as important perspectives on organizational issues.

- Effective teams distribute leadership and responsibility among all team members. Each member has tasks for which he or she is responsible and that make important contributions to team accomplishments.

- Effective teams distribute power among all team members. Power is apportioned on the basis of information and ability and contribution to team activities, not on the basis of place in the formal organizational structure.

- Effective teams match decision-making techniques to types of decision-making situations. Decisions are never made by individuals. Important decisions are usually made through consensus, meaning that the group as a whole comes to agreement about the appropriate course of action.

- Effective teams see periodic controversy and conflict among team members as a positive aspect of team growth and team understanding regarding the processes the team has been initiated to improve.

- Effective teams stay focused on the issues about which they have been convened.

All of this sounds very positive, and those new to the team concept can see the importance of these factors. However, in real situations there is conflict between roles that individuals have in the formal organizational structure and those that are necessary to an effective team structure. Formal organizational roles are often seen to require authority for various functions and responsibilities. Effective teams share authority for the team performance. Therefore, many individuals coming to team approaches to problem solving have to get reoriented, and for some, this reorientation is difficult to accomplish.

Most individuals coming to a PI team role for the first time are unfamiliar with the data collection and analysis aspects of team functioning. Many may not want to have to be involved with such detailed activities and may not have the mathematical skill necessary

Figure 16.3.	**Types of Questions and Their Purposes (After Burns, 1960)**	
Types of Questions		
Type	**Purpose**	**Examples**
Factual	To get information To open discussion	How and all of the *W* questions: what, where, why, when, and who
Explanatory	To find reasons and explanations To broaden discussion To develop additional information	In what way would this help solve the problem? What aspects of this issue should be considered? Just how would this action be done?
Justifying	To challenge old ideas To develop new ideas To find reasons and proof	Why do you think so? How do you know? What evidence do you have?
Leading	To introduce a new idea To advance a suggestion	Should we consider this idea as a possible solution? Would this idea be a feasible alternative?
Hypothetical	To develop new ideas To suggest another, possibly unpopular opinion To change the course of discussion	What would happen if we did it this way? Would it be feasible for us to do this the way company X does it?
Alternative	To choose an alternative To obtain agreement	Which of these solutions is better? Does this solution represent our choice in preference to other alternative solutions?
Coordinating	To develop consensus To obtain agreement To take action	Can we conclude that this is the next step we should take? Is there general agreement on this plan?
Direction of Questions		
Overhead: directed to the group	To open discussion To introduce a new phase To give everyone a chance to comment	How shall we begin? What shall we consider next? What else might be important?
Direct: addressed to a specific individual	To call on an individual for specific information To get an inactive individual involved in the discussion	George, what are your suggestions? Gracie, have you had any experience in this area?
Relay: referred back to another individual or to the group	To help the leader avoid giving his or her own opinion To get others involved in the discussion To call on someone who knows the answer	Would someone like to comment on Peter's question? Mary, how would you answer Paul's question?
Reverse: referred back to the individual who asked the question	To help the leader avoid giving his or her own opinion To encourage the questioner to think for himself or herself To bring out opinions	Well, Bing, how about giving us your opinion first? Heddie, tell us first what your own experience has been in this area?

to perform the activities easily. The team may have to spend some time helping that individual to accomplish his or her team tasks in this area.

Many individuals in healthcare, particularly clinicians, managers, and administrators, may be comfortable with decision making, especially their own style of decision making, whatever that may be. However, effective teams make decisions as groups, often by consensus, acknowledging perspectives of all participants. For many, giving up the right to make decisions is difficult. The team or the leadership of the PI initiative in the organization may have to assist that person in learning new decision-making styles.

Conversely, team members sometimes come to the team with little or no management experience. These individuals often have made few decisions in their work outside of day-to-day job procedures. Dealing with performance improvement issues without carrying out someone else's orders may be difficult for such people. Encouragement to participate and mentoring through the process until this kind of individual develops some new skills are very helpful.

Case Study

Dick Richards was the chief financial officer of Community Hospital of the West. The organization had recently embarked on a performance improvement initiative in response to the increasing competitiveness and regulation of its industry. The administrator had hired a consultant to assist in the implementation of the initiative, and the consultant had been training the administrative group in performance improvement methodologies for the past two months. All of the administrators were being pressured by the board of directors to find something to improve in their divisions, and so Dick had convened a PI team of his managers and their assistants to discuss possible improvement opportunities.

"So what do you think?" asked Dick. "What is there in our areas that needs improvement?"

The managers sat looking at the pictures on the walls of the conference room or doodling on their note pads, silent. They had been sitting there for 20 minutes before Dick had arrived to chair the meeting.

"There has to be something we can improve, doesn't there?" asked Dick. "Nobody's perfect." Again, the managers were silent.

Finally, Marilyn, the director of patient accounting, spoke up. "Well, I don't see why we should spend all this time and money on these phony meetings, when we could just as well be back at our desks getting some real work accomplished. The suspense account report is longer than I've ever seen it since I've been working here. We're waiting on all kinds of accounts to be coded by medical records, and we're sitting here wasting time on this administrative boondoggle. Doesn't the board know we have better things to do?"

Bristling at Marilyn's condemnation of her department, Peggy, the director of health information services, retorted, "You know we don't have enough coders, Dick. I've begged you a multitude of times in the last few months to let me hire some more coders. You just don't seem to understand that when the census decreases, that means more work for us with all those discharged cases, not less. And are Marilyn's billers all working as hard as they can anyway? Half the time I see them sitting in the cafeteria drinking coffee!"

"Now, now, ladies. We're not here to discuss the suspense account report. I know you've got lots of work to do, but I need us to come up with something to improve that the board can see. I've got to be seen as cooperating in this initiative, or we'll all have hell to pay. Now put on your thinking caps. I think we could spruce up the cashier's area a little. It's kind of dull over there. Probably doesn't make much of an impression on the patients when they come to make payments on their bills. That old, yellowed paint is not very appealing, and those fluorescent lights are hideous! I say we come up with a new look for the cashier's window. How's that?"

Several of the managers still just sat there doodling. A couple murmured, "Uh-huh" or "Yeah, okay."

"So let's have another meeting next week to discuss this some more," continued Dick. "I want each of you to go by there before the next meeting and take a good look at that area. Come up with some ideas about how we could make it look better. Then I'll have something to show for quality improvement. Next week same time, okay?" He looked around the table. No one said anything. "Good!" He rose to his feet and ambled out the door of the conference room, leaving the rest to quietly get up and leave.

Case Study Questions

1. Summarize the organizational dynamics at work in this scenario. What is the nature of Dick Richards's leadership style? Does his style work well for performance improvement activities?

2. Is the group performing effectively as a performance improvement team? What recommendations could be made with regard to team performance?

Summary

Developing effective teams probably never will be an easy task for the leadership of a healthcare organization's performance improvement initiatives. It can, however, be done when undertaken with a positive philosophy and firm commitment at the outset and the recognition that much development may have to be done as the program goes along. Important team roles include the facilitator, the recorder/scribe, and the timekeeper. Team members may also need to learn effective listening and questioning techniques and to accept responsibility for participating in collaborative problem solving and other team activities.

References and Suggested Readings

Barczak, N. L. 1996. How to lead effective teams. *Critical Care Nursing Quarterly* 19(1):73–82.

Burns, Robert K. 1960. *The Questioning Techniques.* Chicago: Industrial Relations Center, University of Chicago.

Byham, William C., with Jeff Cox. 1998. *Zapp! The Lightning of Empowerment: How to Improve Quality, Productivity, and Employee Satisfaction.* New York City: Random House.

Byham, William C., with Jeff Cox and Greg Nelson. 1996. *Zapp! Empowerment in Health Care.* New York City: Random House.

Lynch, Robert F., and Thomas J. Werner. 1992. *Continuous Improvement: Teams and Tools.* Atlanta: Qual Team.

Renneker, J. A. 1996. Team building for continuous quality improvement. *Seminar in Perioperative Nursing* 5(1):40–46.

Chapter 17
Managing the Human Side of Change

Learning Objectives

- To understand the importance of applying change management techniques in implementing performance improvements

- To understand the three phases of change

- To recognize the steps in change management

Background and Significance

In today's world, there is no such thing as permanent stability. Change is the norm. The processes and structures that worked last year may be ineffective this year. The products and services that once were cutting edge eventually become obsolete. Healthcare delivery in the United States has been in a state of rapid and unpredictable evolution ever since the Medicare and Medicaid programs were implemented in the 1970s and the prospective payment system was instituted in the 1980s.

As previous chapters have shown, the overarching reason for change in healthcare organizations today is the need to improve the quality of care they provide and at the same time to control the cost of services. Hospitals and other healthcare organizations have institutionalized continuous performance improvement programs to meet this need. Systems, processes, and staff competencies undergo a circular cycle of change as incremental improvements are made in the clinical, administrative, and governance areas of the organization.

Performance improvement is based on the quantitative analysis of data and the qualitative analysis of processes and structures, but performance improvement efforts also have a very human side. After all, healthcare is provided by people working in extremely complex organizations, not by robots that can be reprogrammed or replaced when change is needed. Failure to consider the human side of performance improvement can sink even the most well conceived improvement efforts.

Healthcare professionals have always understood the importance of what they do. Today, during an era of dramatic and ongoing change in the way healthcare is provided and paid for, most clinical and allied health professionals sincerely believe in the goal of improving patient care services and outcomes. Still, most people find changing the way they do things very hard, and healthcare professionals are no exception.

The Three Phases of Change

Every change in the way people do things entails three phases. Whether they are changing the way they eat or the way they write a patient care plan, they go through the same process: ending–transition–beginning. The ending phase is characterized by grief and letting go; the transitional phase by confusion and, ironically, creativity; and the beginning phase by acceptance and hope for the future. The three phases of change are not clear-cut steps. Rather, they overlap one another. At any particular point, one of the three phases is likely to predominate while the emotions and concerns associated with the other two phases fall to the background. The movement is gradual, as one phase gives way to the next.

Grief is a natural human reaction to loss of any kind. Simply defined, *grief* is the conflicting feelings that come along with the end of something familiar or a change in an accepted pattern of behavior. Before people can go on to a new beginning, they need to let go of their old identity or their old way of doing things. According to William Bridges (1991, p. 5), "the failure to identify and be ready for the endings and losses that change produces is the largest single problem that organizations [and individuals] in transition encounter. The organization institutes a quality improvement program, and no one foresees how many people will experience the 'improvements' as a loss of something related to their job."

Between the ending of the old and the beginning of the new lies a transitional zone. People go through this transitional period whether they want to or not, whether they perceive the change as a good thing or a bad thing, whether the change is in our personal life or our work life, and whether the change is slight or overwhelming. The transitional phase is a kind of limbo. The old way of doing things is gone, but the new way of doing things still feels untried and uncomfortable. People tend to become confused and anxious because they have lost their identity as the people who played specific roles in the old way of doing things. Left to their own thoughts and feelings during this phase of organizational change, they may decide to escape their discomfort and confusion by leaving the organization. When people understand the change process they are going through, however, the transitional period can be a time of renewal and creativity.

During the final phase of change, the beginning of the new way of doing things, organizations and the people who make up the organizations settle into a more comfortable state. The new processes or staff structures become familiar, and individuals come to understand and accept their new roles. Some people may still worry that the new way of doing things may not work or that it may even make things worse. Some may feel last regrets about the ideas or coworkers they had to leave behind. Some people may even miss the freedom of the transitional zone and find settling back into a routine rather boring. A beginning can also be a disappointing time when the changes seem to have been made for no discernible reason. Still, eventually, the new way of doing things becomes the accepted way of doing things. Organizations, especially large healthcare organizations, need established structures and processes to function effectively.

Change Management

Like performance improvement, change can be thought of as a process to be understood and managed. Although definitions vary, for the purposes of this chapter, **change management** can be defined as a group of techniques used to help people understand the process of change and accept improvements in the way they perform their work. One or more members of the performance improvement team may take on the role of change manager for the project, or the department or executive managers for the areas affected by the change may play this role. Many organizations hire consultants to handle the change management process when the planned changes will have a significant impact on employees and medical staff.

The steps in the process of change management include the following:

1. Identifying the losses

2. Acknowledging the losses

3. Providing information and asking for feedback

4. Marking the endings

5. Managing the transition

6. Clarifying and reinforcing the beginning

7. Celebrating the successes

Identifying the Losses

When a performance improvement project is still in the planning stage, identifying the losses that will result from changes that need to be made may be difficult, especially if the change affects more than one area of the organization. The performance improvement team should start by describing the proposed improvement in as much detail as possible. Using flowcharts to map out processes may help the team to identify all of the areas that will be involved. Changes made in one area may create the need for secondary changes in other areas. The task of the PI team is to identify all of the people who will need to let go of a current way of doing things before an improvement can be implemented. The team also needs to determine exactly what will need to come to an end for the project to be successful.

Identifying the losses after the improvement has been implemented is much easier. The PI team or change manager for the project needs only to ask the people affected a few questions, such as "What is different for you now?" or "What don't you do anymore now that . . . ?" It is important to remember that nothing new can truly begin before something else has come to an end. Ideally, identifying and acknowledging the losses necessitated by a change should come before the change is implemented, but the ending phase will happen whether it is planned for or not.

Acknowledging the Losses

Depending on the extent of the changes to be made, representatives of the performance improvement team, department managers, or senior executives should explain the planned changes to the people who will be affected. The change manager charged with explaining the changes should be prepared to accept and acknowledge the reactions that result, even when they seem like overreactions.

When endings take place, people may feel angry, sad, anxious, confused, and depressed. All of these feelings are normal reactions to loss. Allowing people to express their emotions openly is difficult but critical to success. Sometimes even minor changes may become symbols of much more comprehensive changes that took place in the past but were never fully acknowledged. Minor changes may also be treated as harbingers of more drastic changes in the future. For example, a process redesign that will result in the elimination of one staff position may be seen by employees as the first of many layoffs to come. The key to effectively handling this step in the change management process is active listening: asking questions about how people feel and sympathetically acknowledging the legitimacy of those emotions.

Providing Information and Asking for Feedback

The timing and content of communications should be carefully planned in advance as an element of project design. It is crucial that the proposed changes be described in specific detail early in the improvement process. If people do not understand the purpose of a change, they will have difficulty accepting it. If they are not sure what the change will entail, they will come to their own conclusions about which processes will need to end and which will stay. And if they are not told how the change will affect them, they may assume the worst.

The performance improvement team or its representative must provide as much information as possible to the people who will be affected directly by the proposed change. Withholding information may lead to intense speculation about the changes to come, and such speculations often create feelings of helplessness and anger. Although some information may need to remain confidential, the change manager should never fabricate answers to questions that he or she cannot answer fully. Rather, the manager should acknowledge the questions and provide as much information as possible. Glossing over the potentially negative aspects of the change can only create mistrust.

Information about the change project should be communicated consistently and often. Repeating the information in a variety of ways will help people accept the change. Newsletters, special announcements, staff meetings, and other forms of communication can all be used to get the message across. The people affected by the change should also be kept up-to-date as the proposed changes are developed, and they should be given the opportunity to provide feedback to the performance improvement team.

The performance improvement team should be sure to seek feedback during every critical stage of the improvement project. They should ask for information about the concerns of stakeholders early in the project's design phase. During testing, stakeholders should be asked for feedback on what is working well and what is not, and they should be directly involved in creating a detailed plan for implementation. During implementation, the people actually applying the change should be asked to suggest refinements and improvements. And after the project is complete, they should be asked to provide feedback on whether the goals of the project were met.

Marking the Endings

Actions always speak louder than words. The change manager should find some method to mark the ending of the old way of doing things. Removing obsolete equipment from a treatment area, rearranging work spaces, or replacing old procedure manuals with new ones can be a symbolic end to the old way. Managers sometimes make the mistake of criticizing the way things were done in the past as a way of introducing improvements. Creating negative pictures of the past is not effective. Instead, the past should be honored for the positive things it accomplished and for the foundations it laid for the future.

Managing the Transition

The length of the transitional period between old and new depends on the extent of the changes to be implemented. Obviously, the restructuring of a whole organization would require a much longer transition than the installation of a new piece of equipment, but both would require that people become accustomed to a new way of doing things. In the first case, everyone in the organization would be affected, clinical staff as well as administrative staff, nurses as well as health information managers. The installation of a new piece of diagnostic equipment, however, might affect only a small number of people. The technicians using the equipment would be affected most directly, but the change might also affect the nursing staff, the patient transport staff, and the medical staff working in that specialty area.

The transitional period is a difficult time for everyone. Productivity is likely to diminish as energy levels fall and people feel unsure of themselves and of the systems on which they depend to accomplish their work. Old resentments may resurface, and staff turnover may increase. During any transition, people tend to put themselves in one of three camps: those who oppose the change, those who endorse the change, and those who have decided to reserve judgment until they see how things turn out. Interpersonal or interdepartmental conflict may result. Everything feels out of control and chaotic, and people may dread going to work every day.

The change manager's task is to help people to understand that the chaos the organization is going through is a necessary part of change. It is during this seemingly chaotic period that people learn new skills, redefine their roles, and work through their questions about the new processes or structures to be implemented. Creative solutions to unforeseen problems are devised, and new relationships are forged. Special training in creative problem solving and team building may be helpful during this period.

The change manager also needs to ensure that nothing falls between the cracks. Temporary systems may be needed to maintain operations. For example, interim team leaders may be assigned to handle staff scheduling, or temporary record-handling procedures may be instituted during the transition between a paper-based and a computer-based health record system.

Above all, the change manager must keep the channels of communication open. Information about the project's progress and the problems being encountered during implementation must be shared between the areas affected and the performance improvement team and/or senior management. New policies and procedures should be developed, and position descriptions should be revised. Change managers may find it helpful to use storyboards to document and explain the improvements being made.

The purpose of the change or the problem that required resolution should be explained and repeated in every communication during the transitional period. The people affected by the change should also be involved in the development of a step-by-step plan for phasing in the new process. The plan should spell out the role that each individual is to play during the transition and after the new system has been fully implemented.

Clarifying and Reinforcing the Beginning

The arrival of a new manager, the installation of new equipment, or the move to new offices only begins the beginning. Before a beginning can be successful, the people affected by the change must have gone through an ending, during which the loss of the old way of doing things was acknowledged; and a transitional phase, during which they built new relationships, learned new skills, accepted new roles, and refined policies and procedures. A true beginning confirms the end of the old way of doing things.

The performance improvement team, the change manager, and other decision makers in the organization need to reinforce new beginnings on every level. Nothing will doom a change effort more quickly than conflicting messages. For example, an improvement that involved making the change from traditional directive management to a self-managed team would not succeed unless the employees were delegated the authority to make decisions. If the former department manager continued to make every important decision, the other people on the team would revert to silence. Similarly, customer service initiatives would not survive if senior managers emphasized cost-cutting over quality in their communications to staff.

Celebrating the Successes

Humans use ceremonies to mark beginnings as well as endings. Baptisms celebrate the birth of new babies, and weddings celebrate the marriage of committed couples. The change manager should find a way to help people celebrate their successes in making meaningful changes in the way they perform their work. A ribbon-cutting ceremony at a new facility, an open house for a reorganized department, and a demonstration of new equipment for colleagues outside the department are some examples of celebrations that mark new beginnings. Even the accomplishment of a minor procedural improvement should be acknowledged with a sincere thank-you to all of the people involved in conceiving, planning, and implementing the change.

Case Study

Faced with rising costs and declining revenues, the board of directors for a community hospital located in a large city on the East Coast decided to combine its obstetrics and pediatrics units. The obstetrics service was located in the oldest part of the facility, and the labor and delivery rooms were cramped and inefficient. A large medical center not far from the hospital offered comfortable, family-centered accommodations and the latest equipment, and several obstetricians had recently moved their practices from the community hospital to the medical center. The board was reluctant to discontinue obstetrics services because the hospital had a long history of providing maternity care to the surrounding community, but overhead costs for the underutilized and obsolete unit were out of control and the cost of replacing the unit was prohibitive.

The pediatrics unit, in contrast, was housed in the newest wing of the hospital. The hospital's emergency department was one of only two in the city equipped to provide pediatric trauma services, and a number of patients were admitted to the service through emergency. In addition, a large physician group that specialized in pediatric oncology admitted hundreds of patients to the facility each year. The physician group was recognized nationwide and handled referrals from pediatricians throughout a four-state area.

The consolidation of services made sense to the board on several levels. From a cost control perspective, closing the obsolete facility would save the hospital millions of dollars in renovation expenses. The consolidation also made sense from a patient care point of view. Expectant mothers who were known to have high-risk pregnancies could plan to deliver their babies at a facility that specialized in treating pediatric patients. In addition, the head of the obstetrics unit was scheduled to retire soon, and the board saw an opportunity to make significant changes in the clinical area. The board believed that the obstetrics service should change its focus from handling routine deliveries to handling high-risk pregnancies and thus overcome the competitive disadvantage the hospital now faced in comparison to the medical center. The board voted to seek funding for a new center of excellence for the care of high-risk mothers and newborns.

Combining the two units will require fundamental changes. The two units are managed in very different ways. The department head of the obstetrics unit is a traditionalist, and the obstetrics staff is accustomed to deferring to his judgment when problems arise. The department head for the pediatrics unit believes in self-managed work teams, and her unit is structured into cross-functional teams with independent decision-making authority. There are other obvious differences as well: one unit treats adults; the other treats children; one unit treats women who stay in the unit for a day or two at most; the other treats infants, children, and adolescents for conditions that require complex treatment regimens and long hospital stays. Parents often sleep in their children's rooms for weeks at a time. Each of the units has a separate identity, and each has taken on a we-versus-them attitude over time.

Case Study Questions

1. How do you think the nurses who work on the two units will feel about the change? The department heads? Who will lose what? How could those losses be acknowledged?

2. Create a communications plan for the project. How would you describe the purpose of the change? What vehicles would you use to communicate information about the project?

3. Who do you think should act as the change manager for the consolidation?

Summary

Performance improvement initiatives sometimes fail when the human factors in change are ignored or mismanaged. By recognizing the steps people go through to accomplish change and managing the transition from old to new, change managers can ensure the success of performance improvement efforts.

References and Suggested Readings

Bridges, William. 1991. *Managing Transitions: Making the Most of Change.* New York City: Perseus Books.

Buckley, D. S. 1999. A practitioner's view on managing change. *Frontiers of Health Services Management,* Fall, pp. 38–43.

Galpin, Timothy J. 1996. *The Human Side of Change.* San Francisco: Jossey-Bass.

Kohles, Mary K., William G. Baker, and Barbara A. Donaho. 1995. *Transformational Leadership: Renewing Fundamental Values and Achieving New Relationships in Health Care.* Chicago: American Hospital Publishing.

Kotter, J. P. 1995. Leading change: why transformation efforts fail. *Harvard Business Review,* March–April, pp. 59–67.

Senge, Peter, et al. 1994. *The Fifth Discipline Fieldbook: Strategies and Tools for Building a Learning Organization.* New York City: Doubleday.

Shortell, S. M., E. M. Morrison, and B. Friedman. 1992. *Strategic Choices for America's Hospitals: Managing Change in Turbulent Times.* San Francisco: Jossey-Bass.

Chapter 18
Developing the Performance Improvement Plan

Learning Objectives

- To recognize the sections of a healthcare organization's performance improvement plan
- To understand the reasons why yearly performance improvement plans are developed

Background and Significance

Performance improvement in healthcare is like any other organized human endeavor. It requires effective planning. Planning, however, requires people to free themselves from the constraints imposed by past experiences and to liberate their most creative energies and ideas, and this can be difficult. Effective planning also requires experience and familiarity with complex healthcare systems. The goal of this chapter is to introduce students to the process of developing performance improvement plans for healthcare organizations.

Strategic Planning

Planning for performance improvement activities in healthcare organizations should be an outgrowth of the organization's overall strategic planning process. The **strategic plan** is developed by the organization's senior administrators and board of directors, whom the public holds accountable for the quality of the organization's products and services. Through annual strategic planning, the administrators and board members validate the mission, vision, goals, and values for the organization as a whole and determine the direction the organization is going as a business entity during the coming year. As part of strategic planning, the board members and administrative officers carefully consider the community the organization serves, the technologies available to it, the expectations of its customers, and the expertise of personnel and medical staff when they craft the mission, vision, goals, and values.

Performance improvement activities should reflect the priorities established by the organization's strategic plan. As discussed in chapter 13, the process of strategic and performance improvement planning is unique to the culture of individual organizations. At

Community Hospital of the West, the managers and employees participate in organization-wide strategic planning. As part of strategic planning in 1998, they identified a list of the important functions and opportunities. (See figure 13.1, p. 200.) The participants used brainstorming techniques and nominal group techniques to identify and prioritize the opportunities. The prioritized ranking shows the number of importance points that the various opportunities for improvement earned upon review by the entire organization. The prioritized opportunities were then reevaluated and regrouped by the hospital's board of directors and senior administrators in light of other survey data. The result was the hospital's list of performance improvement goals for 1999 (appendix A of figure 18.1).

For example, many of the items on the 1998 strategic planning process document were related to patient care. (See the section on assessment of patients, care of patients, and others in figure 13.1.) Before strategic brainstorming, the organization had been collecting data using the Gallup Patient Satisfaction Survey. (See chapter 4.) An in-depth analysis of the data revealed a negative trend in multiple indicators related to nursing care. The indicators included the following:

- Overall nursing care
- Staff showed concern
- Nurses anticipated needs
- Nurses explained procedures
- Nurses demonstrated skill in providing care
- Nurses helped calm fears
- Staff communicated effectively
- Nurses/staff responded to requests

After considerable discussion of the opportunities that had been brainstormed and of the Gallup survey data, the leadership decided to implement a new approach to nursing care as a response to issues affecting nursing care. Specifically, the leadership decided to implement Jean Watson's theory of human caring (Watson, 1985).

The theory of human caring "recognizes the dignity and worth of individuals and that their responses to illness are unique; acknowledges the individual's right to continuous autonomy; helps individuals reach maximum capacity; recognizes that nursing takes place within a human-to-human caring relationship; and supports caring as the core of nursing practice, recognizing that caring is effectively demonstrated and practiced interpersonally." In Watson's theory, caring nursing is exhibited by five behaviors (Dingman, 1999, pp. 31–32):

- Nurse introduces self to patients and explains role in care that day.
- Nurse calls the patient by preferred name.
- Nurse sits at the patient's bedside for at least five minutes per shift to plan and review care.
- Nurse uses a handshake or a touch on the arm.
- Nurse uses the mission, vision, and value statements of the organization in planning care.

Figure 18.1.   Example of a Performance Improvement Plan

Community Hospital of the West
Performance Improvement Plan
1999

I. MISSION

The Board of Trustees of the Community Hospital of the West supports the goal of continuous performance improvement throughout the organization. The goal of the 1999 Performance Improvement Plan is to provide a planned, systematic, and integrated approach to measuring, assessing, and improving the services provided by the organization.

II. PURPOSE

This plan describes the Community Hospital's quality philosophy and explains how this philosophy is put into practice. The plan serves as a standard for the organizationwide approach to performance improvement. The specific purpose of the plan includes the following:

A. To describe the responsibilities for performance improvement throughout the organization
B. To define the requirements and framework for the design, measurement, assessment, and improvement processes
C. To serve as a resource in describing the systematic method for measurement, assessment, and improvement of important functions/processes or the design of new processes
D. To describe the reporting flow through the organization and define responsibility

III. OBJECTIVES OF PERFORMANCE IMPROVEMENT

The objectives of performance improvement at Community Hospital of the West include the following:

A. Improve the performance of the important functions and key processes as prioritized by the organization. Over time, this will include the following:

- Patient rights and organizational ethics
- Patient assessment
- Patient care
- Education
- Continuum of care
- Organizational performance improvement
- Leadership
- Management of the environment of care
- Management of human resources
- Management of information
- Surveillance, prevention, and control of infection
- Governance, medical staff, management, and nursing

B. Focus the organization's performance improvement activities on measuring, assessing, and improving the level of performance in the following dimensions:

- Efficacy
- Appropriateness
- Availability
- Timeliness
- Effectiveness
- Continuity
- Safety
- Efficiency
- Respect and caring

(Continued on next page)

Figure 18.1. *(Continued)*

C. Support the organization's strategic goals in the areas of:

- Performance and service improvement
- Leadership development
- Program development/support
- Marketing and promotion

D. Include in every performance improvement team's objectives, as appropriate, the goals of:

- Decreasing variation in practice
- Decreasing the actual cost of care
- Increasing customer satisfaction
- Increasing volume and market share

E. To promote the collaboration of improvement activities among departments and disciplines. To coordinate medical staff performance improvement activities with those of the organization, integrating efforts whenever appropriate. The organization and medical staff will carry out performance improvement activities for operative and other procedures, blood use, medication use, medical records, utilization review, infection control, and risk management collaboratively.

IV. **RESPONSIBILITIES FOR PERFORMANCE IMPROVEMENT**

A. Responsibilities of the Board of Trustees

1. Clearly communicate the organization's mission, vision, and strategic plan throughout the organization and provide the framework to accomplish the performance improvement goals.
2. Provide an organizationwide mechanism and related policies to assure the provision of quality care.
3. Accept the formal authority and responsibility for the implementation, operation, and assessment of a flexible, comprehensive, and integrated performance improvement program.
4. Determine the extent of the financial support necessary for the program so that administration can provide the specific resources in service, equipment, and personnel required.
5. Participate in the achievement of annual performance improvement priorities.
6. Receive regular reports regarding performance improvement activities and offer recommendations and direction based on the hospital's mission, community needs, care outcomes, and organization strategic goals.

B. Responsibilities of the Organization's Leadership

Leadership collectively and individually is responsible for the planning, design, measurement, assessment, and improvement of performance. The performance improvement activities of patient care, governance, management, clinical and support services, including the functional processes as defined by the JCAHO. This includes the implementation of this plan; setting expectations, and prioritizing improvements, the provision for resources and training needed for these activities, and fostering communication and coordination of performance improvement activities. The organization's leadership includes the leaders of the Board of Trustees, the CEO, and the CNO/COO; elected/appointed leaders of the medical staff and clinical departments; and department managers. The organization's leaders will:

1. Provide for the overall vision, direction, and education required for the development and implementation of the Performance Improvement Program.
2. Coordinate and integrate services throughout the organization, and participate in planning, designing, measuring, assessing, and improving those services.
3. Promote a systemwide approach to performance improvement activities.
4. Develop and implement policies and procedures that guide and support the provision of services.
5. Recommend a sufficient number of qualified and competent persons to provide care and treatment.

Figure 18.1. *(Continued)*

    6. Determine the qualifications and technical and interpersonal competence of the department personnel who provide patient care and organization support services and who are not licensed independent practitioners.

    7. Direct and/or participate in performance improvement activities for the area of responsibility.

    8. Maintain quality control programs and ensure that minimum measurement requirements are met.

    9. Orient and provide in-service training and continuing education of all persons in the organization.

  10. Recommend space and other resources needed by the organization.

  11. Participate in the annual strategic planning process.

C. Medical Staff Responsibilities

The Medical Staff, through its officers, departments, committees, and individual members, is responsible for leading, collaborating, and participating in the implementation of the Performance Improvement Plan. In conjunction with the organization leadership, the Medical Staff will:

    1. Assist in designing and implementing priorities for performance improvement and performance measures to monitor, evaluate, and improve the performance of patient care.

    2. Identify and approve the use of key indicator criteria to conduct continuous surveillance of the professional performance of all individuals who have delineated clinical privileges.

    3. Participate in peer review activities and functions, document conclusions and actions, and maintain technical and interpersonal competencies.

    4. Review and evaluate organization performance measurement data to determine conclusions, recommendations, and actions for improvement, and participate in the implementation of the improvement.

    5. Serve in a leadership role, collaborating with hospital leaders and staff to improve the performance of:
        a. Medical assessment and treatment of patients
        b. Use of operative and other procedures
        c. Use of medications
        d. Use of blood and blood components
        e. Efficiency of clinical practice patterns
        f. Significant departures from established patterns of clinical practice

    6. Serve in a participative role with hospital leaders and staff to improve the performance of:
        a. Education of patients and families
        b. Coordination of care with others
        c. Accurate, timely, and legible completion of patients' medical records

    7. Participate in, advise, support, and recommend formation of hospitalwide (chartered) or department-specific performance improvement teams.

    8. Establish a mechanism for reviewing and assessing performance of outsourced contracted sources of care.

    9. Participate in the annual review and approval of medical staff standing orders.

  10. Participate in the annual strategic planning process.

D. Responsibilities of Departments and Employees

    1. Identify priorities for performance improvement for the department/service based upon the important function(s) performed.

    2. Identify and express their views regarding performance improvement opportunities and participate in performance improvement activities.

    3. Incorporate performance improvement into all work activities by doing the right things well, maintaining technical and interpersonal competencies, and supporting the mission and vision of the organization.

(Continued on next page)

Figure 18.1.   *(Continued)*

E. Responsibilities of the Quality Council

The Quality Council oversees the continuous improvement of performance throughout the organization. Oversight is provided to guide, facilitate, prioritize and reprioritize, and approve performance improvement team activities and to provide for education in team building and problem-solving tools. The Quality Council will:

1. Meet at least quarterly to receive reports of all performance improvement and quality control activities conducted throughout the organization.
2. Provide reports of performance improvement activities and make recommendations as appropriate to the Medical Executive Committee, Administration, Leadership Council, and Board of Trustees regarding hospital-related performance issues. Provide for annual review of the performance improvement plan and program.
3. Provide for interdisciplinary Quality Council representation. Core council members include the Chief Executive Officer (CEO), the Chief Nursing Officer/Chief Operating Officer (CNO/COO), Medical Staff representation, the Quality Resource and Education Manager, and rotating Functional Team Leaders.

F. Responsibilities of the Quality Resources and Education Manager

The Quality Resources and Education Manager will serve as the facility's coordinator of all performance improvement efforts. This will include:

1. Provide direction, education, and support for all PI team activities as they relate to patient care and process evaluation with subsequent reporting to the appropriate organizational/medical staff committees and departments, including the Quality Council, and the Board of Trustees.
2. Maintain an aggregate/comparative database for performance improvement activities including minimum measurement requirements and medical staff related peer review activities.
3. Document the annual evaluation of the performance improvement program. Develop and support mechanisms to conduct detailed analysis of data patterns/trends in order to identify opportunities for the improvement of patient care.
5. Develop and support mechanisms to identify situations in which the results of performance improvement activities are relevant to the performance of an individual, with subsequent reporting to the appropriate person or medical staff/organizational department/service, including clinician profiles for use in recredentialing activities.
6. Assist Leadership in the ongoing training of all staff in the methods/tools of performance improvement.
7. Coordinate activities to maintain ongoing compliance with the JCAHO and other regulatory body standards.

V. EDUCATION

The leaders of the Community Hospital of the West are involved in ongoing educational activities related to performance improvement. This includes the orientation and continuing education of all employees through new employee orientation, department-specific performance improvement orientation, the ongoing participation in performance improvement activities, and "just-in-time training" for performance improvement teams.

VI. PERFORMANCE IMPROVEMENT PROCESSES

A. The planning and design process for collaborative organizationwide performance improvement or the design of new processes will be based upon the following:

1. Alignment with the mission, vision, and strategic plans of the organization.
2. The satisfaction of customers' needs and expectations.
3. Consideration of current information regarding the function, process, or service being designed.
4. Evaluation of the performance and outcomes of the organization's functions, processes, and services.

Figure 18.1.   *(Continued)*

B. The measurement process will be utilized to:

1. Evaluate the maintenance or improvement of processes and outcomes.
2. Evaluate the effectiveness of redesigned processes.
3. Identify opportunities for improvement of existing processes, considering those that are high volume, high risk, or problem prone.
4. Provide baseline information for design of new processes.
5. Assess our customers' needs and expectations and employees' views regarding improvement opportunities.
6. Define minimum measurement requirements that will include monitoring and evaluation (over time) in all the important functions, and continuously in the following areas:
    a. Operative and other procedure processes or outcomes in these categories: selecting the appropriate procedure, preparing the patient, performing the procedure and monitoring the patient, providing postprocedure care and postprocedure education, and performing pathology review
    b. Use of medications in these categories: prescribing or ordering, preparing or dispensing, administering, and monitoring the effects on patients
    c. Use of blood and blood components in these categories: ordering practices; distributing, handling, and dispensing; administration; and monitoring effects on patients
    d. Utilization review activities
    e. Autopsy results
    f. Risk management activities
    g. Quality control activities in the areas of clinical lab, radiology services, nuclear medicine, dietetic services, and pharmacy equipment used to measure and administer medications
7. Measurement will be utilized to compare the organization's performance to external data as available.

C. The assessment process will be utilized:

1. To determine:
    a. Whether design specifications for new processes were met
    b. The level of performance and stability of existing processes
    c. Priorities for possible improvement of existing processes
    d. Actions to improve the performance of processes
    e. Whether change in the processes resulted in improvement
2. In comparing to a frame of reference for interpreting measurement data. The frame of reference may include:
    a. Internal comparisons over time
    b. Comparison to external references
    c. Comparison to internal/external regulations, standards, or policies
3. Intensive assessment is required when one or more of the following situations occur showing undesirable variation in performance:
    a. Occurrences of adverse sentinel events
    b. Adverse variation in the organization's performance in comparison to other organizations or accepted standards
    c. Preoperative to postoperative diagnosis discrepancies
    d. Confirmed transfusion reactions
    e. Significant adverse drug reactions
    f. Adverse variation in relation to an individual's performance

D. The improvement process will follow the organization's model and use team collaboration to improve the performance of existing processes and the quality of outcomes. Anyone at any level of the organization as well as customers can suggest an opportunity for improvement to leadership.

(Continued on next page)

Figure 18.1. *(Continued)*

VII. COMPONENTS SUPPORTING THE PERFORMANCE IMPROVEMENT PROGRAM

A. Risk Management
B. Management of the Environment of Care
C. Infection Control
D. Health Information Management
E. Human Resource Management
F. Utilization Review
G. Pharmacy Department Review
H. Laboratory and Blood Bank Review
I. Medical Staff Credentialing
J. External Benchmarking

VIII. CONFIDENTIALITY

All performance improvement activities set forth in the plan including minutes, reports, and associated work products and documentation tools are considered to be confidential. Such materials are to be held in strictest confidence and carefully safeguarded against unauthorized disclosure. Confidentiality of patients and providers will be achieved by using assigned numbers and not names. Reports, minutes, and other findings may not be released or discussed with any person or agency except those mandated by the hospital policies or state or federal laws. JCAHO or other professional surveyors for programs of accreditation may review these activities. Such professional accreditation reviews will be the sole exception to the confidentiality of performance improvement activities.

IX. APPRAISAL OF PERFORMANCE IMPROVEMENT PLAN

An evaluation of the Performance Improvement Plan will be conducted annually and take into consideration mission, objectives, overall effectiveness, accomplishments, and areas needing improvement. The evaluation will be presented by the Quality Council to the Administration, Leadership Council, the Medical Executive Committee, and the Board of Trustees for approval. Recommendations for improvement will be implemented in the next revision of the Performance Improvement Plan.

APPENDIX A: 1999 PERFORMANCE IMPROVEMENT GOALS

Goal 1:   To improve patient, physician, and employee satisfaction

A. Patient Satisfaction: Improve patient satisfaction as measured by the Gallup Survey.

Action Plan:
- Implement the caring model of nursing.
- Refine and improve the centralized scheduling process.
- Improve patient education and communication in the area of advanced directives.

Measurement:
- Patient responses on the Gallup Survey will shift from satisfied or dissatisfied to increase the very satisfied by 5%.
- The number of positive comments will increase by at least 5%.
- The number of billing complaints will decrease by at least 5%.

B. Physician Satisfaction: Improve physician satisfaction as measured by the biannual medical staff survey.

Action Plan:
- Implement the caring model of nursing.
- Refine/improve the centralized scheduling process.
- Evaluate and downsize committee structure as appropriate.

Measurement: The results of the biannual medical staff survey will shift from satisfied or dissatisfied to increase the very satisfied by 5%.

C. Employee Satisfaction: Improve employee satisfaction.

Action Plan:
- Implement the caring model of nursing.
- Award/recognize employees for years of service.

Figure 18.1. *(Continued)*

- Review/improve the employee evaluation process.
- Implement a system of merit raises.
- Develop department-specific action plans based on employee survey results and exit interview feedback.

Measurement:
- The annual employee turnover rate will decrease by 5%.
- All employees will be surveyed in June/July at department meetings using Gallup Survey questions.
- A system of performing exit interviews will be implemented.

Goal 2:   To improve the infrastructure and systems used to collect, measure, and assess information so that information will be secure, accurate, appropriately accessible, useful, timely, and effective

Action Plan:
- Provide education in basic information management principles and provide tools including software/hardware training for leaders and other staff as needed.
- Improve/develop point-of-service data documentation with associated monitoring and evaluation of outcomes.
- Develop standing agendas for meetings to support appropriate flow of information throughout the organization.
- Develop standardization in documentation measurement including expansion of the organizational data dictionary.
- Improve communication pathways to provide information to and encourage feedback from patients, trustees, physicians, employees, and other customers.

Measurement:
- Performance improvement/risk and safety reports will be complete, accurate, and timely.
- Compliance with documentation requirements as measured by data quality monitoring program will increase.
- Communication as measured by employee, physician, and patient survey results and through unsolicited comments will show improvement.

Goal 3:   To improve leadership orientation, education, and performance

Action Plan:
- Revise/develop executive team and manager orientation and reference manual.
- Provide/attend at least two leadership education programs focusing on assessed needs for trustees, medical executive staff, executive team, and managers.

Measurement:
- Educational program feedback surveys from participants will demonstrate program effectiveness.
- Trustee self-evaluation results will improve.
- Trustee evaluations of the CEO will improve.
- Survey results and self-evaluations will improve.

Goal 4:   To develop and improve employee competence and performance

Action Plan:
- Develop and administer an organizationwide educational needs assessment program including feedback from physicians and employees as well as patient satisfaction survey.
- Develop an educational program calendar to address prioritized needs.

Measurement:
- Educational needs will have been met as measured by the results of posttests and demonstrated competencies.
- Employee perception that needs have been met will be measured by participant evaluations of the educational offerings.

Performance Improvement Planning

Implementation of the caring model was made part of the hospital's strategy for improving patients' perceptions of nursing care. All other opportunities were then to be aligned with that major goal. It was intended that changing the strategy for nursing care in this dramatic way would be evidenced in subsequent measures of nursing effectiveness by the Gallup patient satisfaction survey.

The first part of the performance improvement goals document (figure 18.1) was organized to reflect the needs of the organization's most important customers: patients, physicians, and employees. Opportunities were then listed beneath the customers to which they pertained, maintaining the visibility of customers in the plan and the focus on the customer in the performance improvement approach.

The rest of the 1999 goals document focuses on the important functions of the organization: information improvement, leadership improvement, staff improvement, and overall organizational improvement. Each section identified an action plan and the means by which the efforts at improvement would be measured. These measurements would then provide good data for the organization to assess itself and plan the following year's performance improvement goals, thus maintaining the continuous performance improvement philosophy and cycle in the organization.

Documentation of the Performance Improvement Plan

Documentation of the overall plan for performance improvement activities is an important aspect of maintaining awareness of PI as an issue in the organization and of communicating the organization's efforts in this area to its communities of interest. Obviously, students new to the whole topic of performance improvement in healthcare are not going to be able to write performance improvement plans for healthcare organizations. However, it is hoped that this example may be helpful. Most PI plans outline at least the PI program's mission, purpose, objectives, and responsibilities.

Most PI plan documents begin with the **mission statement** for the performance improvement program in the organization (as opposed to the mission statement for the organization as a whole). For example, the mission statement for the PI plan of Community Hospital of the West reads, "The Board of Trustees of Community Hospital of the West supports the goal of continuous performance improvement throughout the organization. The goal of the 1999 Performance Improvement Plan is to provide a planned, systematic, and integrated approach to measuring, assessing, and improving the services provided by the organization." (See figure 18.1, part I.)

The purpose section explains what the plan is intended to do for the organization. Commonly, discussion centers on communication of the organization's philosophy for performance improvement and communicates that philosophy to its constituencies. General language regarding the content of the plan usually reflects the objectives and responsibilities sections of the plan. (See figure 18.1, part II.)

The objectives section explains planned outcomes of the performance improvement plan. Discussion usually centers on the key processes and functions that the organization seeks to improve, which strategic goals of the organization that PI activities seek to support, and which dimensions of the organization's performance are to be improved. (See figure 18.1, part III.)

The responsibilities section identifies specific responsibilities of the board of trustees, leadership, medical staff, department managers and employees, quality council (if there is one), and quality resources and education management (if there is such a department). (See figure 18.1, part IV.)

The performance improvement plan of Community Hospital of the West also documents the following:

- Other aspects such as how the program will educate individuals in the organization with respect to performance improvement activities (figure 18.1, part V)

- The performance improvement processes and methodologies to be used within the organization (figure 18.1, part VI)

- The standardized components of the program to be undertaken (such as pharmacy and therapeutics and infection control activities) (figure 18.1, part VII)

- The policy on confidentiality to be adhered to with reference to performance improvement activities (figure 18.1, part VIII)

- The appraisal activities to be carried out to evaluate the continuing effectiveness of the performance improvement plan in directing performance improvement activities in the organization (figure 18.1, part IX)

Finally, the appendices of the document usually include the specific performance improvement goals and other supporting documents that the leadership of the initiative believe are important to communication of the program to constituencies within and outside the organization. Only appendix A of the sample PI plan is included in figure 18.1.

Case Study

Students should look at the list of functions and opportunities (figure 13.1) and the performance improvement plan (figure 18.1) for Community Hospital of the West and answer the following questions. Then for an area of student experience at school or at work, they should write a draft of a performance improvement plan. The plan should identify specific performance improvement goals, action plans, and objective measures, as well as the plan's mission, objectives, and responsibilities.

Case Study Questions

1. How is the 1999 performance improvement plan linked to the list of functions and opportunities identified during strategic planning in 1998?

2. Can you identify items in the prioritized 1998 strategic planning process document that are related to goals in the 1999 performance improvement goals?

3. Note that the items in the 1998 strategic planning process document are very specific. Were related items from the list grouped into a more general category for the final 1999 performance improvement goals?

4. Are the measurements identified for the 1999 goals truly quantifiable? That is, will the measurements actually lead to objective data that can be evaluated for evidence of improvement?

Summary

Planning the direction of a healthcare organization's performance improvement program is a complex activity. The program must be created in concert with the organization's overall strategic plan. From the many opportunities for improvement possible, the organization then must decide which opportunities are to be the focus of improvement efforts during the coming year. The planning document for the program includes statements of mission, purpose, objectives, and responsibilities. The document may also include a discussion of the educational initiatives to be developed in support of the PI program, descriptions of the components of the program, methodology to be used, and other information.

References and Suggested Readings

Dingman, Sharon K., et al. 1999. Implementing a caring model to improve patient satisfaction. *Journal of Nursing Administration* 29(12):30–37.

Plisek, P. E. 1995. Techniques for managing quality. *Hospital and Health Services Administration* 40(1):50–79.

Watson, Jean. 1985. *Nursing: Human Science and Human Care, A Theory of Nursing.* Norwalk, Conn.: Appleton-Century-Crofts.

Chapter 19
Evaluating the Performance Improvement Program

Learning Objectives

- To understand the reasons performance improvement programs are evaluated

- To recognize the aspects of the performance improvement program that should be evaluated

- To understand what organizations should do with the information gathered through evaluating the performance improvement program

Background and Significance

Planning the PI program and evaluating the PI program should be mirror images of each other. Taken together, they, too, are a cyclical activity, with planning leading to evaluation and evaluation providing the impetus for new planning.

Performance improvement programs are evaluated for four reasons:

1. *To determine whether the organization's approach to designing, measuring, assessing, and improving its performance is planned, systematic, and organizationwide.* Forethought and deliberation in planning a PI program focus the organization on important issues and lead to better results in program activities. Systematizing the PI program makes it possible for participants to understand what is expected and enables them to anticipate program requirements. Committing to the organizationwide nature of the program ensures that everyone in the organization is in concert with the program's objectives and understands their expected contributions to it.

2. *To determine whether the organization's approach and its activities are carried out collaboratively.* Contemporary expectations of performance improvement activities are that they will be multidisciplinary, that they will improve performance across department lines (that is, that they are *cross-functional*), and that all of the factors that contribute to a problem will be remedied. Participants are expected to contribute as part of a team.

3. *To determine whether the organization's approach needs redesign in light of changes in the strategic plan or organizational objectives.* If the organization's mission, vision, values, organizational structure, or strategic initiatives have changed since the performance improvement program was planned, then new measures and assessment activities may have to be undertaken. Modifications should be implemented as soon as possible after major changes in the organization's objectives have been implemented.

4. *To determine whether the program was effective in the improvement of overall organizational performance.* It is important to identify whether the PI program was responsible for important improvements in organizational performance or whether those improvements were due to other factors. It is also important to identify whether any improvement was achieved at all. Review of program performance should identify whether program processes are efficient, effective, timely, and appropriately supported with personnel, budget, and other resources.

Components of Program Review

During program review, each of the areas discussed in this text should be examined for continuing focus and relevance. Each area should document the opportunities for improvement that were identified and what outcomes of performance improvement were accomplished. Each should document what problems remain unresolved from prior evaluation periods or have not shown significant signs of impending improvement. Each area should identify issues in the performance improvement program that, if changed, could better support the area's performance improvement efforts. For example:

- *The performance improvement model:* Does the performance improvement methodology currently used in the organization continue to support its PI activities well? Could the model be made more efficient or formalities lessened in some activities? Do all members of the organization understand the model and the ways it can helpfully structure performance improvement activities?

- *Improvement opportunities:* Have the organization's members been able to identify improvement opportunities? Have they been able to recognize impending sentinel events? Have they been able to identify measures for important processes, customers, products, and services in their areas of responsibility? Have they discovered benchmarks to evaluate their division's performance against?

- *Teamwork in PI activities:* Have the organization's members been able to work effectively in teams? Are they willing and able to take on the important roles in team activities? Do they participate and interact well at team meetings to work through PI processes? Can they document important team milestones with appropriate tools? Have they learned to use the QI toolbox techniques effectively and appropriately? Have they learned to listen and question effectively in interpersonal communication? Can they communicate the team's process and outcomes effectively to the rest of the organization?

- *Customer satisfaction:* Have internal and external customers been identified for all performance improvement projects? Have customers' requirements been identified in detail? Has customer satisfaction been measured objectively and with appropriate tools?

- *Continuum of care:* Are clients and patients provided with care using appropriate resources and settings? Are required changes in level of care identified and resource utilization redesigned appropriately? Are transfers of patients between care settings carefully orchestrated and care needs communicated effectively? Are relations among payers, providers, and patients positive? Are care processes regarding the continuum examined and improved as opportunities are identified?

- *Infectious disease:* Are means to prevent the transmission of infectious disease always in place? Are surveillance measures undertaken to track infectious disease in the facilities and appropriate containment procedures employed when necessary? Are care processes regarding infectious disease examined and improved as opportunities are identified?

- *Risk exposure:* Is adherence to procedures monitored and appropriate education undertaken when necessary? Are the right services always rendered to the right patient, at the right time, with the right procedure? Are unforeseen occurrences always reported per policy and procedure? Are care processes modified when necessary to prevent injury to patients, visitors, and employees?

- *Care of patients:* Are every patient's care needs assessed, planned, carried out, and reassessed appropriately? Do members of the care team redesign more effective care processes when necessary? Are care outcomes systematically examined for opportunities for improvement? Are routine care assessments such as pharmacy and therapeutics, blood usage, mortality and morbidity, and so on, carried out and opportunities for improvement identified? Is all care documented appropriately in paper-based or computer-based information systems? Is continuing education of caregivers undertaken with respect to important practice areas? Are care processes examined and improved as opportunities are identified?

- *Care environment and safety:* Has the care environment been monitored for opportunities for improvement? Has environment and safety training been carried out for all new employees and on anniversary dates for continuing employees? Has all training of employees been documented in personnel files? Are all employees process-capable with respect to fire suppression, smoke suppression, disaster preparedness, evacuation of facilities, and so forth?

- *Human resources development:* Are appropriate hiring, staffing, development, and assessment activities occurring in all departments? Are employees being screened for disease as required by state health regulations? Are required documents being maintained on all employees? Are required credentials and licenses being verified on all employed staff? Are required credentials and licenses being verified on all independent practitioners? Are appropriate reviews of practice capability being performed on all clinical staff?

- *Accreditation and licensure:* Is the organization continuously ready for review by accrediting and licensing agencies?

In addition to reviewing the aspects of quality improvement programs identified, evaluation of the program should also review any focused performance improvement projects that were undertaken in the preceding year. Focused performance improvement projects are those organizationwide opportunities that may have been identified at the beginning of the current performance improvement cycle, such as those that were chartered by the quality council.

Each of these program goals should have an action plan and a measurement section. During program evaluation, each of the action plans and measurement sections must be examined to determine whether the action plan was implemented and, if it was, whether appropriate and acceptable changes in measurement were effected. If change in measurement was in a positive direction, it may be that the goal can be removed from the goals for the following year. If the change in measurement was negative, the action plan should be reconsidered to identify reasons for its lack of success. Redesign of the action plan should then be undertaken to provide guidance to the organization for the following year.

For example, Community Hospital of the West had decided to implement Jean Watson's caring model in its approach to nursing services during 1999. (See the discussion in chapter 18.) The hospital's goal was that nursing services would show an increase in patient satisfaction as measured on the Gallup patient satisfaction survey. In strategic planning for year 2000, the leadership reviewed the Gallup data and found that an increase in satisfaction had occurred in all areas but two, "nurses anticipated needs" and "staff communicated effectively." The leadership decided to continue training nursing staff in Watson's caring model and to place increased emphasis on those two aspects of nursing interaction with patients.

Finally, it must be recognized that program evaluation activities should provide a foundation for subsequent program planning. If the kinds of questions asked in each of the areas are answered in the negative, then the leadership should be ready to respond with redirection and/or support of PI program activities to bring the negative response to a positive one.

Case Study

Students should recall the case study for chapter 3 (pp. 23–24). The team at Western States University Medical Center continued to work on the issue. Over the ensuing months, the team elected a team leader and found a facilitator. Its vision statement was constructed: "Patient location is correctly identified in ACIS and SMS systems at all times." It tentatively identified process customers as nursing staff, patient accounting staff, admitting staff, and patients.

The team decided early on that it did not have sufficient data to make decisions about system capabilities or to recommend solutions to the problem, and so it began to develop data collection activities to get a handle on the realities of patient location in the institution. It spent the first four months of its work collecting data. It collected data on the number of patients admitted, discharged, and transferred in the system. It examined the procedure of users who entered the admissions, discharges, and transfers in the system and summarized the amount of admitting, discharging, and transferring that each performed. It did observational studies of the patient transfer procedure, identifying how long the typical patient transfer took from one unit to another, the exact times of initiation and completion, and the time of transfer input into the information system. It identified the number and type of errors occurring concerning patient admission, discharge, and transfer and the effects those errors had in the census and in other departments.

At the end of this first four months of activity, the quality council of Western States University Medical Center began its annual review of the important aspects of the PI program. The team leader of the patient transfer team was asked to submit a one-page synopsis of the team's activities, for which he submitted a brief description of team activities and a complete set of the data collected by the team.

Case Study Questions

1. What would be your assessment of the patient transfer team's accomplishments thus far if you were a member of the quality council?

2. What recommendations would you make with reference to the team's future activities?

Summary

The annual evaluation of performance improvement programs ensures that the programs focus on opportunities for improvement that are truly important to the organization. Evaluation should encompass all areas of the program, including the organization's PI methodology, team training and functioning, and the use of QI toolbox techniques as well as standing components of healthcare performance improvement such as infection control, continuum of care management, risk management, human resources development, and environment of care management. The findings of the evaluation should be incorporated into the following year's performance improvement plan.

References and Suggested Readings

Dingman, Sharon K., et al. 1999. Implementing a caring model to improve patient satisfaction. *Journal of Nursing Administration* 29(12):30–37.

Watson, Jean. 1985. *Nursing: Human Science and Human Care: A Theory of Nursing.* Norwalk, Conn.: Appleton-Century-Crofts.

Chapter 20
Understanding the Legal Implications of Performance Improvement

Learning Objective

- To recognize and understand the legal aspects of performance improvement activities conducted in healthcare organizations

Background and Significance

In healthcare organizations, performance improvement activities are affected by a number of laws, rules, and regulations. Because performance improvement projects and processes may be complex and sometimes controversial, understanding the legal context in which the activities are carried out is critical. This chapter applies familiar legal theories to performance improvement in healthcare. Specifically, this chapter covers the legal implications of performance improvement in relation to the following areas:

- Copyright law and the ownership of performance improvement and quality management methodologies, data, and studies

- Contract law

- Tort law and the standard of care

- Privacy and confidentiality issues

- Peer review, immunity, and sentinel event reporting

Copyright Law

The Copyright Act of 1976 guarantees the creators of intellectual works the right to control how their works will be used. In other words, the law establishes ownership rights for intellectual property. Copyright in a work generally extends through the life of the author plus 50 years. When the copyright is held by an organization, the term of the copyright is

Note: The information in this chapter was provided by Dorothy Grandolfi Wagg, JD, RHIA.

75 years from the date of publication or 100 years from the date of creation, whichever is longer.

Copyright law protects the original expression contained in an intellectual work. In this context, *expression* means the words, sounds, and/or images used by an author or authors to express an idea or to describe a process. It is important to understand that copyright law protects only the expression and not the actual ideas or facts that make up the content of the work. Two descriptions of the same facts may be copyrighted by two individual authors as long as the second version is not a copy of the first. For example, any number of books could be written about the Second World War, and the author of each book could own the copyright on the book he or she wrote.

All original work is automatically covered by copyright law from the time it first appears in recognizable form. Copyrightable materials include magazine articles, books, databases, audio and video recordings, illustrations, photographs, reports, and lectures. The copyright law also applies to less substantial intellectual property such as computer programs and software applications.

Original intellectual work can be created by an individual, a group of individuals, or an organization. For this reason, the copyright on an original work can be held by a single author, a group of authors, or an organization.

Federal copyright law also recognizes works "made for hire." When employees prepare copyrightable materials as part of their employment responsibilities, the employer is considered the author for copyright purposes. Similarly, when one person or organization hires another person or organization to prepare an original work, the copyright is owned by the person or organization that requested that the work be created.

Copyright law treats intellectual property like personal or physical property. Therefore, the ownership of intellectual property can be transferred to another party in whole or in part. For example, writers often transfer their copyrights on original written works to the organizations that publish their articles and books.

In addition, the copyright holder can permit another person or organization to use his or her property. In such cases, a **permissions** agreement gives a second party legal permission to use previously copyrighted material. For example, an author may enter into an agreement that allows another party to reprint her whole book or just a chapter or chart from the book.

Software licenses are another example of limited rights of use for copyrighted intellectual property. A software license generally allows a person to use the software, but the user does not "own" the code that forms the basis of the software. The owner of the copyright is the original software developer or another party to whom the copyright was transferred or sold.

One notable exception to copyright law is any work that is created through the workings of the federal government. Such works are considered to be in the **public domain;** that is, they can be used freely but they cannot be copyrighted by anyone. Works on which the copyright has expired also fall into the public domain.

Copying the original work of another author and claiming it as one's own is a serious violation of copyright law known as **plagiarism.** In addition, using previously copyrighted work without the owner's permission may be illegal even when the copyright holder is given credit as the author.

Under some very limited circumstances, copyrighted materials may be used without the owner's written permission. Such exceptions to copyright law fall under the **doctrine**

of fair use. The intent of the fair use exceptions to copyright law is to allow limited use for purposes usually associated with nonprofit activities. The fair use of copyrighted works includes making photocopies for purposes of criticism, comment, news reporting, education (including multiple copies for classroom use), scholarship, and research. Copyrighted works may also be quoted in materials published for similar purposes.

In determining whether the use made of a work in any particular case is a fair use, all of the following factors should be considered carefully:

- The purpose and character of the use, including whether such use is of a commercial nature or is for nonprofit educational purposes

- The nature of the copyrighted work

- The amount of material used in relation to the whole copyrighted work

- The effect of the use on the potential market for, or value of, a copyrighted work

In practical terms, the provisions of copyright law are relevant to performance improvement projects in two areas: first, in protecting the results of PI efforts as intellectual property and, second, in respecting the ownership rights of other copyright holders.

The results of most performance improvement initiatives are documented in written reports. Some projects require the development of unique research methodologies. Because the work is performed by employees as part of their regular jobs or by consultants under contract, the copyright on such materials is usually owned by the healthcare organization. Any databases or process tools developed during PI projects are also subject to copyright ownership.

To protect the organization's copyright on such materials, a copyright notice should be included at the beginning of every written report and computer database. Materials distributed as single pages should carry a copyright notice on the bottom of each page. Formal registration is not necessary to protect the copyright on such original work. The author of the material needs only to place a notice of copyright on the work using the following language:

Copyright *(year)*, by *(name of organization)*.
All rights reserved.

When a project requires a significant investment of resources or results in products that will be sold or licensed to other organizations, it may be advantageous to formally register the copyright. The federal government has established an office for copyright registration. Registration of a copyright provides enhanced legal protection by documenting a clear public notice of the copyright's existence and establishing the owner as the first party to copyright the material. Instructions on registering a copyright can be obtained from the Copyright Office in Washington, DC, or from its Web page (http://lcweb.loc.gov/copyright/).

Protecting an organization's ownership rights by copyrighting its intellectual property will not ensure the confidentiality of clinical and business-related information. Privacy and confidentiality issues are discussed later in this chapter.

Participants in performance improvement projects often use published and unpublished materials from sources outside the organization. Such sources may include publishers, other healthcare organizations, standards organizations, consulting firms, and software developers. When copyrighted written materials are used for internal research and education, photocopying is usually allowable under the doctrine of fair use. When photocopies of copyrighted materials are to be distributed to a number of participants, a reference to the original source of the material and a notice of the source's copyright should be placed on every copy.

It should be remembered, however, that photocopying is not an acceptable alternative to buying books and publishers' reprints when they are available. The same is true of materials developed for clinical improvement projects. Organizations such as third-party payers often invest enormous amounts of time and money in developing criteria to be used in the evaluation of patient care. Such criteria are often sold or licensed by the copyright owner in an effort to recoup investments in the project, and such materials cannot be used or photocopied without permission.

The need to obtain a license to use copyrighted software is more familiar. Copyright owners of software products often grant site licenses to healthcare organizations. Many educational products available on the Internet are also sold through site licenses. It is important to remember that materials made available on Web sites are protected under the provisions of the copyright law and should be used with the same consideration as print materials.

To avoid allegations of copyright violation, the performance improvement team should take the following steps:

- Clarify ownership rights when dealing with consultants by executing written work-for-hire agreements.

- Execute confidentiality agreements when materials will be reviewed by parties outside the organization.

- Attach copyright notices to works developed in the healthcare organization, and register the copyrights with the federal copyright office when appropriate.

- Purchase multiple copies of products to which the doctrine of fair use does not apply.

Contract Law

A **contract** is a mutual promise between two or more parties that the law recognizes and considers enforceable. Promises are made every day by all sorts of people under all sorts of circumstances. What distinguishes an enforceable promise—one that is considered a contract—from those that are not considered enforceable?

In order for the law to recognize a contract as valid and enforceable, four conditions must be met. First, there must be **mutual assent** between or among the parties. This assent (or agreement) should be made in writing. Without a written agreement, genuine issues related to proof may arise. The courts are reluctant to take into consideration any contract terms that are not expressly written down. Therefore, it is critical that all the items the parties want to be binding are reflected in the language of the contract.

The test of whether mutual assent exists is determined by the answers to two questions: Was a valid offer communicated by one party, and was a valid acceptance of the offer communicated by the other party? A common example of a contract is the agreement entered into when a house is sold. Did the buyer make an offer that the seller understood? Did the seller communicate her acceptance of the offer to the buyer in a way that the buyer understood? When the answer to both questions is yes, the condition of mutual assent has been met.

The second legal consideration in the validity of a contract is whether the contract has a **legal purpose.** For example, the courts will not enforce agreements or contracts between individuals if the transaction involved the transport or selling of illegal drugs.

The third consideration is **competency,** that is, whether the parties are competent to enter into a binding agreement. Individuals may be judged to be incompetent owing to immature age or mental impairment. For example, most states require that parties to contracts must be at least 18 years old.

Finally, a contract must be supported by what is referred to as **legal consideration.** All parties to an agreement must promise to do something that they are not otherwise legally obligated to do. Generally, consideration involves making a monetary payment on the part of one party and doing some specified task on the part of the other party. For example, a software vendor might agree to provide software with certain characteristics necessary to perform certain tasks, and the buyer might agree to pay for the software as well as not to violate the copyright or license granted for the software. If one party failed to perform his obligation, the other party could sue for breach of contract.

A contract should contain the following information and provisions:

- *Identification of the parties:* The contract should include the legal names and addresses of the persons or organizations that are party to the contract. Post office box numbers should not be used as legal addresses because they would not be sufficient for serving legal notices such as subpoenas.

- *Terms of the agreement:* The contract should include a clear statement of the purpose of the agreement as well as the beginning and ending dates of the agreement. This is particularly important when work is to be performed within rigid deadlines. Provisions related to penalties for not performing the work in a timely manner may also be included.

- *Provisions for termination:* The contract should include termination provisions. Termination of the agreement "for cause" should be allowed. That is, the contract could be terminated if one of the parties failed to perform or performed inadequately or one of the parties otherwise breached the agreement. A termination-without-cause clause would allow termination of the agreement with 60 or 90 days' written notice. Agreements that terminate for cause usually include provisions that assign costs to the party who does not fulfill the contract.

Contract issues often arise in the context of performance improvement when a healthcare organization engages a vendor or consultant to perform a quality study or to lead the organization in developing its performance improvement processes. Contracts are also involved when the organization agrees to buy a certain type of software or to use a certain copyrighted data-gathering methodology. Confidentiality agreements are another example of contracts that are commonly used in the field of healthcare performance improvement.

When vendors or consultants are engaged to provide support for performance improvement projects, several considerations should be covered during the contracting process. First, the organization's representative should make sure that the vendor or consultant holds adequate professional liability and worker's compensation insurance.

When an agreement covers certain goods and services with a value of $10,000 or more and the organization is a Medicare contractor, the vendor or consultant must agree to provide access to certain records. The books and records needed to verify the costs related to the contracted services must be made available to appropriate state and federal agencies for four years after the services are rendered.

The parties to contracts should also warranty that they will not participate in any activity that violates state or federal law prohibiting fraud and abuse and kickbacks or other prohibited activity. Vendors and consultants should also provide assurance that they have not been suspended from participation in any federal program. In addition, the parties should agree to comply with other laws, rules, and regulations such as the Americans with Disabilities Act, the Civil Rights Act, and the Drug Free Workplace Act.

The contract should also make it clear that the work to be performed by the vendor or consultant is to be considered work for hire under the copyright law. The contract should indicate who owns copyright to any product or report developed, including, but not limited to, any graphic art, photographs, videos, and computer images. The agreement should also make it clear which party will be responsible for obtaining permissions and licenses or for filing copyright applications.

Contracts with vendors and consultants should also state that the vendor or consultant is not allowed to use the organization's name in any promotional materials without the express written permission of the organization. Every contract should contain a clause that disallows subcontracting of the work to another organization not party to the contract. Amendment of the agreement should not be allowed without the written consent of all parties.

The agreement should contain confidentiality language. The terms of the contract must acknowledge that, if during the period of the agreement the vendor comes into contact with proprietary, copyrighted, or trade secret information using organizational resources, such information may not be disclosed to others by the vendor without consent. In healthcare, this is particularly relevant to patient-identifiable information.

During the contracting process, the vendor or consultant should be informed of the organization's corporate compliance program and should receive and agree to comply with the organization's code of conduct and business standards. The vendor should also be required to report first to the party that hired it before consulting with any outside entity or government official regarding any alleged violation of law or regulation that the vendor may have reason to believe has occurred.

For example, problems may arise when a vendor supplies a proposal for a quality management information system, which a healthcare organization accepts. However, these kinds of proposals are often so detailed that the entirety of the terms may not always be included in the contract. In that instance, a contract may include the proposal's terms with simple language that the proposal is "attached and its terms and obligations are incorporated by reference." In this way, the vendor can be held to promises it made in the marketing and sales of its product.

Tort Law and the Standard of Care

A **tort** is a wrongful act committed against a person or a piece of property. A tort is a civil wrong and as such is considered separately from criminal acts and breaches of contract. A tort can be either intentional or nonintentional. Intentional torts are committed with the intent to do something wrong, and nonintentional torts are committed without such intent.

Tort law in the United States is based on English law. It provides a way for individuals, groups, businesses, corporations, and other nongovernmental organizations to resolve disputes. Many kinds of actions, or lawsuits, can be brought under the general heading of tort law in civil courts, as one private party sues another private party. For example, a patient can sue a physician for battery, or a pedestrian can sue a bus driver for personal injury.

In contrast, wrongful acts that violate criminal laws are prosecuted in criminal courts. In criminal cases, a unit of government is the party pursuing a claim against an individual accused of committing a crime (for example, a murder or a robbery). Under some circumstances, both a criminal claim and a civil claim can be made for the same wrongful act. Criminal cases result in fines and jail sentences; civil cases result in fines.

In healthcare, the most notable tort is the tort of negligence. *Negligence* is generally defined as a failure to perform an act that a reasonably prudent person would perform (omission) or the performance of an act that a reasonably prudent person would not perform (commission) under a given set of circumstances. Negligent conduct represents a departure from the way a reasonable person would act or a departure from the usual or normal standard of behavior. In healthcare, negligence is a departure from the usual standard of care.

Four elements must be present to prove that a tort of negligence occurred. These items must be present whether the plaintiff is suing a physician for providing negligent care or a CEO is suing his lawyer for negligent advice in handling of his company's affairs. All four of the following elements must be present:

1. *Duty to use due care:* A relationship must have been established between the parties in which one party has an obligation to act as a reasonably prudent person would act toward the other. The relationship between a physician and a patient is an example of such a relationship. The requirement that the physician must conform to a specified standard of care is necessary in order to establish liability for a breach of that standard of care.

2. *Breach of duty:* One party failed to conform to a specific duty owed a party.

3. *Injury:* The party to whom the duty was owed was harmed because the duty was breached.

4. *Cause:* A connection between the breach of the duty and the injury or harm can be established. This element is known as a causal connection. To establish a causal connection, there must be a reasonably close relationship between the breach of the duty and the harm, and the harm must have been foreseeable.

The goal of all performance improvement initiatives is to develop the best possible clinical practices. All performance improvements should be fair and reasonable, because they establish a standard of care in the eyes of the law. For example, a professional organization might establish a standard that requires that the organization assign four nurses for every ten patients in a certain patient care unit. If fewer than four nurses were working on the unit at a particular time, the staffing level could be deemed to be below the standard of care.

In determining whether a person or an organization breached an established standard of care, the law looks to several sources to determine just what the standard should be. First, a court or jury would look at what the law sets out as a standard of care. It would review what if anything state or federal laws and regulations say about appropriate behavior. Evidence of the established standard of care for certain professional activities might also be found in regulations and guidelines promulgated by governmental agencies or in guidelines, codes of ethics, and other treatises published by professional associations or societies. For example, the Joint Commission on Accreditation of Healthcare Organizations identifies a standard of care for hospitals and other healthcare organizations such that failing to meet the standard could be said to be negligent if injuries occurred that could have been prevented had the standard been followed.

Changes in the standard of care occur over time with advancements in technology and medical science. Changes in any established medical practice must be supported by reliable research. Studies can result in a new standard of care, and restudying an issue to validate a suggested change in the accepted course of action may be the most prudent approach to performance improvement.

Privacy and Confidentiality Issues

Performance improvement initiatives involve reviewing the medical care provided in the healthcare organization. To accomplish this review, healthcare professionals look at multiple episodes of care for particular types of patients. Most often, the review is accomplished by referring to the health records of specific, name-identified patients. Healthcare professionals involved in peer review activities occupy a unique position. They must understand the rights of all of the parties involved: patients, providers, and healthcare organizations. In addition, they must mediate among the parties in a way consistent with the law and yet serving the legitimate needs of patients and providers, the public good, the requirements of healthcare research, and the responsibilities of healthcare organizations.

Healthcare organizations are responsible for developing, implementing, and enforcing strict policies on the privacy of health information. They are also responsible for educating all of the parties involved in handling patient-identifiable information. Where health record information is available on-line, patient privacy is mandated by the Health Insurance Portability and Accountability Act (HIPAA) and other regulations.

The act and the regulations for implementing the act cover every use of patient data, even use by the entity that is deemed to be the legal owner of patient records, the healthcare organization. The notice of rulemaking for the standards for privacy of individually identifiable health information, which were published in the November 3, 1999, *Federal Register,* contains provisions specifically related to removing the patient identifier from health records to be used for purposes other than patient care. The federal regulation singles out quality studies as one purpose for which patient identity should be protected. Specifically, the proposed regulations state the following:

> There are many instances in which such individually identifiable health information is stripped of the information that could identify individual subjects and is used for analytical, statistical and other related purposes. Large data sets of de-identified information can be used for innumerable purposes that are vital to improving the efficiency and effectiveness of health care delivery, such as epidemiological studies, comparisons of cost, quality or specific outcomes across providers or payers,

studies of incidence or prevalence of disease across populations, areas or time, and studies of access to care or differing use patterns across populations, areas or time. Researchers and others often obtain large data sets with de-identified information from providers and payers (including from public payers) to engage in these types of studies. This information is valuable for public health activities (e.g., to identify cost-effective interventions for a particular disease) as well as for commercial purposes (e.g., to identify areas for marketing new health care services).

Using patient-identifiable health records and other identifiable health information is common practice in performance improvement initiatives and quality studies. Therefore, a working knowledge of HIPAA regulations is essential. Some states have also enacted legislation or have legislation pending that requires that patient-specific identifying information be removed from a health record before that record can be used in any study.

Privacy advocates suggest that patient-identifiable information should be used only with the express written consent of the patient or the patient's legal representative.

In general, healthcare entities provide medical staff, employees, and agents of the organization access to patient-identifiable information to perform quality studies. At a minimum, all individuals who have access to patient-identifiable information should be required to undergo annual training in the patient's right to privacy and the confidentiality of health records as well as relevant laws and regulations related to patient privacy and release of information. They should be provided copies of relevant policies and procedures, and they should certify that they understand the organization's policies and agree to abide by them.

A **confidentiality agreement** similar to the ones shown in figures 20.1 and 20.2 should be imposed on the organization's employees, independent practitioners, agents, contractors, vendors, and others.

It is important to remember also that independent practitioners have the same rights to privacy in the course of performance improvement review and study. Study findings regarding the practice of a particular provider deserve the same level of confidentiality as do the records of patients used to perform the review. Selection of cases for review in committee must be performed by predefined policy and procedure and must adhere to review criteria applied uniformly across all providers. Access to the patient records of a provider must be accorded only for the purposes of the review. Information developed for review activities and known to review committee members must remain confidential and within the confines of committee discussion and records only. Release of information may only occur for the purposes of further review by higher-level committees in the performance improvement organizational structure or for review by state licensing entities. Quality management policy and procedure must make this necessity clear to all persons involved in performance improvement review activities.

Peer Review, Immunity, and Sentinel Event Reporting

Performance improvement activities and quality assurance studies in healthcare organizations are conducted under the control and direction of peer review committees. A **peer review committee** is a group of like professionals, or peers, established according to an organization's medical staff bylaws, the organization's policy and procedure, or the requirements of state law. The peer review system allows medical professionals to critique and criticize the work of their colleagues candidly and without fear of reprisal. Organizations

---

Figure 20.1.   Sample Confidentiality Agreement

HEALTHCARE ENTITY, INC.
CONFIDENTIALITY AGREEMENT

Healthcare Entity, Inc. ("the Entity"), has a legal and ethical responsibility to safeguard the privacy of all patients and to protect the confidentiality of health, business, and proprietary information. In the course of its business relationship with the Entity, _____ ("Contractor") may come into possession of confidential patient information, even though it may not be directly involved in providing patient care services, or confidential and proprietary business and legal information.

In consideration of and as a condition to its business relationship between the parties, Contractor, its employees and agents, will hold the following information ("confidential information") in strictest confidence, and in accordance with the Entity's policies and procedures:

(1) Any information supplied by the Entity;
(2) Any information that is the direct result of services provided to the Entity by Consultant; and
(3) Any information about the Entity's business operations, services, products, or patients.

Contractor further agrees, on behalf of itself, its employees and agents, as follows:

(1) To maintain the confidentiality of patient information in accordance with the Entity's confidentiality policies;
(2) To make a copy of the Entity's policies available to its agent and employees for reference and to adopt and observe policies and procedures that meet the Entity's standards with regard to maintaining patient information in a secure manner and properly disposing of information which is no longer needed or is converted to another medium;
(3) To review the Entity's confidentiality policies with its employees and agents and instruct them that:
   • they are to access patient information only as necessary to carry out the responsibilities of their employment or agency;
   • they are to maintain confidentiality of patient information in accordance with the Entity's policies;
   • violation of patient confidentiality may be grounds for disciplinary action up to and including termination of employment or contract.
(4) To obtain from each employee or agent who uses or has access to patient information on Contractor's behalf a written statement that he or she has been informed about and understands the obligation to protect confidentiality and agrees to do so. This signed statement shall be maintained in the employee or agent's personal or contract files and shall be renewed annually.
(5) That the Entity may at its sole discretion revoke access to patient information at any time, if it has a good faith belief that patient confidentiality may be breached by Contractor, its agents or employees. Contractor further agrees to immediately suspend or terminate access to patient information by any agent or employee so requested by the Entity.
(6) That the Entity may audit access to and use of its patient information by Contractor, its agents or employees at any time on an ongoing basis and ask for and receive copies of the agent and employee statements required pursuant to paragraph (4) above.

This agreement is effective as of the date signed and shall remain in effect until revoked by either party. Provisions related to maintaining confidentiality of patient information shall survive the termination of this agreement.

For Contractor: For the Entity:

_____   _____
Signed   Signed
Type Name: Type Name:
Type Title: Type Title:

_____   _____
Date   Date

Figure 20.2.   Sample Confidentiality Agreement

1. I _____ (agent or employee name) do hereby acknowledge my obligation to maintain patient confidentiality and agree to not divulge, discuss, or otherwise disclose any information relating to a patient or any aspect of his or her care unless otherwise expressly allowed by the Entity. I further acknowledge and understand that (1) I will access patient information only as necessary to carry out the responsibilities of my employment or agency; (2) I will maintain confidentiality of patient information in accordance with the Entity's policies; and (3) that violation of patient confidentiality may be grounds for disciplinary action up to and including termination of employment or contract.

2. I have read the above statement and understand the consequences for breach of patient confidentiality.

_____

Signature of employee or agent

Name:

Title:

Department:

Date:

---

that use peer review to assess treatment protocols and quality improvement efforts benefit from the feedback neutral peer reviewers provide.

The process of establishing peer review committees varies from organization to organization and from state to state. It is important to recognize that there are two levels of peer review to which an independent practitioner may be subject. The first level is the peer review undertaken within healthcare organizations to improve practitioner performance or to validate that the practitioner's standard of care is commensurate with that of the community of practitioners to which he belongs. Generally, this review is undertaken routinely during the credentialing process (discussed in chapter 10). Occasionally, when a practitioner sustains negative outcomes in his or her treatment of a patient or patients, a special review will be undertaken by peers in the same department or specialty to ensure that the care provided by the practitioner was appropriate.

For example, one neurosurgeon at Community Hospital of the West routinely got his laminectomy patients up and walking the day after surgery. At the time (the early 1970s), his neurosurgical peers believed that allowing patients to get out of bed and to walk so soon after surgery exposed the patient and the healthcare organization to excessive risk of a negative outcome. After extensive peer review over a series of years, the neurosurgeon's privileges were withdrawn at the institution because he refused to comply with the standard of care of his community of fellow neurosurgeons. Interestingly, getting patients up and walking on the day following surgery became the standard of care in the late 1990s. The disciplined neurosurgeon apparently was ahead of his time.

When a practitioner is deemed by organizational peer review to practice in a dangerous or completely unacceptable manner, he or she may then be referred to the second level of peer review processes, that of the professional licensing bodies of a state government. Referral to state licensing bodies may also occur when the public at large complains to the licensing body about the practitioner. Usually, the licensing of independent practitioners is undertaken in close cooperation with medical and other societies in a particular state, and so peers are again used to review and validate practice at the state level. Determinations made at this level could result in disciplinary action or even revocation of the practitioner's license.

In general, institutional peer review committees perform the following activities (institutional level I review most commonly considers the first two issues on the list; state level II review would more often consider the last three issues on the list):

- Evaluating the quality of care rendered by providers of healthcare services

- Determining whether the services provided were performed in compliance with applicable standards of care

- Determining whether the cost of the services rendered was reasonable in a given geographic area

- Determining fitness to practice (that is, whether an individual provider was impaired by reason of alcohol abuse, drug abuse, physical disability, mental instability, or other limitation)

The medical professionals involved in evaluating the work of their peers are provided certain legal protections, or **peer review privileges.** Peer review privileges are established by medical staff bylaws at level I and by state law at level II and may vary from state to state. The protections have two goals: to ensure the confidentiality of peer review activities and records and to protect committee members from civil liability for good-faith participation in the peer review process.

Level II peer review committees are organized under strict legal guidelines. They must adhere to the rules established by state law or regulation in order to be eligible for peer review privileges. At level I, the medical staff bylaws are more concerned with ensuring objectivity and appropriate due process for each practitioner undergoing routine or special review.

Generally, the proceedings and records of peer review committees are not subject to legal **discovery.** (That is, any written documentation of a committee's activities is not admissible as evidence in a legal proceeding.) Original documents or records available from sources outside the peer review committee are not immune from discovery or use in civil proceedings merely because they were presented during the proceedings of a peer review committee. For example, if a patient filed a malpractice action against a physician, the patient's medical record would still be admissible in court. However, the minutes of peer review discussion of that patient's case would generally not be discoverable. In addition, any peer review processes authorized by state law and carried out in good faith are exempt from state antitrust law.

The American Health Information Management Association recommends the following steps for improving the confidentiality of peer review information:

1. Make certain that the purposes of peer review committees, as stated in medical staff bylaws and other corporate documents, conform to the terminology and requirements of state law.

2. Make certain that peer review committees are constituted in accordance with the applicable state law.

3. Act cautiously regarding the use of ad hoc investigations and special committees.

4. Ensure that the information loop includes only individuals who are covered by peer review privilege.

5. Be careful in structuring peer review outside the hospital setting when state statute protects only hospital-based settings.

6. Protect the physical security of peer review records.

7. Educate the members of the peer review committee regarding the nature and limitations of peer review privilege.

8. Use medical staff bylaws and hospital policies to protect peer review confidentiality.

9. Periodically audit peer review policies and practices.

Sentinel Events

On April 2, 1998, the mandate on sentinel events from the Joint Commission on Accreditation of Healthcare Organizations (JCAHO) became effective. This standard requires healthcare organizations to report certain events or occurrences that the JCAHO calls sentinel events. A **sentinel event** is an unexpected occurrence involving death or serious physical or psychological injury or the risk thereof to either patients or employees. Serious injury specifically includes loss of limb or function. The phrase "or the risk thereof" includes any process variation for which a recurrence would carry a significant chance of a serious adverse outcome. Such events are termed sentinel because they signal the need for immediate investigation and response.

The standard requires that a **root-cause analysis** or a detailed investigation be performed when a sentinel event occurs. The JCAHO stated four purposes for requiring the reporting of sentinel events:

- To have a positive impact on improving patient care

- To focus the attention of an organization that has experienced a sentinel event on understanding the causes that underlie the event and on making changes in the organization's systems and processes to reduce the probability of such an event reoccurring in the future

- To increase the general knowledge about sentinel events, their causes, and strategies for prevention

- To maintain the confidence of the public in the accreditation process

Root-cause analysis is a process for identifying the underlying problems that result in variations in care and outcome or the sentinel event. The analyses focus on systems and processes with the goal of identifying opportunities for improvement. The product of the root-cause analysis is an action plan that identifies the strategies that the organization intends to implement to reduce the risk of similar events occurring in the future.

The subset of sentinel events that is subject to review by the JCAHO includes any occurrence that meets either of two basic criteria. Only those sentinel events that affect the recipients of care (patients, clients, or residents) and that meet the following criteria are reportable to the JCAHO:

- The event resulted in an unanticipated death or a significant and permanent loss of function not related to the natural course of the patient's illness or underlying condition.

- The event was one of the following (even if the outcome was not death or major permanent loss of function):

  —Suicide of a patient in a setting where the patient received around-the-clock care (for example, a hospital, residential treatment center, or crisis stabilization center)

  —Infant abduction or discharge to the wrong family

  —Rape

  —Hemolytic transfusion reaction involving administration of blood or blood products with major blood group incompatibilities

  —Surgery on the wrong patient or the wrong body part

Obviously, these kinds of events are likely to trigger investigations and quality studies to improve patient care.

The JCAHO's policy on sentinel event reporting raises issues related to the access of outside accrediting bodies to performance improvement information. Sentinel event information includes reports and investigative materials that traditionally have been created as part of a healthcare organization's peer review process. As such, the information has been deemed confidential and was not available to outside third parties. Although the information related to any studies or investigations that occur after a sentinel event contributes to an understanding of quality concerns or breakdowns in systems that affect delivery of quality care, vigorous and candid discourse might be discouraged if the parties did not believe that the information was protected from disclosure. Oftentimes, such occurrences trigger a quality study to determine whether certain problems or systems flaws are chronic quality problems.

What then should an organization do when faced with this dilemma? If the facility decided to report a sentinel event to the JCAHO, it would essentially waive its peer review privilege. If, however, it decided not to report the event, it would face sanction from the accreditation body.

The JCAHO has indicated that the reporting policy is voluntary. Healthcare organizations will not be automatically placed under greater accreditation scrutiny for choosing not to self-report sentinel events as long as a credible root-cause analysis is conducted and appropriate actions are taken. Healthcare organizations, however, remain concerned about third-party access to peer review information.

Although organizations are granted limited confidentiality when they report sentinel events and follow up with credible root-cause analysis and appropriate action plan, the potential for discovery of the facts of the situation is real. Healthcare organizations must weigh carefully their decision and should consider at a minimum conducting thorough root-cause analyses through existing peer review mechanisms. The decision to report a sentinel event should be made by the organization after careful review of the risks and benefits of reporting. Certainly any quality study that is ordered following a sentinel event should be done through the auspices of the peer review committee process to maximize confidentiality and immunity.

Case Study

Helen James, director of quality management at the Community Hospital of the West, was at home watching television one evening when the telephone rang. On the other end of the line was one of the clerks from Health Information Services at the hospital.

"Hello, Ms. James?" the clerk asked.

"Yes, this is Helen James," she responded.

"Ms. James, Dr. Alan Cooper is here," said the clerk. "You know, the neurosurgeon?"

"Yes, I remember him," Ms. James answered. "What's up?"

"Well, he wants me to pull all the records of spinal anesthesia for Dr. Johnson. . . . You know, the anesthesiologist?" said the clerk. "He says that he wants to review all the cases tonight and tomorrow. He said it's for something called peer review for quality improvement. But, Ms. James, I have a lot of other work I'm supposed to be getting done. I don't even know how to begin looking up one doctor's records if they're not incomplete."

Ms. James pondered the situation for a moment. She did not recall that Dr. Johnson, the anesthesiologist, was on the list for credentials review this year, and none of his cases had come up for surgical case review committee. Why would Dr. Cooper need Dr. Johnson's records?

Case Study Questions

1. What should Ms. James say to Dr. Cooper?

2. Because it is unlikely that Dr. Johnson is eligible for peer review, what should her policy be regarding access to his records?

Summary

Performance improvement activities in healthcare organizations are affected by a number of laws, rules, and regulations. Understanding the legal context in which PI activities are carried out is critical. The following areas of law have practical application in PI projects: copyright law, contract law, tort law and the standard of care, and privacy and confidentiality issues. Legal issues must also be considered in peer review activities and sentinel event reporting.

Reference

McWay, Dana C. 1997. Risk management and quality assurance. In *Legal Aspects of Health Information Management*, pp. 155–73. New York City: Delmar Publishers.

Glossary and Index

Glossary

Absolute frequency: The number of times that a score or value occurs in a data set.

Accreditation: The act of granting approval to a healthcare organization based on whether the organization has met a set of voluntary standards developed by the accreditation agency.

Accreditation standards: An accrediting agency's published rules, which serve as the basis for comparative assessment during the review or survey process.

Action plan: A set of initiatives that are to be undertaken to achieve a performance improvement goal.

Adverse drug reaction: A patient's detrimental response to a medication that is undesired, unintended, or unexpected in dosages recognized in accepted medical practice.

Affinity diagram: A graphic tool used to organize and prioritize ideas after a brainstorming session.

Agenda: A list of the tasks to be accomplished during a meeting.

Bar graph: A graphic data display tool used to show discrete categories of information.

Benchmarking: The systematic comparison of the products, services, and outcomes of one organization with those of a similar organization or the systematic comparison of one organization's outcomes with regional or national standards.

Blitz team: A type of PI team that constructs relatively simple "fixes" to improve a work process without going through the complete PI cycle.

Brainstorming: An idea generation technique in which a team leader solicits creative input from team members.

Case management: The principal process by which healthcare organizations optimize the continuum of care for their patients.

Cause-and-effect diagram: An investigational technique that facilitates the identification of the various factors that contribute to a problem; also called a fishbone diagram.

Certification: The act of granting approval for a healthcare organization to provide services to a specific group of beneficiaries; also, the act of granting a healthcare professional approval to practice. *See also* Credential.

Change management: A group of interpersonal and communication techniques used to help people understand the process of change and accept improvements in the way they perform their work.

Check sheet: A data collection tool used to identify patterns in sample observations.

Clinical guidelines: The descriptions of medical interventions for specific diagnoses in which treatment regimens and the patients' progress are evaluated on the basis of nationally accepted standards of care for each diagnosis.

Clinical Laboratory Improvement Amendments (CLIA):   The 1988 reenactment of the 1967 Clinical Laboratory Improvement Act, the federal regulations outlining the quality assurance activities required of laboratories that provide clinical services.

Clinical path: A graphic tool used to communicate established standards of patient care for specific diagnoses; also called clinical pathway, care map, and critical path.

Clinical practice standards: The established criteria against which the decisions and actions of healthcare practitioners and other representatives of healthcare organizations are assessed in accordance with state and federal laws, regulations, and guidelines; the codes of ethics published by professional associations or societies; the criteria for accreditation published by accreditation agencies; or the usual and common practice of equivalent clinicians or organizations in a geographical region.

Clinical privileges: The accordance by a healthcare organization to a licensed, independent healthcare practitioner (physician, nurse practitioner, or another professional) of permission to practice in a specific area of specialty within that organization.

Closed record review: The examination of patient records assumed to be complete with respect to all necessary and appropriate documentation by surveyors from accreditation organizations.

Compliance: The process of meeting a prescribed set of standards or regulations in order to maintain active accreditation, licensure, or certification status.

Community-acquired infection: An infection that was present in a patient before he or she was admitted to the hospital.

Compulsory review: The examination of a healthcare facility and its processes and infrastructures as required by state laws and regulations.

Conditions of Participation: A set of regulations published by the Health Care Financing Administration to outline requirements of approved programs providing healthcare services to beneficiaries of Medicare and Medicaid programs.

Confidentiality agreement: A document that outlines the responsibility of healthcare workers for complying with their employer's policies and procedures for protecting patient and corporate information and information systems; such documents usually include a stipulation that violations of confidentiality may result in termination.

Continuous data: An infinite number of possible values in measurements that can be expressed in decimal values.

Continuous monitoring: The regular and frequent assessment of healthcare processes and their outcomes and related costs.

Continuous quality improvement (CQI):   A component of total quality management (TQM) that emphasizes ongoing performance assessment and improvement planning.

Continuum of care: The totality of healthcare services provided in all settings, from the least intensive to the most intensive; the emphasis is on treating individual patients at the level of care required by their course of treatment.

Contract: A mutual promise between two or more parties that the law recognizes and considers enforceable.

Control areas: Physical facilities within an organization where utilities are turned on or off or are otherwise monitored.

Control chart: A data display tool used to show changes in key processes over time.

Copyright: A legal principle that protects the original expression contained in an intellectual work, that is, the words, sounds, and/or images used by an author or authors to express an idea or to describe a process.

Cost: The amount of financial resources consumed in the provision of healthcare services to the U.S. population.

Credential: A formal agreement granting an individual permission to practice in a profession, usually conferred by a national professional organization dedicated to a specific area of healthcare practice; or the accordance by a healthcare organization to a licensed, independent practitioner (physician, nurse practitioner, and another professional) of permission to practice in a specific area of specialty within that organization.

Credentialing process: The examination of an independent healthcare practitioner's licenses, specialty credentials, and professional performance upon which a healthcare organization bases its decision to confer or withhold permission to practice (privileges) in the organization.

Criterion: *See* Indicator.

Critical path: *See* Clinical path.

Critical performance measures: Those outputs by which the quality of an organization's services will be measured by patients, clients, visitors, and community leaders.

Cross-functional: A term used to describe an entity or activity that involves more than one healthcare department, discipline, or profession.

Customers: Those individuals who receive a product or a service from a process; *internal* customers are those individuals within the organization who receive products or services from an organizational unit or department, and *external* customers are those individuals from outside the organization who receive products or services from an organizational unit or department.

Deemed status: The term used for the Health Care Financing Administration's assumption that an organization meets the Medicare and Medicaid *Conditions of Participation* when the organization is currently accredited by the JCAHO or CARF.

Direct observation: A means of gathering data about a process in which participants in the process are observed.

Discovery: The pretrial disclosure on the part of one or both litigants of any facts or documents considered germane and admissible in a legal proceeding.

Discrete data: Numerical values that represent whole numbers.

Doctrine of fair use: A convention that permits the limited use of copyrighted intellectual property for purposes usually associated with nonprofit activities, including making photocopies for purposes of criticism, comment, news reporting, education, scholarship, and research.

Document review: An in-depth study performed by accreditation surveyors of an organization's policies and procedures, administrative records, human resources records, performance improvement documentation, and other similar documents as well as a review of closed patient records.

Due process: The right of individuals to fair treatment under the law.

Effectiveness: In the language of the Joint Commission on Accreditation of Healthcare Organizations, the degree to which a healthcare intervention is provided in the correct manner, given the current state of knowledge, with the goal of achieving the desired/projected outcome for the patient.

Efficacy: In the language of the Joint Commission on Accreditation of Healthcare Organizations, the degree to which the treatment intervention used for a patient has been shown to accomplish the desired/projected outcomes.

Efficiency: In the language of the Joint Commission on Accreditation of Healthcare Organizations, the ratio of the outcomes for a patient to the resources consumed in delivering the care.

Evidence-based medicine: The care processes or treatment interventions that researchers performing large, population-based studies have found to achieve the best outcomes in various types of medical practice.

Exit conference: A meeting that closes a site visit during which the surveyors representing an accreditation organization summarize their findings and explain any deficiencies that have been identified; at this time, the leadership of the organization is also allowed an opportunity to discuss the surveyors' perspectives or provide additional information related to any deficiencies the surveyors intend to cite in their final reports.

Expectations: The characteristics that customers want to be evident in a healthcare product, service, or outcome.

Facility Quality Indicator Profile: A report based on the data gathered via the Long-Term Care Minimum Data Set that indicates what proportion of the facility's residents have deficits in each area of assessment during the reporting period and specifically which residents have which deficits; the profile also provides data comparing the facility's current experience with a preestablished comparison group.

Fishbone diagram: *See* Cause-and-effect diagram.

Flowchart: An analytical tool used to illustrate the sequence of activities in a complex process.

Food and drug interactions: An unexpected condition that results from the physiologic incompatibility of therapeutic drugs and food consumed by a patient.

Formulary: A list of drugs approved for use in a healthcare organization; the selection of items to be included in the formulary is based on objective evaluations of their relative therapeutic merits, safety, and cost.

Gantt chart: A type of data display tool used to schedule a process and track its progress over time.

Ground rules: An agreement concerning attendance, time management, participation, communication, decision making, documentation, room arrangements and cleanup, and so on developed by PI team members at the initiation of the team's work on an opportunity for improvement.

Hard issues: The processes and products upon which customers base their perceptions of quality.

Healthcare Integrity and Protection Data Bank (HIPDB): A national database that maintains reports on civil judgments and criminal convictions issued against licensed healthcare providers.

Histogram: A type of bar graph used to display data proportionally.

Icon: A graphic symbol used to represent a critical event in a process flowchart.

Incident report: *See* Occurrence report.

Independent practitioner: Any individual permitted by law to provide healthcare services without direction or supervision, within the scope of the individual's license as conferred by state regulatory agencies.

Indicator: A performance measure used to monitor the outcomes of a process; also called a criterion.

Information management standards: Chapter 7 of the *Accreditation Manual for Hospitals* of the Joint Commission on Accreditation of Healthcare Organizations, which promulgates the JCAHO's requirements regarding the data and information used for various purposes in healthcare organizations.

Interview: A discussion of the qualifications and experiences of a job applicant with respect to the employment process; or a discussion of an organization's conditions with its leadership during the accreditation or licensure survey process.

Leadership: The senior governing, administrative, and management groups of a healthcare organization, which are responsible for setting the mission and overall strategic direction of the organization.

Legal purpose: An element of a legal contract that states the reason the contract is being created.

License: The legal authorization granted by a state to an entity that allows the entity to provide healthcare services within a specific scope of services and geographical location; states license both individual healthcare professionals and healthcare facilities.

Licensure: The process of granting a facility or healthcare professional a license to practice.

Material safety data sheet (MSDS):   Documentation maintained on the hazardous materials used in a healthcare organization; the documentation outlines such information as common and chemical names, family name, and product codes; risks associated with the material, including overall health risk, flammability, reactivity with other chemicals, and effects at the site of contact; descriptions of the protective equipment and clothing that should be used to handle the material; and other similar information.

Mean: The average value in a range of values that is calculated by summing the values and dividing the total by the number of values in the range.

Medication error: A mistake that involves an accidental drug overdose, an administration of an incorrect substance, an accidental consumption of a drug, or a misuse of a drug or biological during a medical or surgical procedure.

Minimum Data Set (MDS):   The data set that the Health Care Financing Administration requires long-term care facilities to collect on all residents who are federal program beneficiaries.

Minutes: The written record of key events in a formal meeting.

Mission: A broad statement describing what a healthcare organization does; or a statement of the goals and purpose of a performance improvement initiative.

Mutual assent: A written agreement describing the promises made by each party to a contract.

National Practitioner Data Bank (NPDB):   A federally sponsored national database that maintains reports on medical malpractice settlements, clinical privilege actions, and professional society membership actions against licensed healthcare professionals.

Nominal data: Values assigned to specific categories; also called categorical data.

Nominal group technique: A QI technique that allows groups to narrow the focus of discussion or to make decisions without becoming involved in extended, circular discussions.

Nosocomial infection: An infection acquired as a result of an exposure that occurred in a healthcare facility after the patient was admitted.

Occurrence report: A structured data collection tool that risk managers use to gather information about potentially compensable events; also called an incident report.

Opening conference: A meeting conducted at the beginning of the accreditation site visit during which the surveyors outline the schedule of activities and list any individuals whom they would like to interview.

Opportunity for improvement: A healthcare structure, product, service, process, or outcome that does not meet its customers' expectations and, therefore, could be improved.

Ordinal data: Values assigned to rank the comparative characteristics of something according to a given set of criteria; also called ranked data.

Outcomes: The end results of healthcare services in terms of the patient's expectations, needs, and quality of life; may be positive and appropriate or negative and diminishing.

Outputs: The measurable products of an organization's work.

Pareto chart: A type of bar graph used to determine priorities in problem solving.

Peer review committee: A group of like professionals, or peers, established according to an organization's medical staff bylaws, organizational policy and procedure, or the requirements of state law; the peer review system allows medical professionals to candidly critique and criticize the work of their colleagues without fear of reprisal.

Peer review organization: Private or public agencies contracted by the Health Care Financing Administration to undertake examination and evaluation of the quality of healthcare rendered to beneficiaries of federal healthcare programs.

Performance improvement council: The leadership group that oversees performance improvement activities in some healthcare organizations.

Performance improvement team: Members of the healthcare organization who have formed a cross-functional group to examine a performance issue and make recommendations with respect to its improvement.

Performance measures: Those outputs by which the quality of the organization and its work units is assessed by patients, clients, visitors, and community leaders.

Permissions: The means by which a copyright holder formally allows another person or organization to use his or her intellectual property.

Pharmacy and therapeutics (P and T) committee: The multidisciplinary committee that oversees and monitors the drugs and therapeutics available for use, the administration of medications and therapeutics, and the positive and negative outcomes of medications and therapeutics used in a healthcare organization.

Pie chart: A data display tool used to show the relationship of individual parts to the whole.

Plagiarism: The act of copying the original work of an author and claiming it as one's own.

Potentially compensable event (PCE):   An occurrence that results in injury to persons in the healthcare organization or to property loss.

Process: The interrelated activities of healthcare organizations, which include governance, managerial support, and clinical services, that affect patient outcomes across departments and disciplines within an integrated environment.

Public domain: Intellectual property that, because of its age, expiration of copyright, or development by a public agency, can be used freely but cannot be copyrighted by anyone.

Quality assurance (QA):   A term commonly used in healthcare to refer to quality-monitoring activities during the 1970s and 1980s, at which time it connoted a retrospective review of care provided with admonishment of providers for substandard care.

QI toolbox techniques: Tools that facilitate the collection, display, and analysis of data and information and that help team members stay focused include cause-and-effect diagrams, graphic presentations, and others.

Ranked data: *See* Ordinal data.

Recall logs: Documentation of communications from manufacturers regarding problems with equipment.

Relative frequency: The percentage of times that a characteristic appears in a data set.

Risk: A formal insurance term denoting liability to compensate individuals for injuries sustained in a healthcare facility.

Root-cause analysis: Analysis of a sentinel event from all aspects (human, procedural, machinery, materiel) to identify how each contributed to the occurrence of the event and to develop new systems that will prevent reoccurrence.

Run chart: A type of data display tool used to plot information on the progress of a process over time.

Sentinel event: An occurrence that led or could have led to injuries to patients, staff, or other individuals; such injuries are life-threatening or result in serious compromise of an individual's physiologic functioning or health.

Site visit: An in-person review conducted by a survey team from an accreditation agency; the visit involves document reviews, staff interviews, an examination of the organization's physical plant, and other activities.

Soft issues: Staff attitudes upon which customers base their perceptions of quality.

Software licenses: A formal agreement that allows a person to use a copyrighted software application.

Special treatment procedures (STPs):   A term used by the Joint Commission on Accreditation of Healthcare Organizations to denote the use of seclusion, restraints, and protective devices during the care of a patient.

Standard deviation: A statistic used to show how the values in a range are distributed around the mean.

Standard of care: An established set of clinical decisions and actions taken by clinicians and other representatives of healthcare organizations in accordance with state and federal laws, regulations, and guidelines; codes of ethics published by professional associations or societies; regulations for accreditation published by accreditation agencies; or usual and common practice of equivalent clinicians or organizations in a geographical region.

Storyboards: A graphic display tool used to communicate the details of PI activities.

Strategic plan: The document in which the leadership of a healthcare organization identifies the organization's overall mission, vision, goals, and values and sets the long-term direction of the organization as a business entity.

Structures: The foundations of caregiving, which include buildings, equipment, technologies, professional staff, and appropriate policies.

Survey team: A group of individuals sent by an accrediting agency to review a healthcare organization for accreditation purposes.

Survey tools: Research instruments that are used to gather data and information from respondents in a uniform manner through the administration of a predefined and structured set of questions and possible responses.

Team charter: A document that explains the issues the team was implemented to improve, describes the goals and objectives and desired end state (vision), and lists the initial members of the team and their respective departments.

Team facilitator: A PI team role primarily responsible for ensuring that an effective performance improvement process occurs by serving as advisor and consultant to the PI team; remaining a neutral, nonvoting member; suggesting alternative PI methods and techniques to keep the team on target and moving forward; managing group dynamics; acting as coach and motivator for the team; assisting in consensus building when necessary; and recognizing team and individual achievements.

Team leader: A PI team role responsible for championing the effectiveness of PI activities in meeting customers' needs and for the *content* of a team's work.

Team member: A PI team role responsible for participating in team activities, identifying opportunities for improvement, gathering and analyzing data, sharing knowledge, and planning improvements.

Team recorder/scribe: A PI team role responsible for maintaining the records of a team's work during meetings, including any documentation required by the organization.

Timekeeper: A PI team role responsible for notifying the team during meetings of time remaining on each agenda item in an effort to keep the team moving forward on its PI project.

Tort: A wrongful act committed against a person or a piece of property in a civil rather than a criminal context.

Total quality management (TQM):   A management philosophy developed in the midtwentieth century by W. Edwards Deming and others that encouraged industrial organizations to focus on the quality of their products as their paramount mission.

Transfusion reaction: Signs, symptoms, or conditions caused by a patient's having been given an incompatible transfusion.

Universal precautions: The application of a set of procedures specifically designed to minimize or eliminate the passage of infectious disease agents from one individual to another during the provision of healthcare services.

Vision: A description of the ideal end state or a description of the best way a process should function.

Voluntary review: An examination of an organization's structures and processes conducted at the request of a healthcare facility seeking accreditation from a reviewing agency.

Index